**Prentice Hall Brief Review
for the New York Regents Exam**

# Chemistry:
# The Physical Setting

## Patrick Kavanah

**Order Information**

Send orders to:

PEARSON CUSTOMER SERVICE

P.O. BOX 2500

LEBANON, IN 46052-3009

or

CALL TOLL FREE 1-800-848-9500
(8:00 A.M.-6:00 P.M. EST)

• Orders can be placed via phone

## About the Author

Patrick Kavanah graduated from the University of Notre Dame with a Bachelor of Science degree in 1957, and pursued graduate work at Georgetown University and Columbia Teachers' College, earning a Master's Degree in Science Education at the University of Northern Iowa in 1964. He has taught at Mahopac High School in Mahopac, NY, at Lago High School in Aruba, Netherlands Antilles, and for 31 years at Monroe-Woodbury High School in Central Valley, NY, where he was a Chemistry teacher and Chairman of the Science Department.

Acknowledgments begin on page I-7 and constitute an extension of this copyright page.

ISBN-13: 978-0-13-317394-9
ISBN-10: 0-13-317394-1

2 3 4 5 6 7 8 9 10 V011 15 14 13 12 11

# Brief Review in
# Chemistry: The Physical Setting

## New York Standards

Standard  Key Idea

**KEY**

## 4.2.1

Major Understanding

| | | |
|---|---|---|
| 4.3.1a | 4.3.1k | 4.PS3.1i |
| 4.3.1b | 4.3.1l | 4.PS3.1ii |
| 4.3.1c | 4.3.1m | 4.PS3.1iii |
| 4.3.1d | 4.3.1n | 4.PS3.1iv |
| 4.3.1e | 4.3.1q | 4.PS3.1v |
| 4.3.1f | 4.3.1r | 4.PS3.1vi |
| 4.3.1g | 4.3.1s | 4.PS3.1x |
| 4.3.1h | 4.3.1t | 4.PS3.1xi |
| 4.3.1i | 4.3.1u | 4.PS3.1xii |
| 4.3.1j | 4.3.1cc | 4.PS3.1xxii |

| | | |
|---|---|---|
| 4.3 | 4.3.2b | 4.PS3.2ii |
| 4.3.1w | 4.3.3a | 4.PS3.2iii |
| 4.3.1x | 4.3.3d | 4.PS3.2v |
| 4.3.1cc | 4.4.1b | 4.PS3.3i |
| 4.3.1dd | 4.5 | 4.PS3.3ii |
| 4.3.1ee | 4.5.2g | 4.PS3.3iii |
| 4.3.2a | 4PS3.2i | |

| | | |
|---|---|---|
| 4.3.1ee | 4.3.3d | 4.PS3.3vii |
| 4.3.3c | 4.PS3.3iv | 4.PS3.3viii |
| 4.3.3e | 4.PS3.3v | 4.PS3.3ix |
| 4.3.3f | 4.PS3.3vi | 4.PS3.4vii |

| | | |
|---|---|---|
| 4.3.1s | 4.4.2a | 4.PS4.2ii |
| 4.3.1w | 4.4.2b | 4.PS4.2iii |
| 4.3.1dd | 4.4.2c | 4.PS4.2iv |
| 4.3.1jj | 4.PS3.1xviii | |
| 4.3.1kk | 4.PS3.1xxii | |
| 4.3.1nn | 4.PS3.1xxiv | |
| 4.3.4a | 4.PS3.4i | |
| 4.3.4b | 4.PS3.4ii | |
| 4.3.4c | 4.PS3.4iii | |
| 4.4 | 4.PS4.2i | |

| | | |
|---|---|---|
| 4.3.1g | 4.3.1z | 4.PS3.1xiii |
| 4.3.1v | 4.3.1aa | 4.PS3.1xiv |
| 4.3.1w | 4.3.1bb | 4.PS3.1xv |
| 4.3.1x | 4.5.2f | 4.PS3.1xvi |
| 4.3.1y | 4.PS3.1x | 4.PS3.1xviii |

New York Standards

| | | |
|---|---|---|
| 4.5.2a | 4.5.2i | 4.PS3.1viii |
| 4.5.2b | 4.5.2j | 4.PS3.2xix |
| 4.5.2c | 4.5.2k | 4.PS5.2i |
| 4.5.2d | 4.5.2l | 4.PS5.2ii |
| 4.5.2e | 4.5.2m | 4.PS5.2iv |
| 4.5.2h | 4.5.2n | 4.PS5.2v |

| | |
|---|---|
| 4.3.1nn | 4.PS3.1xxvi |
| 4.3.1oo | 4.PS3.1xxiv |
| 4.3.1pp | 4.PS3.1xxviii |
| 4.3.1qq | 4.PS3.1xxx |
| 4.PS3.1xxiv | |
| 4.PS3.1xxv | |

| | | |
|---|---|---|
| 4.3.1ll | 4.3.4g | 4.PS3.1xxiii |
| 4.3.1mm | 4.3.4h | 4.PS3.4v |
| 4.3.4a | 4.3.4i | 4.PS3.4vi |
| 4.3.4b | 4.3.4j | 4.PS3.4vii |
| 4.3.4c | 4.4.1c | 4.PS4.1i |
| 4.3.4d | 4.4.1d | 4.PS4.1ii |
| 4.3.4f | 4.PS3.1iv | |

| | | |
|---|---|---|
| 4.3.1ll | 4.3.4g | 4.PS3.1xxiii |
| 4.3.1mm | 4.3.4h | 4.PS3.4v |
| 4.3.4a | 4.3.4i | 4.PS3.4vi |
| 4.3.4b | 4.3.4j | 4.PS3.4vii |
| 4.3.4c | 4.4.1c | 4.PS4.1i |
| 4.3.4d | 4.4.1d | 4.PS4.1ii |
| 4.3.4f | 4.PS3.1iv | |

| | |
|---|---|
| 4.3.1rr | 4.3.1zz |
| 4.3.1ss | 4.PS3.1xxxi |
| 4.3.1tt | 4.PS3.1xxxii |
| 4.3.1uu | 4.PS3.1xxxiii |
| 4.3.1vv | 4.PS3.1xxxiv |
| 4.3.1ww | 4.PS3.1xxxv |
| 4.3.1xx | |

**Separate Answer Key Contents:**

Answers for Review and Practice Questions
Answers for Regents Examinations
Diagnostic Tests and Answers

# About This Book

This book is designed to enhance review of the concepts, skills, and application of the Physical Science/Chemistry Core Curriculum that may be tested on the Regents Examination for The Physical Setting: Chemistry. Students can use the book in any order as each topic is independent except for the introduction of vocabulary words.

## Features

### Content Review

The presentation features aids for accessing the basic content that will be tested on the Regents Examination. Some material that will not be tested has been added to a few topics to enhance understanding, but that material is not assessed in the Practice Questions.

**Illustrations** Graphics visualize the concepts and vocabulary of chemistry as well as the types of drawings students will be required to interpret on the exam.

**Vocabulary** Many exam questions require an understanding of the language of chemistry.

**Bold Words** Vocabulary listed at the beginning of a topic and defined within that topic.

**Underlined Words** Terms that appear as bold in other topics or describe basic chemistry concepts.

**Sample Problems** Step-by-step detailed solutions guide the problem-solving process, reinforce content knowledge, and provide examples of problems found on the exam.

### Sidebars

**Memory Jogger** Recalls relevant information covered elsewhere in this book or previous science courses.

**Digging Deeper** Provides specific examples of some concepts or expands core content.

**Review Questions** Questions similar to those on the exam, totaling more than 900, clarify and reinforce understanding.

## Practice Questions for the New York Regents Exam

A total of more than 500 Practice Questions are written and organized to mimic the exam.

**Part A** Multiple-choice questions test knowledge.

**Part B** Both multiple-choice and constructed-response questions test skills and understandings.

**Part C** Questions often require an extended constructed response with a more detailed answer supported by applications or examples. Numbers in brackets tell how many points the question is worth on an actual exam.

## Reference and Support

**Strategies for Answering Test Questions** Support to help you interpret and answer the range of exam questions.

**Appendix 1** The *Reference Tables for Physical Setting/Chemistry* are integral to this content review and are annotated with an ®. Review and Practice Questions refer you to them.

**Appendix 2** *Graphing and Math Skills* provides a review of basic math and graphic skills, which are an integral part of some exam questions.

**Glossary** Defines all bold vocabulary words and underlined words.

**Index** Cross-references concepts in the topics.

## Regents Examinations

The most recent released Regents Examinations are reproduced at the end of this book to provide practice in taking actual Regents Examinations.

### Answer Key with Diagnostic Tests

A separate Answer Key includes all answers to the Review and Practice Questions along with topic-by-topic Diagnostic Tests to help determine which concepts require more intense review.

This section provides strategies to help you answer various types of questions on the Regents Examination for The Physical Setting/Chemistry. Strategies are provided for answering multiple-choice and constructed-response questions as well as for questions based on diagrams, data tables, and graphs and questions that use the *Reference Tables for Physical Setting/Chemistry*, which are reproduced in the Appendix.

## Strategies for Multiple-Choice Questions

Multiple-choice questions will likely account for more than 50% of the Regents Examination for The Physical Setting/Chemistry. Part A is comprised totally of multiple-choice questions, whereas Part B contains some, but not all, multiple-choice questions. Therefore, it is important to be good at deciphering multiple-choice questions. Here are a few helpful strategies. For any one question, not all strategies will need to be used. The numbers are provided for reference, not to specify an order (except for Strategies 1 and 2).

1. Always read the entire question, but wait to read the choices. (See Strategy 4.)

2. Carefully examine any data tables, diagrams, photographs, or relevant part(s) of the *Reference Tables for Physical Setting/Chemistry* associated with the question.

3. Underline key words and phrases in the question that signal what you should be looking for in the answer. This will make you read the question more carefully. This strategy applies mostly to questions with a long introduction.

4. Try to think of an answer to the question before looking at the choices given. If you think you know the answer, write it on a separate piece of paper before reading the choices. Next, read all of the choices and compare them to your answer before making a decision. Do not select the first answer that seems correct. If your answer matches one of the choices, and you are quite sure of your response, you are probably correct.

Even if your answer matches one of the choices, carefully consider all of the answers because the obvious choice is not always the correct one. If there are no exact matches, re-read the question and look for the choice that is most similar to your answer.

5. Eliminate any choices that you know are incorrect. Lightly cross out the numbers for those choices on the exam paper. Each choice you can eliminate increases your chances of selecting the correct answer.

6. If the question makes no sense after reading through it several times, leave it for later. After completing the rest of the exam, return to the question. Something you read on the other parts of the exam may give you some ideas about how to answer this question. If you are still unsure, go with your best guess. There is no penalty for guessing, but answers left blank will be counted as wrong. If you employ your best test-taking strategies, you just may select the correct answer.

## Strategies for Constructed-Response Questions

Some questions in Part B and all questions in Part C of the Regents Examination for Physical Setting/Chemistry require a constructed response. Some of these questions may require you to write one or two sentences. No matter which type of answer is requested, the following strategies will help you write constructed responses.

1. Always read through the entire question.

2. Underline key words and phrases in the question that signal what you should be looking for in the answer. This will make you read the question more carefully.

3. Look over the *Reference Tables for Physical Setting/Chemistry* for any helpful information related to the question.

4. Write a brief outline, or at least a few notes to yourself, about what should be included in the answer.

5. Pay attention to key words that indicate how to answer the question and what you

need to say in your answer. Several of these words are very common. For example, you might be asked to discuss, describe, explain, define, compare, contrast, or design. The table below lists key words and directions for your answers.

6. When you write your answer, don't be so general that you are not really saying anything. Be very specific. You should use the correct terms and clearly explain the processes and relationships. Be sure to provide details, such as the names of processes, names of structures, and, if it is appropriate, how they are related. If only one example or term is required, do not give two or more. If one is correct and the other is wrong, your answer will be marked wrong.

7. If a question has two or three parts, answer each part in a separate sentence or paragraph. This will make it easy for the person scoring your paper to find all of the information. When writing your answer, don't shortchange one part of the question by spending too much time on another part.

8. If sentences are called for in the answer, be sure that you write sentences. A sentence should always have a subject and a verb,

and it should not start with the word *because*. Note that you will not lose points for incorrect grammar, spelling, punctuation, or poor penmanship. However, such errors and poor penmanship could impair your ability to make your answer clear to the person scoring your paper. If that person cannot understand what you are trying to say, you will not receive the maximum number of points.

9. When the question calls for you to write the answer in paragraphs, do not write a "standard" essay such as you would write for social studies. Do not spend time writing an introduction, several short paragraphs, and a conclusion. Write your outline, and then answer the question directly.

## Strategies for Questions Based on Diagrams

Both multiple-choice and extended-response question frequently include diagrams or pictures. Usually the diagrams provide information needed to answer the question. The diagrams may be realistic, or they may be schematic. Schematic drawings show the relationships among parts and sometimes the sequence in a system. Follow these strategies:

| Using Key Words to Direct Your Answers | |
|---|---|
| **Key Word** | **What Direction Your Answer Should Take** |
| Analyze | • Break the idea, concept, or situation into parts, and explain how they relate.<br>• Carefully explain relationships, such as cause and effect. |
| Discuss | • Make observations about the topic or situation using facts.<br>• Thoroughly write about various aspects of the topic or situation. |
| Describe | • Illustrate the subject using words.<br>• Provide a thorough account of the topic.<br>• Give complete answers. |
| Explain | • Clarify the topic of the question by spelling it out completely.<br>• Make the topic understandable.<br>• Provide reasons for the outcome. |
| Define | • State the exact meaning of the topic or word.<br>• Explain what something is or what it means. |
| Compare | • Relate two or more topics with an emphasis on how they are alike.<br>• State the similarities between two or more examples. |
| Contrast | • Relate two or more topics with an emphasis on how they are different.<br>• State the differences between two or more examples. |
| Design | • Plan an experiment or component of an experiment. Map out your proposal being sure to provide information about all of the required parts. |
| State | • Express or tell in words.<br>• Explain or describe using at least one fact, term, or relationship. |

1. First study the diagram and think about what the diagram shows you. Be sure to read any information, such as titles or labels, that go with the diagram.

2. Read the question. Follow the strategies for either multiple-choice or constructed-response questions listed previously.

## Strategies for Questions Based on Data Tables

Most data tables contain information that summarizes a topic. A table uses rows and columns to condense information and to present it in an organized way. Rows are the horizontal divisions going from left to right across the table, while columns are vertical divisions going from top to bottom. Column headings name the type of information included in a table. Sometimes different categories of information are listed down the left-hand column of the table. When answering a question with a data table, use the following strategies.

1. Find the title of the table. It is usually located across the top.

2. Determine the number of columns in the table and their purpose.

3. Determine the number of rows and their purpose.

4. Read across the rows and down the columns to determine what the relationships are.

5. Now you are ready to read the question with the data table. Answer the question by using the suggested strategies for multiple-choice or constructed-response questions listed previously.

## Strategies for Questions Based on Graphs

Graphs represent relationships in a visual form that is easy to read. Three different types of graphs commonly used on science Regents Examinations are line graphs, bar graphs, and circle graphs. Line graphs are the most common, and they show the relationship between two changing quantities, or variables. When a question is based on any of the three types of graphs, the information you need to correctly answer the question can usually be found on the graph.

When answering a question that includes a graph, first ask yourself these questions:

- What information does the graph provide?
- What are the variables?
- What seems to happen to one variable as the other changes?

After a careful analysis of the graph, use the appropriate strategies for multiple-choice or constructed-response questions.

## Strategies for Questions Based on Readings

Some questions in Part C of the Regents Examination will require the reading of a chemistry-related passage. The answers to the questions will be based upon the article's content and your knowledge of chemistry. The key to doing well on these questions is a thorough reading and comprehension of the article and a strong overall knowledge of chemistry. To help prepare for this portion of the Regents Examination, read the following sample reading passages and answer the related questions.

**Base your answers to questions 1 through 3 on the information below, the *Reference Tables for Physical Setting/Chemistry*, and your knowledge of chemistry.**

Radioactivity and radioactive isotopes have the potential for both benefiting and harming living organisms. One use of radioactive isotopes is in radiation therapy as a treatment for cancer. cesium-137 is sometimes used in radiation therapy.

A sample of cesium-137 was left in an abandoned clinic in Brazil in 1987. Cesium-137 gives off a blue glow because of its radioactivity. The people who discovered the sample were attracted by the blue glow and had no idea of any danger. Hundreds of people were treated for overexposure to radiation, and four people died.

1. Using Reference Table N, complete the equation below for the radioactive decay of Cs-137. Include both atomic number and mass number for each particle. [1]

$$^{137}_{55}\text{Cs} \rightarrow {}^{0}_{-1}e + {}^{137}_{56}\text{Ba}$$

**2.** If 12.5 grams of the original sample of cesium-137 remained after 90.69 years, what was the mass of the original sample? [1]

**3.** Suppose a 40-gram sample of iodine-131 and a 40-gram sample of cesium-137 were both abandoned in the clinic in 1987. Explain why the sample of iodine-131 would not pose as great a radiation risk to people today as the sample of cesium-137 would. [1]

**Base your answers to questions 4 through 6 on the information below.**

A glass tube is filled with hydrogen gas at low pressure. An electric current is passed through the gas causing it to emit light. This light is passed through a prism to separate the light into the bright, colored lines of hydrogen's visible spectrum. Each colored line corresponds to a particular wavelength of light. One of hydrogen's spectral lines is a red light with a wavelength of 656 nanometers.

Tubes filled with other gases produce different bright-line spectra that are characteristic of each kind of gas. These spectra have been observed and recorded.

**4.** Explain, in terms of electron energy states and energy changes, how hydrogen's bright-line spectrum is produced. [1]

**5.** Explain how the elements present on the surface of a star can be identified using bright-line spectra. [1]

**6.** A student measured the wavelength of hydrogen's visible red spectral line to be 647 nanometers. Show a correct numerical setup for calculating the student's percent error. [1]

**Base your answers to questions 7 through 10 on the information below.**

Propane is a fuel that is sold in rigid, pressurized cylinders. Most of the propane in a cylinder is liquid, with gas in the space about the liquid level. When propane is released from the cylinder, the propane leaves the cylinder as a gas. Propane gas is used as a fuel by mixing it with oxygen in the air and igniting the mixture, which is represented by the balanced equation below.

$$C_3H_8(g) + 5O_2(g) \rightarrow 3CO_2(g) + 4H_2O(\ell) + 2219.2 \text{ kJ}$$

A small amount of methanethiol, which has a distinct odor, is added to the propane to help consumers detect a propane leak. In methanethiol, the odor is caused by the thiol functional group (-SH). Methanethiol, $CH_3SH$, has a structure very similar to the structure of methanol.

**7.** Draw a particle diagram to represent propane in a pressurized cylinder. Your response must include at least six molecules of propane in the liquid phase and six molecules of propane in the gaseous phase. [1]

**8.** Draw a potential energy diagram for this reaction. [1]

**9.** Determine the total amount of energy released when 2.50 moles of propane is completely reacted with oxygen. [1]

**10.** Draw a structural formula for a molecule of methanethiol. [1]

# Use of Reference Tables for Physical Setting/Chemistry to Help Answer Questions

In recent Regents Examinations between 20% and 35% of the questions have involved the use of the *Reference Tables for Physical Setting/ Chemistry*. You should become thoroughly familiar with all details of these tables. Sometimes the questions will specifically refer you to the reference tables, but most often you will be expected to know what information is included within the reference tables.

The text helps you become more familiar with the content of the reference tables by referring to the tables within the text presentation. These references are indicated by an ⓡ on the page.

# The Atom

## How Scientists View Atomic Composition

**? Look at your desk. What do you think it is made of? ?**

You might say wood, metal, or plastic. If you were living in Greece 2500 years ago, you would have said "earth." At that time, the Greek philosopher Empedocles claimed that all matter was composed of fire, air, water, and earth.

Empedocles also described two other components—love and discord. It was love that held the other components together in matter and discord that kept them apart. In that way, an object, substance, or organism could be described as a ratio of fire, air, water, earth, love, and discord.

These components were considered eternal and could not be explained. Yet about 2000 years later, scientists did begin to explain them and the nature of matter itself.

## Vocabulary

| | | |
|---|---|---|
| atom | excited state | neutron |
| atomic mass | ground state | nucleus |
| atomic mass unit | heterogeneous | orbital |
| atomic number | homogeneous | proton |
| compound | isotope | pure substance |
| electron | mass number | valence |
| element | mixture | wave-mechanical model |

## Topic Overview

Chemistry is the study of <u>matter,</u> which is anything that has mass and volume. The desk that you are sitting at, the air around you, and your body are all made up of matter. <u>Chemistry</u> deals with the composition of matter and the changes that matter may undergo.

Scientists have long sought the answers to solve the question, "What are we, the earth, and the stars made of?" Our present answer is that there are only about 100 different building blocks that explain the composition of the entire visible universe. Our present model has been the result of the thinking and experiments of scientists over a few thousand years. Today's model adequately explains how so many different objects can be made from such a few fundamental building blocks. These fundamental particles, called atoms, are themselves made of even smaller parts.

## Early Studies of Atoms

The Greeks' view of the nature of matter as being composed of fire, air, water, and earth lasted until the 1600s when Robert Boyle identified gold and silver as themselves being elemental; that is, they are not themselves made of fire, air, earth, or water. As Boyle's ideas were slowly accepted, additional elements were discovered, and the Greek concept of what makes up matter faded.

### Dalton's Atomic Theory

The work of Boyle led John Dalton to propose his revolutionary theory in the 1700s. He theorized that the basic unit of matter is a tiny particle called an **atom.**

Dalton's theory of the atom can be summarized by the following points.

- All elements are composed of indivisible atoms.
- All atoms of a given element are identical.

- Atoms of different elements are different; that is, they have different masses.
- Compounds are formed by the combination of atoms of different elements.

Although we now know that some of Dalton's theory was not correct, it laid the important groundwork for the current concept of the atom.

## Structure of the Atom

Experimental studies of the atom soon showed that it was not indivisible but was made up of even smaller parts.

**Electrons** J. J. Thomson used a cathode ray tube to show one of these smaller units that make up an atom. Because the ray produced in the tube was deflected a certain way by an electrical or magnetic field, he concluded that the ray was formed by particles and that the particles were negatively charged. The only source available for the particles was the atoms present. Thus, Thomson theorized that an atom contains small, negatively charged particles, which he named **electrons.**

A concept of the atom developed in which these negatively charged particles were visualized as being embedded in atoms, just as we might find raisins in bread. This model was called the "plum pudding" model. In this model, the mass of the rest of the atom was evenly distributed and positively charged, taking up all of the space not occupied by the electrons.

**The Nucleus** If electrons are present in atoms, what makes up the rest of the atom? One scientist who studied this question was Ernest Rutherford. A group of scientists that included Rutherford conducted the following experiment, with surprising results. Look at Figure 1-1A. They directed <u>alpha particles,</u> which are positively charged particles that are much smaller than an atom, at a thin piece of gold foil. If the plum pudding model of the atom were correct, all of the alpha particles would pass through the foil with just a few being slightly deflected.

As the scientists expected, most of the particles passed straight through the foil, and a few were slightly deflected. But to their amazement, some of the alpha particles were greatly deflected, and some even bounced back, as shown in Figure 1-1B. From this experiment, Rutherford concluded that atoms have a dense central core, called a **nucleus,** while the remainder of the atom is essentially empty space. Because alpha particles are positively charged and

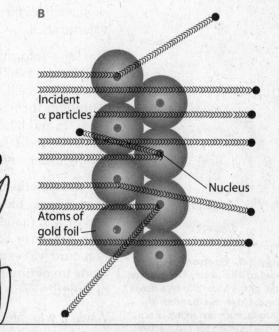

**Figure 1-1. The Rutherford gold-foil experiment:** (A) Scattering of alpha particles (B) The deflections of the alpha particles showed that atoms have a dense, positively charged center. Experimental results showed that only about one alpha particle out of each 10,000 was dramatically deflected.

**Figure 1-2. The Bohr model of the atom:** Protons and neutrons are in the dense central nucleus with electrons orbiting in valence shells.

were repelled by the nucleus, the nucleus must also be positively charged because like charges repel each other.

**Protons and Neutrons** Since atoms are electrically neutral, scientists reasoned that there must be positive charges to offset the negatively charged electrons, and these charges must be located in the nucleus. These positively charged particles are called **protons.** In addition to protons it was later discovered that there are additional particles in the nucleus that do not have either a positive or negative charge. These neutral particles are called **neutrons.**

## Modern Atomic Theory

Scientists used the information derived from this and other experiments to further describe atomic structure.

**The Bohr Model of the Atom** In the early 20th century the common model of the atom was the Bohr or "planetary" model. The model showed a center, the nucleus, and rings of orbiting electrons.

Normally, composition of the nucleus shows the number of positively charged protons and the number of neutral neutrons present as shown in Figure 1-2. The electrons are shown in concentric circles or shells around the nucleus, designated by the letters K, L, M, N, O, P, and Q or the numbers 1 through 7. The K shell can hold a maximum of 2 electrons, the L shell a maximum of 8. The outermost shell of an atom may not contain more than 8 electrons. These outermost electrons are called **valence** electrons.

When a valence shell is filled, the element is a noble gas. When a shell is filled, the next element begins to fill the next higher energy valence shell.

The same information can be shown in a linear form. The symbol of the element is followed by showing the number of electrons in each succeeding shell. Thus Na-2-8-1 represents the sodium atom. The "Na" represents the nucleus and the 2-8-1 shows the electron arrangement in the K, L, and M shells. The electron structure of each element is shown on the Periodic Table of the Elements in the *Reference Tables for Physical Setting/Chemistry.* Ⓡ

**The Wave-Mechanical Model** Advances in the study of energy aided in modifying the atomic model. Energy had been viewed as being waves, and matter as particles. By the 1900s, energy and matter were both viewed as acting as both waves and particles. The wave aspect of nature was expanded, and it was also proposed that energy was made up of tiny packets called quanta. These energy packets acted like particles.

When it was later determined that the electron not only has properties of mass but also has wavelike properties, this concept of a dual nature was incorporated into the current model of the atom, the **wave-mechanical model.** This modern model of the atom pictures the atom as having a dense, positively charged nucleus as proposed in the planetary model. The major difference between the wave-mechanical model and the Bohr model is found in the manner in which the electrons are pictured. Instead

A

Most probable electron location

B

**Figure 1-3. Electron cloud model of the atom:** The modern model of the atom shows a dense nucleus. (A) In this diagram of hydrogen, each dot represents a possible location for the electron. The ring shows the most probable location of an electron. (B) In this model of a cross-section of a multielectron atom, the dots represent probable locations of electrons. Each of the darker circles represents an orbital.

of moving in definite, fixed orbits around the nucleus as suggested in the Bohr model, the wave-mechanical model portrays electrons with distinct amounts of energy moving in areas called orbitals. An **orbital** is described as a region in which an electron of a particular amount of energy is most likely to be located. Models of orbitals are shown in Figure 1-3.

Thus, the modern model of the atom is not the invention of a single scientist, but rather one that has evolved over a long period of time. Figure 1-4 summarizes some of the atomic models involved in the evolution of the current atomic model.

| Dalton | Thomson | Rutherford | Bohr | Present |

**Figure 1-4. Changing views of atomic structure over time:** The representations show the cannonball, plum pudding, nuclear, planetary, and wave-mechanical atomic models.

# Review Questions

1. The concept that matter is composed of tiny, discrete particles is generally attributed to the

   (1) Greeks
   (2) Romans
   (3) English
   (4) Germans

2. The first subatomic particle discovered was the

   (1) proton      (3) electron
   (2) neutron     (4) photon

3. According to the law of the conservation of mass, if the products of a reaction have a mass of 64.0 g, then the total mass of the reactants

   (1) must be less than 64.0 g
   (2) must be equal to 64.0 g
   (3) must be more than 64.0 g
   (4) is not related to the mass of the products

4. The gold-foil experiment led scientists to conclude that an atom's

   (1) positive charge is evenly distributed throughout its volume
   (2) negative charge is mainly concentrated in its nucleus
   (3) mass is evenly distributed throughout its volume
   (4) volume is mainly unoccupied

5. The model of the atom that pictured the atom with electrons stuck randomly throughout the mass of the atom was called the

   (1) cannonball model
   (2) plum pudding model
   (3) planetary model
   (4) wave-mechanical model

6. After bombarding a gold foil sheet with alpha particles, scientists concluded that atoms mainly consist of

   (1) electrons
   (2) empty space
   (3) protons
   (4) neutrons

7. Experimental evidence indicates that the nucleus of an atom

   (1) contains most of the mass of the atom
   (2) contains a small percentage of the mass of the atom
   (3) has no charge
   (4) has a negative charge

8. Dalton's atomic theory states that
   (1) all atoms of an element are positively charged
   (2) different elements can have the same mass
   (3) atoms of a given element must be identical
   (4) all the atoms in a compound are identical

9. Modern theory pictures an electron as
   (1) a particle only
   (2) a wave only
   (3) both a particle and a wave
   (4) neither a particle nor a wave

10. What are the major differences between the plum pudding and planetary models of the atom?

11. Why did Rutherford conclude that the atom was mostly empty space?

12. What is a major difference between the Rutherford and the wave-mechanical models of the atom?

## Digging Deeper

The concept of protons, electrons, and neutrons as fundamental particles can be used to explain most of the chemical behavior of an atom. However, recent research has shown that protons and neutrons are themselves made of smaller particles called quarks. Each quark has a fractional charge of either $\frac{2}{3}+$ or $\frac{1}{3}-$. Each proton and neutron is composed of three quarks. Because it has a total 1+ charge, a proton must be composed of two quarks each with a charge of $\frac{2}{3}+$ and one quark with a charge of $\frac{1}{3}-$. A neutron has no charge, so it must be composed of one quark with a charge of $\frac{2}{3}+$ and two quarks each with a charge of $\frac{1}{3}-$.

## Subatomic Particles

You have seen that all atoms are composed of a small, dense, positively charged nucleus surrounded by a large space occupied by electrons. The nucleus contains two types of particles—protons with a positive charge, and neutrons with no charge.

Protons have a mass of only $1.67 \times 10^{-24}$ g. Because the mass of a proton is so small, it is more convenient to use a different scale whose units are called **atomic mass units** to represent its mass. A proton is assigned 1.0 atomic mass unit (amu). A neutron has approximately the same mass as a proton.

Each atom of a specific element must contain the same number of protons as every other atom of that element. The number of protons in the nucleus of an atom is the **atomic number** of that element. For example, chlorine has an atomic number of 17. Each chlorine atom contains 17 protons in its nucleus.

Electrons occupy the space of an atom outside the nucleus and have a charge equal to, but opposite of, a proton. Electrons are much less massive than either the proton or neutron, having a mass of only 1/1836 amu. Table 1-1 summarizes information about each of the particles that make up an atom.

It has been mentioned that the mass of an atom is extremely small. The atomic mass scale replaces grams as the unit used to describe the masses of atoms. The nucleus of a carbon atom containing 6 protons and 6 neutrons is taken as the standard mass, and the mass of any atom is a ratio between its mass and that of the carbon nucleus. The sum of the numbers of protons and neutrons in the nucleus is called the **mass number** of the nucleus. Thus, a nucleus with 7 protons and 7 neutrons has a mass number of 14. When determining the mass of an atom, the mass of the electrons is so small it is not considered in the calculation.

| Table 1-1. Some Subatomic Particles | | | | |
|---|---|---|---|---|
| Particle | Charge | Mass | Location | Symbol |
| Proton | +1 | 1 amu | nucleus | ${}_{1}^{1}H$ or $p_{1}^{1}$ |
| Neutron | 0 | 1 amu | nucleus | ${}_{0}^{1}n$ |
| Electron | −1 | 1/1836 amu | outside | ${}_{-1}^{0}e$ |

| Table 1-2. Isotopes of Hydrogen | | | | |
|---|---|---|---|---|
| Particle | Protons | Neutrons | Mass Number | Symbol |
| Protium | 1 | 0 | 1 amu | $_1^1\text{H}$ |
| Deuterium | 1 | 1 | 2 amu | $_1^2\text{H}$ |
| Tritium | 1 | 2 | 3 amu | $_1^3\text{H}$ |

**Isotopes** Although all the atoms of a given element must contain the same number of protons, the number of neutrons may vary. Most atoms of hydrogen contain only a proton. Remembering that the mass number of an atom is the sum of its protons and neutrons, this atom of hydrogen has a mass of 1 amu. In addition to this atom with a mass of 1 amu, there are some atoms of hydrogen that have a nucleus with both a proton and a neutron. While this is still an atom of hydrogen, it has a mass number of 2. There is still another type of hydrogen with a nucleus containing two neutrons in addition to a proton; this atom has a mass number of 3. These different forms of an atom are called isotopes. **Isotopes** are atoms of the same element that have different numbers of neutrons, and hence have different mass numbers. Table 1-2 describes the isotopes of the element hydrogen.

**Isotope Symbols** Isotopes can be identified by using a symbol that indicates both the element and its mass number. Thus, C-12 represents a carbon atom with a mass number of 12. The mass number represents the sum of the protons and neutrons. The difference between the atomic number of an atom and its mass number is the number of neutrons. Because the atomic number (number of protons) of C-12 is 6, the number of neutrons will also be 6. Different ways to symbolize carbon-14 isotopes are shown in Figure 1-5.

C-14    $^{14}\text{C}$

Carbon-14   $_6^{14}\text{C}$

**Figure 1-5. Some symbols of isotopes:** Common isotopic notations of carbon atoms that contain six protons and eight neutrons

## Atomic Masses

You have seen that the mass number of a given nucleus must be an integer because it is the sum of the numbers of protons and neutrons in the nucleus. However, when you examine the periodic table of the elements, you will notice that most of the elements have masses that are fractional values. These masses are called the **atomic masses** of the elements, and they are the average mass of all the isotopes in a sample of the element.

## SAMPLE PROBLEM

Find the number of neutrons in an atom of $_{34}^{79}\text{Se}$.

**SOLUTION:** Identify the known and unknown values.

*Known*
atomic number = 34
mass number = 79

*Unknown*
number of neutrons = ?

**1.** Write the relationship for number of neutrons, atomic number, and atomic mass.

Neutrons = Mass number − Atomic number

**2.** Substitute the known values and solve for the number of neutrons.

Neutrons = 79 − 34 = 45

Atomic mass can be calculated from the mass and the abundance of naturally occurring isotopes. Carbon has two naturally occurring stable isotopes. Most carbon atoms—98.89%—are C-12, while the remaining 1.108% are C-13. What is the atomic mass of carbon?

**SOLUTION:** Identify the known and unknown values.

_Known_
98.89% C-12
1.108% C-13

_Unknown_
atomic mass = ? amu

**1.** Convert the percentages to decimal numbers, and multiply the mass of each isotope by its decimal abundance.

12 amu × 0.9889 = 11.87 amu
13 amu × 0.01108 = 0.1440 amu

**2.** Add these masses of isotopes.

11.87 amu + 0.1440 amu = 12.01 amu

How can chlorine have an atomic mass of 35.454 amu? The answer is found in the relative numbers of the isotopes of chlorine. There are two major isotopes of chlorine, Cl-35 and Cl-37. The atomic mass of chlorine is the average of the two isotopes. But the average of Cl-35 and Cl-37 would seem to give chlorine an average mass of 36 amu. That would be true if Cl-35 and Cl-37 were equally abundant in nature, but such is not the case.

If you had four test grades, 90%, 90%, 90% and 80%, you would not have an average test grade of 85%. Your average would be 87.5%. In the same way, if there are many more atoms of Cl-35 than Cl-37, the average mass would be closer to 35 amu. Consult either the periodic table or a table of properties of the elements for average atomic masses.

## Location of Electrons

Remember that electrons are found in the space of the atom around the nucleus. Experiments have shown that the electrons are not found just anywhere around the nucleus; they are found in orbitals. An orbital is a region where an electron can most probably be found.

**Energy Levels** The orbitals in an atom form a series of energy levels in which electrons may be found. Each electron in an atom has its own distinct amount of energy that corresponds to the energy level that it occupies. Electrons can gain and lose energy and move to different energy levels, but they do so in a unique way. Instead of being able to absorb any amount of energy, an electron can only absorb a discrete, or fixed amount of energy that would allow it to move to a higher energy level. While this concept is difficult for us to understand, an analogy may help. When we climb up or down a set of stairs, we must exert enough energy to move from one step to another. We can't stop at a half step. In a like manner, if an electron moves from one energy level to a different energy level, it must give off or absorb the energy difference between those two levels.

**Ground and Excited States** When the electrons occupy the lowest available orbitals, the atom is said to be in the **ground state.** The electrons in a ground state atom have filled the available spaces from the lowest energy level to higher levels until all the electrons are accounted for. The linear symbol Na-2-8-1 shows the electron arrangement for a ground state sodium atom.

When electrons are subjected to stimuli such as heat, light, or electricity, an electron may absorb energy and temporarily move to a higher energy level. This unstable condition is called an **excited state.** Na-2-7-2 is one of the many possible arrangements for an excited atom of sodium. An excited-state electron quickly returns to a lower available level, emitting the same amount of energy it absorbed to go to the higher energy level.

The energy emitted may be in the form of infrared, ultraviolet, or visible light. The light given off from a fluorescent or a neon light is caused by excited electrons returning to lower energy levels. While the light appears as one color to our eyes, it is actually composed of many different wavelengths, each of which is seen as a different line when viewed through an instrument called a spectroscope.

Unlike a continuous spectrum produced by holding a prism in sunlight, the visible light produced by electrons is confined to narrow lines of color called bright line spectra. Each atom has its own distinct pattern of emission lines (or bright line spectrum), and these spectra are used to identify elements.

## SAMPLE PROBLEM

What element is represented by the following line spectrum?

Bright-line spectrum of an element

**SOLUTION:** Identify the known and unknown values.

*Known*
Spectra of several
   elements

*Unknown*
Identity of the
   element = ?

1. Compare the lines on the spectrum of the element shown above to those in Figure 1-6.

2. Notice that the first line shown for the unknown element is at 4600. Two elements on the reference table have spectral lines at that frequency, Li and Sr. The second line of the unknown is at 4960. Both elements have lines approximately at this reading, but Sr has two lines between 4600 and 4960 that are not in the unknown. The unknown is Li. Check for accuracy by noting that Li has a line at 6090, while Sr does not.

# Spectra

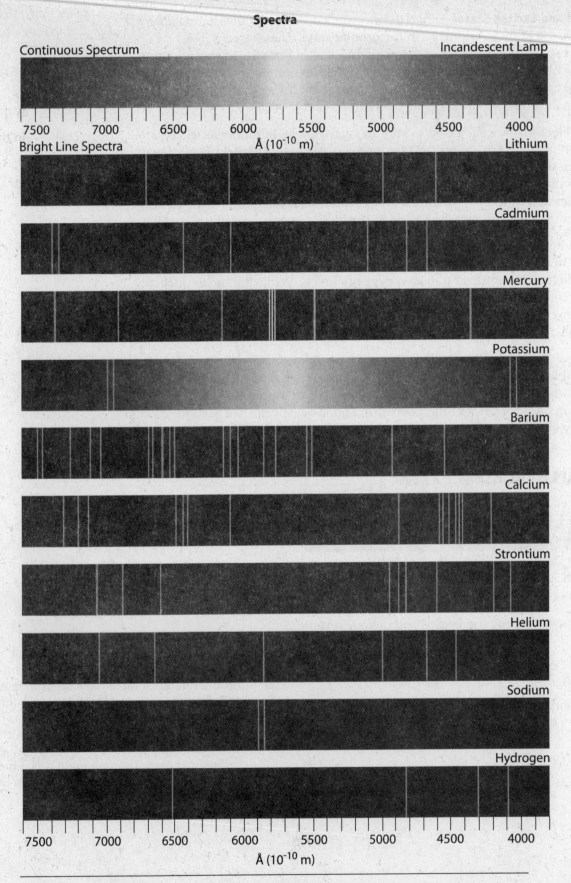

**Figure 1-6. Emission spectra:** The bright lines are emission lines and are unique to each type of atom.

**13.** The atomic mass of an element is defined as the weighted average mass of that element's

(1) most abundant isotope
(2) least abundant isotope
(3) naturally occurring isotopes
(4) radioactive isotopes

**14.** Element X has two isotopes. If 72.0% of the element has an isotopic mass of 84.9 amu and 28.0% has an isotopic mass of 87.0 amu, the average atomic mass of element X is numerically equal to

(1) $(72.0 + 98.9)(28.0 + 87.0)$
(2) $(72.0 - 84.9)(28.0 - 87.0)$
(3) $(0.720)(84.9) + (0.280)(87.0)$
(4) $(72.0)(84.9) + (28.0)(87.0)$

**15.** A neutral atom with 6 electrons and 8 neutrons is an isotope of

(1) carbon      (3) nitrogen
(2) silicon     (4) oxygen

**16.** The average isotopic mass of chlorine is 35.5 amu. Which mixture of isotopes (shown as percents) produces this mass?

(1) 50% C-12 and 50% C-13
(2) 50% Cl-35 and 50% Cl-37
(3) 75% Cl-35 and 25% Cl-37
(4) 75% C-12 and 25% C-13

**17.** The major portion of an atom's mass consists of

(1) electrons and protons
(2) electrons and neutrons
(3) neutrons and positrons
(4) neutrons and protons

**18.** Which atoms have the same number of neutrons?

(1) H-1 and He-3     (3) H-3 and He-3
(2) H-2 and He-4     (4) H-3 and He-4

**19.** Atoms of $^{16}$O, $^{17}$O and $^{18}$O have the same number of

(1) neutrons but a different number of protons
(2) protons but a different number of neutrons
(3) protons but a different number of electrons
(4) electrons but a different number of protons

**20.** A neutron has approximately the same mass as

(1) an alpha particle     (3) an electron
(2) a beta particle       (4) a proton

**21.** The total number of protons and neutrons in the nuclide $^{35}_{17}$Cl is

(1) 52      (2) 35      (3) 18      (4) 17

**22.** The nuclides $^{14}_{6}$C and $^{14}_{7}$N are similar in that they both have the same

(1) mass number
(2) atomic number
(3) number of neutrons
(4) nuclear charge

**23.** What is the nuclear charge of an atom with a mass of 23 and an atomic number of 11?

(1) 11+      (2) 12+      (3) 23+      (4) 34+

**24.** Compared to the charge and mass of a proton, an electron has

(1) the same charge and a smaller mass
(2) the same charge and the same mass
(3) an opposite charge and a smaller mass
(4) an opposite charge and the same mass

**25.** Which of the following statements is correct?

(1) A proton is positively charged; a neutron is negatively charged.
(2) A proton is negatively charged; a neutron is positively charged.
(3) A proton is positively charged; an electron is negatively charged.
(4) A proton is negatively charged; an electron is positively charged.

**26.** Which symbols represent atoms that are isotopes of each other?

(1) $^{14}$C and $^{14}$N      (3) $^{131}$I and $^{131}$I
(2) $^{16}$O and $^{18}$O      (4) $^{222}$Rn and $^{222}$Ra

**27.** When electrons in an excited state fall to lower energy levels, energy is

(1) absorbed
(2) released
(3) neither absorbed nor released
(4) both released and absorbed

**28.** The characteristic bright-line spectrum of an atom is produced when

(1) nuclei undergo fission
(2) nuclei undergo fusion
(3) electrons move from higher to lower energy levels
(4) electrons move from lower to higher energy levels

## Electron Arrangement

Although the electrons in an atom contribute little to the mass of an atom, their arrangement determines its chemical properties. The chemical properties of an element are based on the number of electrons in the outer energy level of its atoms. These outer electrons are called <u>valence electrons.</u> How can you determine how the electrons are arranged in an atom and, therefore, how many valence electrons an atom has?

### Quantum Numbers

Remember that the first energy level in an atom can contain two electrons and the second can contain eight. We can't see the electron arrangement in an atom. How were these numbers determined? A theory, called the <u>quantum theory</u>, was developed to explain the chemical behavior of atoms.

Electrons can be described by a set of four numbers called <u>quantum numbers</u>. The first number describes the major energy level of the electron and is called the principal quantum number. The principal quantum number is the same as the number of the energy level that contains the electron. If an electron has a principal quantum number of 2, it is in the second energy level from the nucleus.

Each energy level has one or more sublevels associated with it. Each energy level contains as many sublevels as the number of the level. For example, energy level three has three sublevels.

The first sublevel of any energy level is designated the s sublevel. If a second sublevel is present, it is $p$. The third is $d$, and the fourth is $f$. Sublevels are described by using the number of the principal energy level together with the letter designation of each sublevel. For example, 3$s$ describes the first sublevel of the third energy level.

The third quantum number relates to the orbitals in the sublevels and their orientations. Remember that an orbital is a location inside the atom where an electron is most likely to be found.

Electrons that are in s sublevels are found in orbitals with spherical shapes without sharp edges surrounding the nucleus. There is only one way a sphere can be arranged, so there is only one orbital in an $s$ sublevel.

The $p$ orbital is somewhat dumbbell in shape. There are three of these orbitals at each principal energy level higher than energy level one. The $p$ orbitals are arranged at right angles to each other and can be designated as $p_x$, $p_y$, and $p_z$. Thus, each $p$ sublevel contains three orbitals. Figure 1-7 shows the shapes of $s$ and $p$ orbitals.

At levels three and higher, there is another type of sublevel, the $d$ sublevel containing five orbitals. From principal level four and higher, $f$ sublevels with seven orbitals are found. The shapes of the orbitals in both the $d$ and $f$ sublevels are complex, so only $s$ and $p$ orbitals are shown.

The fourth quantum number relates to the spin of an electron. This number indicates that each orbital can contain two electrons spinning in opposite directions.

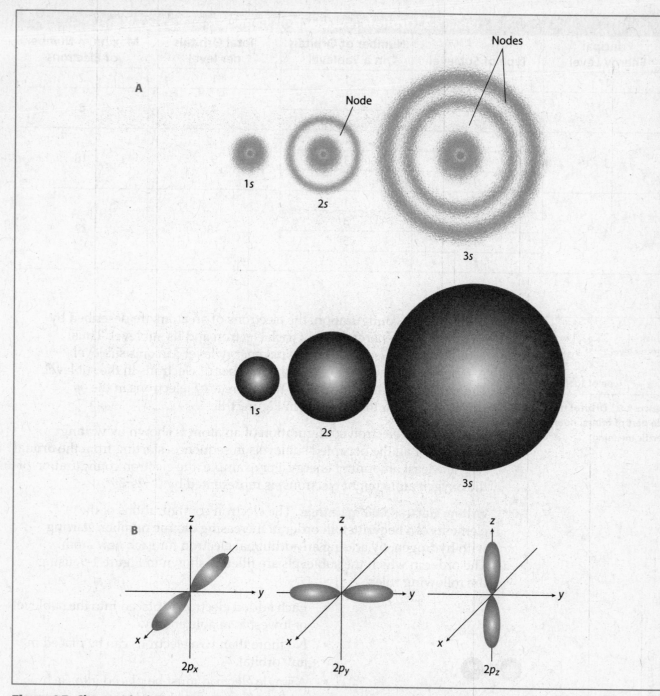

**Figure 1-7. Shape and relative sizes of orbitals:** (A) Look at the shape and relative sizes of 1*s*, 2*s*, and 3*s* orbitals. The upper diagrams are cross sections of the diagrams beneath. The dark areas show where electrons are most probably located. Notice that there are areas, called nodes, where it is unlikely to find an electron. (B) Shapes and orientations of *p* orbitals

Table 1-3 summarizes how the maximum number of electrons per energy level is determined using these four quantum numbers.

## Electron Configurations

Quantum numbers describe the distribution of the electrons in an atom when you remember that electrons will occupy the lowest sublevel possible. This distribution of the electrons in an atom is called its <u>electron configuration</u>.

## Table 1-3. Orbitals and Electron Capacity

| Principal Energy Level | Type of Sublevel | Number of Orbitals in a Sublevel | Total Orbitals per level | Maximum Number of Electrons |
|:---:|:---:|:---:|:---:|:---:|
| 1 | s | 1 | 1 | 2 |
| 2 | s | 1 | 4 | 8 |
|   | p | 3 |   |   |
| 3 | s | 1 | 9 | 18 |
|   | p | 3 |   |   |
|   | d | 5 |   |   |
| 4 | s | 1 | 16 | 32 |
|   | p | 3 |   |   |
|   | d | 5 |   |   |
|   | f | 7 |   |   |

Principal energy level → $3p^4$ ← Number of electrons in sublevel

↑ Type of sublevel

**Figure 1-8. Orbital notation:** Each part of orbital notation has a specific meaning.

In an electron configuration, the electrons of an atom are described by identifying the energy level of each electron and its sublevel. Thus, $3s$ describes an electron at principal energy level 3 in an s sublevel. A superscript is added to show the number of electrons in the sublevel. The notation $4p^5$ tells the reader that there are 5 electrons in the $4p$ sublevel. Look at the example in Figure 1-8.

The complete electron configuration of an atom is shown by writing symbols for all the occupied sublevels in sequence, starting from the orbital with the least amount of energy. For example, the electron configuration of the oxygen atom (eight electrons) is represented by $1s^2 2s^2 2p^4$.

**Writing Electron Configurations** The electron configurations of the elements can be written in order of increasing atomic number, starting with hydrogen, by adding an additional electron for each new atom. The order in which the sublevels are filled is shown in Figure 1-9, using the following rules.

- Each added electron is placed into the sublevel of lowest available energy.
- No more than two electrons can be placed in any orbital.
- A single electron must be placed into each orbital of a given sublevel before any pairing takes place. (Hund's Rule)
- The outermost principal energy level can only contain electrons in s and p orbitals.

**Order of Electron Fill** While there are many locations that electrons might fill in an atom, the most stable condition exists when they fill the lowest available energy orbitals. This simply means that the first energy level, which is less energetic than any other, is filled first. In level two, the s orbital, then the p orbitals, are filled. Next, the s and p orbitals of the third level are

Energy decreases

Energy decreases

**Figure 1-9. Electron configurations:** To find the electron configuration of an atom, simply begin adding electrons to the 1s sublevel and continue adding them in the order shown.

filled, but the 3d level is not filled next. Instead, the 4s sublevel is filled, followed by the 3d. Why does this change in order occur? As the number of sublevels per energy level increases, the space taken up by the sublevels increases and the energy levels begin to overlap.

**Orbital Notation** While electron configuration notation is useful, it does not show how electrons are distributed in each sublevel. Figure 1-10 shows two ways of illustrating the distribution of electrons in an atom. A circle or square can be used to represent an orbital. An electron is represented either by a line or an arrow. When two lines are drawn in an orbital they represent an orbital pair with opposite spins. If arrows are used to represent the electrons, two arrows pointed in opposite directions represent a pair of electrons with opposite spin.

**Figure 1-10. Two methods of showing orbital notation:** The arrows in an orbital are drawn in opposite directions to indicate that the electrons have opposite spins.

## SAMPLE PROBLEM

A phosphorus atom has an electron configuration of $1s^22s^22p^63s^13p^4$. Is the atom in its ground state, or is it in an excited state?

**SOLUTION:** Identify the known and unknown values.

| *Known* | *Unknown* |
|---|---|
| electron configuration of $1s^22s^22p^63s^13p^4$ | excited or ground state |

1. Look at Figure 1-10 for order of filling of orbitals.

2. If the order is changed, or if a sublevel other than the last one is unfilled, the atom is probably in an excited state. The ground state configuration of a phosphorus atom would be $1s^22s^22p^63s^23p^3$. In the known configuration, one electron is in a higher sublevel than it would be in its ground state, so the atom is excited.

# Review Questions

**29.** Which is the electron configuration of an atom in the excited state?

(1) $1s^22s^22p^2$
(2) $1s^22s^22p^1$
(3) $1s^22s^22p^53s^2$
(4) $1s^22s^22p^63s^1$

**30.** Which atom in the ground state contains one completely filled p orbital?

(1) Ne      (3) He
(2) O        (4) Be

**31.** What is the total number of electrons in the second principal energy level of a calcium atom in the ground state?

(1) 6      (3) 8
(2) 2      (4) 18

**32.** Which is the correct orbital notation of a lithium atom in the ground state?

33. The atom of which element in the ground state has two unpaired electrons in the 2p sublevel?

(1) fluorine
(2) nitrogen
(3) beryllium
(4) carbon

34. What is the total number of occupied s orbitals in an atom of nickel in the ground state?

(1) 1     (2) 2     (3) 3     (4) 4

35. Which atom in the ground state has only three electrons in the 3p sublevel?

(1) phosphorus     (3) argon
(2) potassium      (4) aluminum

36. What is the total number of occupied principal energy levels in a neutral atom of neon in the ground state?

(1) 1     (2) 2     (3) 3     (4) 4

37. Which is the electron configuration of an atom in the excited state?

(1) $1s^12s^1$
(2) $1s^22s^1$
(3) $1s^22s^22p^1$
(4) $1s^22s^22p^2$

38. Which orbital notation correctly represents the outermost principal energy level of a nitrogen atom in the ground state?

39. Which electron configuration represents a potassium atom in the excited state?

(1) $1s^22s^22p^63s^23p^3$
(2) $1s^22s^22p^63s^13p^4$
(3) $1s^22s^22p^63s^23p^64s^1$
(4) $1s^22s^22p^63s^23p^54s^2$

40. In an atom of lithium in the ground state, what is the total number of orbitals that contain only one electron?

(1) 1     (2) 2     (3) 3     (4) 4

41. What is the total number of completely filled principal energy levels in an atom of argon in the ground state?

(1) 1     (2) 2     (3) 3     (4) 4

42. What is the total number of electrons needed to completely fill all the orbitals in an atom's second principal energy level?

(1) 16     (2) 2     (3) 8     (4) 4

43. An atom in the excited state can have an electron configuration of

(1) $1s^22s^2$
(2) $1s^22p^1$
(3) $1s^22s^22p^5$
(4) $1s^22s^22p^6$

44. What is the total number of sublevels in the fourth principal energy level?

(1) 1     (2) 2     (3) 3     (4) 4

45. Which electron configuration represents an atom in the excited state?

(1) $1s^22s^22p^63s^2$
(2) $1s^22s^22p^63s^1$
(3) $1s^22s^22p^6$
(4) $1s^22s^22p^53s^2$

46. Which element has atoms in the ground state with a sublevel that is only half filled?

(1) helium     (3) nitrogen
(2) beryllium  (4) neon

47. Which sublevel contains a total of five orbitals?

(1) s     (2) p     (3) d     (4) f

48. What is the maximum number of electrons that can occupy the fourth principal energy level of an atom?

(1) 6     (2) 8     (3) 18     (4) 32

49. What is the total number of unpaired electrons in an atom of oxygen in the ground state?

(1) 6     (2) 2     (3) 8     (4) 4

50. Which of the following sublevels has the highest energy?

(1) 2p     (2) 2s     (3) 3p     (4) 3s

51. What is the maximum number of electrons in an orbital of any atom?

(1) 1     (2) 2     (3) 6     (4) 10

**52.** What is the electron configuration of a Mn atom in the ground state?

(1) $1s^2 2s^2 2p^6 3s^2$
(2) $1s^2 2s^2 2p^6 3s^2 3p^6 s3d^5 4s^2$
(3) $1s^2 2s^2 2p^6 3s^2 3p^6 3d^5 4s^1 4p^1$
(4) $1s^2 2s^2 2p^6 3s^2 3p^6 3d^7$

**53.** Which orbital notation correctly represents a noble gas in the ground state?

**54.** Which atom in the ground state has three half-filled orbitals?

(1) P          (3) Al
(2) Si         (4) Li

**55.** What is the total number of completely filled sublevels found in an atom of krypton in the ground state?

(1) 10         (3) 8
(2) 2          (4) 4

**56.** Assuming that the orbitals of nickel fill in the order described in Figure 1-10, what is the total number of sublevels that contain electrons in the third principal energy level of a nickel atom in the ground state?

(1) 1          (3) 3
(2) 2          (4) 4

**57.** The third row of the periodic table (Na to Ar) follows the same pattern of electron filling as the second row (Li to Ne). Write the electron configurations and orbital structure for the elements from Na to Ar.

## Types of Matter

The world is composed of millions of different materials, and they are all combinations of atoms. As we look at the world around us, two categories of matter can be distinguished.

### Homogeneous and Heterogeneous Matter

Some matter looks uniform and doesn't seem to be made up of parts. A sample of pure water does not have distinguishable parts and has the same composition throughout. When a material has uniform composition throughout, the sample is said to be **homogeneous.** Homogeneous matter can contain more than one type of particle, but particles are uniformly distributed. Sugar dissolved in water is an example of matter that contains both sugar and water but is homogeneous because the smallest particles that make up sugar and water are uniformly distributed.

Other materials are obviously made up of parts. A chocolate chip cookie has pieces of chocolate embedded in the cookie dough. When you examine a piece of concrete, you can see tiny pebbles and pieces of sand embedded in the cement. Such materials, which have varying composition, are said to be **heterogeneous.** Heterogeneous materials are made up of parts with different chemical and physical properties. These parts are not uniformly mixed or dispersed.

Matter can be divided into the major categories of pure substances and mixtures. Pure substances are homogeneous; mixtures can be either heterogeneous or homogeneous.

## Pure Substances

A sample of matter is a **pure substance** if its composition is the same throughout the sample. The two types of pure substances are elements and compounds. Oxygen gas, an element, and water, a compound, are examples of pure substances.

**Elements** **Elements** are substances that cannot be broken down or decomposed into simpler substances by chemical means. There are 91 elements that occur naturally, and more than a dozen elements are synthesized in laboratories. Most elements are metals, such as gold, iron, and aluminum. Examine a periodic table of the elements to see how many different elements you recognize.

**Compounds** **Compounds** are composed of two or more elements that are chemically combined in definite proportions by mass. Although all compounds contain at least two different types of atoms, the composition of a compound is the same throughout.

The law of definite proportions is the statement that types of atoms in a compound exist in a fixed ratio. Examine the law of definite proportions as shown in Figure 1-11. Water is a compound composed of two elements—hydrogen and oxygen—that are chemically combined. Water can be decomposed into these two elements in a mass ratio of 1:8. When any sample of water is decomposed it will always yield one part by weight of hydrogen for each eight parts of oxygen. When 9 g of water are decomposed they will always produce 1 g of hydrogen and 8 g of oxygen. If 36 g of water decomposed, how many grams of oxygen would be produced? Because the proportions remain the same, 32 g of oxygen would be produced.

Pure substances have a constant composition, both within a given sample and from one sample to another. There is another type of matter that does not have a constant composition.

18 g $H_2O$ → 16 g $O_2$ + 2 g $H_2$

**Figure 1-11. The law of definite proportions:** This diagram is a model of the decomposition of water. Notice that for every 18 g of water, 16 g of oxygen and 2 g of hydrogen form.

## Mixtures

**Mixtures** are combinations of two or more pure substances that can be separated by physical means. Mixtures are different from compounds because their composition is not definite or "fixed," and the parts can be separated by physical means. For example, different amounts of sugar can be dissolved in a liter of water, and each result would be a water solution of sugar. Even though the sugar seems to disappear and become part of the water, it really doesn't. If the water evaporates, the sugar is left behind; the water and sugar separate.

Some mixtures are homogeneous, and some are heterogeneous. Solutions are mixtures that are homogeneous. Most mixtures are heterogeneous. Soil and concrete are good examples of heterogeneous mixtures. The different parts of each can be easily seen.

## Distinguishing Between Mixtures and Compounds

Look at Figure 1-12. Both mixtures and compounds contain two or more different elements. However, the two categories are quite different when one considers their composition and properties.

In a mixture, elements such as iron and sulfur can be present in different ratios. Each substance that makes up the mixture retains its properties. Iron is magnetic and can be separated from a mixture of iron and sulfur with a magnet. Sulfur retains its elemental yellow color in the mixture.

However, if these two elements chemically react, they combine in a mass ratio of 1.74 parts of iron to 1.00 part of sulfur. In the compound the iron is no longer magnetic, and the sulfur loses its yellow color. The compound has its own properties. For example, iron sulfide has a different melting point than either elemental sulfur or iron.

In a later topic, you will learn about different methods that can be used to separate the parts of a mixture.

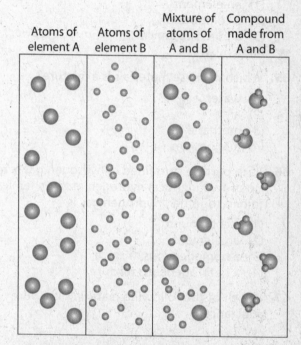

**Figure 1-12. Elements, compounds and mixtures:** Study the models and notice the differences among elements, compounds, and mixtures.

# Review Questions

**58.** Which of the following cannot be decomposed by chemical means?

(1) sodium     (3) sucrose
(2) ethanol     (4) water

**59.** A compound differs from an element in that a compound

(1) is homogeneous
(2) has a definite composition
(3) has a definite melting point
(4) can be decomposed by a chemical reaction

**60.** A compound differs from a mixture in that a compound always has a

(1) homogeneous composition
(2) maximum of two elements
(3) minimum of three elements
(4) heterogeneous composition

**61.** Most elements are

(1) metals     (3) gases
(2) nonmetals     (4) made in a laboratory

**62.** A pure substance that is composed only of identical atoms is classified as

(1) a compound
(2) an element
(3) a heterogeneous mixture
(4) a homogeneous mixture

**63.** Which is characteristic of all mixtures?

(1) They are homogeneous.
(2) They are heterogeneous.
(3) Their compositions are in a definite ratio.
(4) Their compositions may vary.

**64.** A heterogeneous material may be

(1) an element
(2) a compound
(3) a pure substance
(4) a mixture

**65.** Which of these materials is a mixture?

(1) water
(2) air
(3) methane
(4) magnesium

**66.** Each particle contained in hydrogen gas is made up of two identical hydrogen atoms chemically joined together. Hydrogen gas is

(1) a compound
(2) an element
(3) a homogeneous mixture
(4) a heterogeneous mixture

**67.** Which of the following materials is a pure substance?

(1) air
(2) water
(3) fire
(4) earth

**68.** Which statement is an identifying characteristic of a mixture?

(1) A mixture can consist of a single element.
(2) A mixture can be separated by physical means.
(3) A mixture must have a definite composition by weight.
(4) A mixture must be homogeneous.

**69.** Which substance can be decomposed by a chemical change?

(1) ammonia        (3) magnesium
(2) aluminum       (4) manganese

**Answer the following questions using complete sentences.**

**70.** A sample of a material is passed through a filter paper. A white deposit remains on the paper, and a clear liquid passes through. The clear liquid is then evaporated, leaving a white residue. What can you determine about the nature of the sample?

**71.** A substance is found to contain only calcium and sulfur. How would you determine whether the substance is a compound or a mixture?

**72.** Using ⬤⬤ to represent a hydrogen molecule and ⬤⬤ to represent an oxygen molecule, draw a picture of a mixture of hydrogen and oxygen gases.

**73.** What are some of the differences between a mixture of iron and oxygen and a compound composed of iron and oxygen?

**74.** Is a pepperoni pizza homogeneous or heterogeneous? Explain your answer.

**75.** Examine the contents of the four containers shown below. Use complete sentences to identify each as containing only elements, only compounds or a mixture of these. Explain each of your answers.

**76.** Are the contents of Container D in question 75 homogeneous or heterogeneous? Explain your answer.

**77.** A chemist receives two samples. Analysis of one sample shows it to be 88.88% oxygen by mass and 11.12% hydrogen. Analysis of the other sample shows it to be 94.12% oxygen and 5.88% hydrogen. Are these samples of the same material? Explain your answer.

**Directions**

Review the Test-Taking Strategies section of this book. Then answer the following questions. Read each question carefully and answer with a correct choice or response.

## Part A

1 The model of the atom that pictured the atom with electrons traveling in circular orbits was called the
(1) planetary model
(2) cannonball model
(3) wave-mechanical model
(4) plum pudding model

2 Which sequence represents a correct order of historical developments leading to the modern model of the atom?
(1) the atom is a hard sphere → most of the atom is empty space → electrons exist in orbitals outside the nucleus
(2) the atom is a hard sphere → electrons exist in orbitals outside the nucleus → most of the atom is empty space
(3) most of the atom is empty space → electrons exist in orbitals outside the nucleus → the atom is a hard sphere
(4) most of the atom is empty space → the atom is a hard sphere → electrons exist in orbitals outside the nucleus

3 Compared to the entire atom, the nucleus of the atom is
(1) smaller and contains most of the atom's mass
(2) smaller and contains little of the atom's mass
(3) large and contains most of the atom's mass
(4) large and contains little of the atom's mass

4 In a famous experiment, positively charged particles were aimed at a thin sheet of gold foil. The results of this experiment were that
(1) most of the particles failed to pass through the foil
(2) most of the particles were repelled, showing that gold has a negative core
(3) a few of the particles were repelled, showing that the gold has a positive core
(4) a few of the particles were repelled, showing that the gold was neutral

5 Neutral atoms must contain equal numbers of
(1) protons and electrons
(2) protons and neutrons
(3) protons, neutrons, and electrons
(4) neutrons and electrons

6 Which of the following is true of a compound but not a mixture?
(1) A compound contains more than one element.
(2) All the nuclei in a compound contain the same number of protons.
(3) A compound may be heterogeneous.
(4) The composition of a compound does not vary.

7 Compared with an electron, a proton has
(1) more mass and the same charge
(2) more mass and an opposite charge
(3) equal mass and the same charge
(4) equal mass and an opposite charge

8 The total number of electrons in a neutral atom of any element is always equal to the atom's
(1) mass number
(2) number of neutrons
(3) number of protons
(4) number of nucleons

9 All isotopes of neutral atoms of sodium have
(1) 11 protons and 12 neutrons
(2) 12 protons and 11 neutrons
(3) 11 protons and 11 electrons
(4) 12 protons and 12 electrons

10 There are three isotopes of hydrogen, H-1, H-2, and H-3. All of these isotopes have
(1) a mass of 2 amu
(2) an atomic number of 1
(3) 1, 2, or 3 neutrons
(4) 1, 2, or 3 protons

11 An atom in the excited state contains
(1) more electrons than an atom in the ground state
(2) more protons than an atom in the ground state
(3) more potential energy than an atom in the ground state
(4) more mass than an atom in the ground state

12 As an electron moves from the excited state to the ground state, the potential energy of the electron
(1) decreases
(2) increases
(3) remains the same
(4) becomes zero

13 Which of the following particles has the smallest mass?
(1) neutron
(2) electron
(3) proton
(4) hydrogen atom

14 An element occurs as a mixture of isotopes. The atomic mass of the element is based upon
(1) the mass of the individual isotopes, only
(2) the relative abundances of the isotopes, only
(3) both the masses and the relative abundances of the individual isotopes
(4) neither the masses nor the relative abundances of the individual isotopes

## Part B

15 100 g of a clear liquid is evaporated and a few grams of white crystals remain. The original liquid was a
(1) heterogeneous compound
(2) heterogeneous mixture
(3) homogeneous compound
(4) homogeneous mixture

16 Two samples of bronze, a uniform material, are analyzed and found to contain different percentages of tin. Based on this information, bronze is likely a
(1) homogeneous compound
(2) heterogeneous compound
(3) homogeneous mixture
(4) heterogeneous mixture

17 Many companies around the world manufacture ammonia, $NH_3$. Which of the following is true?
(1) No matter where it is manufactured, it will have the same composition.
(2) Its composition will vary from place to place because different amounts of nitrogen and hydrogen are used.
(3) Some samples may contain more nitrogen than others.
(4) Some samples may contain more hydrogen than others.

18 There are three isotopes of oxygen: O-16, O-17, and O-18. These neutral atoms contain
(1) equal numbers of protons, neutrons, and electrons
(2) equal numbers of protons and neutrons, but different numbers of electrons
(3) equal numbers of protons and electrons, but different numbers of neutrons
(4) different numbers of protons, neutrons, and electrons

19 What is the charge on a particle that contains 9 protons, 10 neutrons, and 9 electrons?
(1) It is neutral.
(2) It has a net charge of 1+.
(3) It has a net charge of 1−.
(4) It has a net charge of 28+.

20 An element has two isotopes. 90% of the isotopes have a mass number of 20 amu, while 10% have a mass number of 22 amu. The atomic mass of the element
(1) cannot be determined without knowing the atomic number
(2) is 21 amu
(3) is closer to 20 amu than to 22 amu
(4) is closer to 22 amu than to 20 amu

21 If the atomic number of a neutral element is 35, and its nucleus contains 40 neutrons, which of the following is correct?
(1) The atom is bromine, and it has 35 electrons.
(2) The atom is bromine, and it has a mass number of 40.
(3) The atom is zirconium, and it has a mass number of 75.
(4) The atom is zirconium, and it has 40 electrons.

22 Examine the diagram of the atom. What element does it represent?

(1) hydrogen
(2) helium
(3) lithium
(4) carbon

23 An atom of Cl-35 contains
   (1) 17 protons, 17 neutrons, and 18 electrons
   (2) 17 protons, 18 neutrons, and 17 electrons
   (3) 18 protons, 17 neutrons, and 17 electrons
   (4) 18 protons, 18 neutrons, and 18 electrons

24 Which must be a mixture of substances?
   (1) solid
   (2) liquid
   (3) gas
   (4) solution

# Part C

25 When electrons move from the fourth energy level to the second energy level, they emit visible light. Explain why the light emitted when an electron makes this move in a sodium atom is a different color than the light emitted by an electron moving from the fourth to the second level of a hydrogen atom. [2]

26 A chemist analyzes two samples. One sample contains 14 g of element X and 6.0 g of element Y. The second sample contains 28 g of element X and 6.0 g of element Y. Does it appear that the two samples are the same substance? Explain the reasons for your answer. [3]

27 Ernest Rutherford performed an experiment in which alpha particles (helium nuclei) were aimed at gold foil. When a few of the particles bounced back instead of passing through with little or no deflection, Rutherford is quoted as saying, "I was as surprised as if I had aimed a 14-inch artillery shell at a piece of paper and it bounced back." Why was he so surprised, and how did he modify the model of the atom to explain his results? [4]

28 Samples of two different compounds were heated in a flame, and a spectral analysis was performed on each compound. Many of the lines from the two samples matched, but others did not. Use your knowledge of chemistry to explain how this is possible. [2]

29 Complete the following: [6]

| Composton of Some Neutral Atoms | | | |
|---|---|---|---|
| Symbol | H | | U |
| Atomic number | | 19 | |
| Mass number | 3 | | 238 |
| Number of neutrons | | 20 | |
| Number of electrons | | | |

30 A moon sample was analyzed in a lab. The carbon in the sample was found to be 97.78% carbon-12 and 2.22% carbon-13. According to these data, what is the atomic mass of carbon? Show all of your work. [3]

Base your answers to questions 31 through 33 on the data table, which shows three isotopes of neon.

| Some Isotopes of Neon | | |
|---|---|---|
| Isotope | Atomic Mass (atomic mass units) | Percent Natural Abundance |
| Ne-20 | 19.99 | 90.9% |
| Ne-21 | 20.99 | 0.3% |
| Ne-22 | 21.99 | 8.8% |

31 In terms of atomic particles, state one difference between these three isotopes of neon.

32 Based on the atomic masses and the natural abundances shown in the data table, show a correct numerical setup for calculating the average atomic mass of neon.

33 Based on the natural abundances, the average atomic mass of neon is closest to which whole number?

Base your answers to questions 34 and 35 on the information below.

Naturally occurring elemental carbon is a mixture of isotopes. The percent composition of the two most abundant isotopes is listed below.

• 98.93% of the carbon atoms have a mass of 12.00 amu.

• 1.07% of the carbon atoms have a mass of 13.00 amu.

34 Show a correct numerical setup for calculating the average atomic mass of carbon. [1]

35 Describe, in terms of subatomic particles found in the nucleus, one difference and one similarity in the nuclei of the two isotopes. The response must include both isotopes. [2]

# Formulas and Equations

## How Scientists Communicate With Symbols

**?** *Which "water" would all scientists around the world understand?*  **?**

l'eau

wasser

acqua

agua

$H_2O$

вода

ύδωρ

water

Find the answer in this topic.

# Formulas and Equations

## Vocabulary

| | | |
|---|---|---|
| analysis | exothermic | qualitative |
| chemical change | formula | quantitative |
| coefficient | molecular formula | reactant |
| decomposition | molecule | single replacement |
| diatomic molecule | physical change | subscript |
| double replacement | polyatomic ion | symbol |
| empirical formula | product | synthesis |
| endothermic | | |

## Topic Overview

Chemists in every country of the world speak many different languages. Despite their language differences, it is necessary for them to communicate with each other in a clear and concise manner. Chemists have agreed to a universal language of symbols to identify the elements of the earth, and a system of formulas and equations to explain how the elements interact. In this topic you will explore how the symbols are used to identify the different elements and how they can be combined into formulas representing the millions of different compounds. Then you will learn how these formulas can be combined into chemical equations to show the quantitative and qualitative aspects of chemical reactions.

## Chemical Symbols and Formulas

While the names of the elements are often different in various languages of the world, it is important that a person in any country can quickly and accurately determine which element is being referred to.

### Chemical Symbols

A system for a universal shorthand to identify the elements has been agreed upon. Each element has been assigned a unique one-, two-, or three-letter **symbol** for its identification. The first letter of a symbol is always capitalized. If there are any other letters in the symbol, they are lower case.

Some of the more common elements have a single letter symbol, such as O for oxygen and H for hydrogen. Other elements have symbols with two letters. Only recently discovered elements that don't yet have permanent names are given three-letter symbols. These elements are given systematic names that represent their atomic number until a name can be agreed upon by the International Union of Pure and Applied Chemists (IUPAC).

Symbols are usually easy to remember, as the letters in the symbol often relate to the English name of the element, such as He for helium and Al for aluminum. Sometimes the letters of the symbol do not correspond to the common English element name but relate instead to the Latin or Greek name, such as K (Latin *kalium*) for potassium, and Na (Latin *natrium*) for sodium. Table 2-1 shows the names and symbols of elements with atomic numbers 1–20.

| Table 2-1. Names and Symbols for the First 20 Elements | | | | | |
| --- | --- | --- | --- | --- | --- |
| Atomic Number | Name | Symbol | Atomic Number | Name | Symbol |
| 1 | hydrogen | H | 11 | sodium | Na |
| 2 | helium | He | 12 | magnesium | Mg |
| 3 | lithium | Li | 13 | aluminum | Al |
| 4 | beryllium | Be | 14 | silicon | Si |
| 5 | boron | B | 15 | phosphorus | P |
| 6 | carbon | C | 16 | sulfur | S |
| 7 | nitrogen | N | 17 | chlorine | Cl |
| 8 | oxygen | O | 18 | argon | Ar |
| 9 | fluorine | F | 19 | potassium | K |
| 10 | neon | Ne | 20 | calcium | Ca |

**Diatomic Molecules** When writing the symbols of uncombined elements, almost all are written as monatomic, that is, without a subscript. A **subscript** is a number to the right and slightly below a symbol that tells the number of atoms present. A subscript is not written if only one atom is present. Therefore, the symbol for iron is Fe, neon is Ne, and carbon is C.

There are, however, several important exceptions. Some elements exist in nature as two identical atoms covalently bonded into a **diatomic molecule.** Oxygen normally exists as $O_2$, a diatomic molecule. Other elements that exist as diatomic molecules are hydrogen ($H_2$), nitrogen ($N_2$), and the elements of Group 17 of the periodic table ($F_2$, $Cl_2$, $Br_2$, and $I_2$). Be sure that whenever you write the formulas for any of these uncombined elements, that you write them as diatomic molecules.

## Chemical Formulas

Compounds are composed of combinations of elements chemically combined in definite proportions by weight (mass). **Formulas** use chemical symbols and numbers to show both qualitative and quantitative information about a substance. **Qualitative** information relates to things that cannot be counted or measured, such as what elements are in the compound. **Quantitative** information deals with things that can be either counted or measured, such as the number of atoms of each element present in a unit of the compound.

In a formula of a compound, the symbols for the elements supply the qualitative information. The formula CO tells the reader that the compound consists of carbon and oxygen. Notice the difference between CO and Co. The first is a combination of two elements in a compound, carbon monoxide, while the second is the symbol for an element, cobalt.

Carbon monoxide

## CO
**one carbon atom,
one oxygen atom**

Carbon dioxide

## CO$_2$
**one carbon atom,
two oxygen atoms**

**Figure 2-1. Subscripts in a formula:** The use of subscripts shows the relative number of atoms of each type in a compound. No subscript is written if only one atom of an element is present.

Recall that the numbers to the right and slightly below a symbol, called subscripts, supply quantitative information, telling us the number of atoms of those elements in a unit of the compound. For example, the symbols in the formula $H_2SO_4$ give us the qualitative information that the compound contains hydrogen, sulfur, and oxygen. The subscript 2 after the H indicates that there are two atoms of hydrogen present. No subscript is written after the S, so there is one sulfur atom. The 4 after O informs the reader that there are four atoms of oxygen present. Figure 2-1 shows the use of subscripts for the two compounds of carbon and oxygen. Table 2-2 shows some formulas for elements and compounds. Notice that the formula for a monatomic element is just its symbol.

| Table 2-2. Formulas for Some Elements and Compounds | | | |
|---|---|---|---|
| Name | Formula | Name | Formula |
| neon | Ne | calcium hydroxide | Ca(OH)$_2$ |
| sulfuric acid | H$_2$SO$_4$ | magnesium nitrate | Mg(NO$_3$)$_2$ |
| glucose | C$_6$H$_{12}$O$_6$ | sodium chloride | NaCl |
| uranium | U | gold | Au |
| chlorine | Cl$_2$ | dihydrogen oxide | H$_2$O |
| ammonia | NH$_3$ | hydrochloric acid | HCl |
| methane | CH$_4$ | sodium hydroxide | NaOH |
| iron | Fe | benzene | C$_6$H$_6$ |
| ammonium phosphate | (NH$_4$)$_3$PO$_4$ | silver nitrate | AgNO$_3$ |

**Types of Formulas** Two basic types of formulas provide different types of information about a compound. Empirical formulas include all types of compounds. Molecular formulas are important when considering compounds formed from atoms sharing electrons.

**Empirical Formulas** An **empirical formula** represents the simplest integer ratio in which atoms combine to form a compound. Ionic substances do not form discrete units or molecules, but rather an array of ions (charged particles). Ionic formulas indicate the ratio of the ions in a compound. The formula MgCl$_2$ tells us that for every magnesium ion in the compound there are two chloride ions. Formulas of ionic substances are empirical formulas.

**Molecular Formulas** Covalently bonded substances form discrete units called **molecules.** In some cases, such as H$_2$O, the empirical formula not only represents the simplest ratio, but it also represents the actual ratio of the atoms in a molecule of water. In other cases, the **molecular formula** may be a multiple of the empirical formula. For example the molecular formula of glucose is C$_6$H$_{12}$O$_6$, which is six times the empirical formula CH$_2$O.

## Atoms, Compounds, and Ions

It's easy to interpret a formula for an element or a compound, but it's a bit more complicated to write the formula for a compound. How do you know what elements form the compound and in what proportion? To understand how elements form compounds, an understanding of atoms and ions is essential.

Memory Jogger

proton = positive charge
electron = negative charge
neutron = no charge

Atoms and compounds are electrically neutral; that is, they do not have a net charge. Both atoms and compounds contain positively charged protons and negatively charged electrons, but there are equal numbers of positive and negative charges, producing a neutral atom or compound.

Ions, however, are not neutral and may be either positively or negatively charged. An ion that contains more protons than electrons will be positively charged, while an ion with more electrons than protons will have a negative charge. Positively charged ions attract negatively charged ions in a ratio that produces a neutral compound.

## Ionic Charges

The charge of an ion is indicated by a superscript following the symbol of the ion. When the ion has a charge of either $1+$ or $1-$, the number $1$ is omitted, and only the sign of the charge is shown. Thus the sodium ion with a charge of $1+$ is written as $Na^+$, and chlorine with a charge of $1-$ is $Cl^-$. The symbols of all other ions show both the size and sign of the charge. An aluminum ion is written as $Al^{3+}$, and an oxygen ion is shown as $O^{2-}$.

**Polyatomic Ions** A **polyatomic ion** is a group of atoms covalently bonded together, possessing a charge. Selected Polyatomic Ions in the *Reference Tables for Physical Setting/Chemistry* is a list of common polyatomic ions and their charges.

On Table 2-2 you will notice that three of the formulas contain symbols enclosed in parentheses. Parentheses are used to enclose polyatomic ions when there is more than one of the ions in a unit of a compound. The subscript written after the parentheses tells the reader how many of the ions are present in the compound. The subscript refers to each of the elements in the ion. For example, $(NH_4)_3PO_4$ tells the reader that there are three $NH_4^+$ ions, each containing one nitrogen atom and four hydrogen atoms, for a total of three nitrogen atoms and 12 hydrogen atoms. $NH_4^+$ is a polyatomic ion called the ammonium ion and has a charge of $1+$. The second part of the formula, $PO_4^{3-}$, is the formula of one phosphate ion that contains one phosphorus atom and four oxygen atoms. Like the ammonium ion, it has a charge, but it is $3-$. Figure 2-2 shows formulas, names, and models of some common polyatomic ions.

**Forming a Compound** Compounds can form in several different ways. One way is by the attraction of oppositely charged ions. Monatomic or polyatomic ions attract each other in a ratio that produces a neutral compound. Many of the compounds listed in Table 2-2 are formed in this manner.

## Coefficients

You know what information a subscript provides in a chemical formula. However, sometimes there is a number called a **coefficient** written in front of a formula. The coefficient tells how many units of the formula are present, and it applies to the entire formula. To determine the number of atoms present, consider the formula without the coefficient, and then multiply each value by the coefficient to find the total of each type of atom. For example, $2H_2O$ means that there are two molecules of water. These two molecules contain four hydrogen atoms and two oxygen atoms.

**Figure 2-2. Polyatomic ions:** Names, formulas, and models show the relationship of atoms in these polyatomic ions.

Hydroxide ion

$OH^-$

Nitrate ion

$NO_3^-$

Ammonium ion

$NH_4^+$

Sulfate ion

$SO_4^{2-}$

| Table 2-3. Atoms in Calcium Nitrate | |
| --- | --- |
| **Formula** | **Atoms** |
| $Ca(NO_3)_2$ | 1 calcium |
| | 2 nitrogen |
| | 6 oxygen |
| $3Ca(NO_3)_2$ | 3 calcium |
| | 6 nitrogen |
| | 18 oxygen |

The expression $4Mg(NO_3)_2$ contains four magnesium atoms, eight nitrogen atoms, and 24 oxygen atoms. As another example, consider Table 2-3.

## Hydrates

When water from some ionic solutions evaporates, the solute forms a crystal lattice that binds water within the structure. Such a compound is called a <u>hydrate.</u> These crystals have a definite number of water molecules for each unit of the compound. Barium chloride ($BaCl_2$) traps two water molecules as shown by the formula of the hydrate, $BaCl_2 \cdot 2H_2O$. Copper sulfate ($CuSO_4$) has five water molecules and a formula of $CuSO_4 \cdot 5H_2O$. Alum ($NaAl(SO_4)_2$) has 12 water molecules attached, $NaAl(SO_4)_2 \cdot 12H_2O$. The anhydrous (not hydrated) compound can be obtained by heating the crystals to drive off the water.

In a chemical reaction, the water in a hydrate does not react. However, it adds mass to the compound. For example, 10.0 g of a truly dry crystal of copper(II) sulfate contains more $CuSO_4$ than 10.0 g of the hydrated crystal, which contains both $CuSO_4$ and $H_2O$. If a certain amount of a material is made from a hydrated crystal, the mass of water must be considered in determining how much of the compound must be used.

# Review Questions

1. In a sample of solid $Ba(NO_3)_2$ the ratio of barium ions to nitrate ions is

   (1) 1:3:2  (2) 1:2  (3) 2:1  (4) 1:6

2. A chemical formula is an expression used to represent

   (1) mixtures only     (3) compounds only
   (2) elements only     (4) elements and compounds

3. Which formula represents a compound?

   (1) Ca  (2) Cr  (3) CO  (4) Co

4. What is the total number of atoms in the formula $Ca(NO_3)_2$?

   (1) 7  (2) 2  (3) 3  (4) 9

5. What is the total number of sulfur atoms in the formula $(NH_4)_2SO_4$?

   (1) 1  (2) 2  (3) 3  (4) 4

6. What is the total number of hydrogen atoms in the formula $3Mg(C_2H_3O_2)_2$?

   (1) 3  (2) 6  (3) 12  (4) 18

7. An example of an empirical formula is

   (1) $S_2H_2$  (2) $H_2O_2$  (3) $C_2Cl_2$  (4) $CaCl_2$

8. Which is an empirical formula?

   (1) $C_2H_2$  (2) $C_2H_4$  (3) $Al_2Cl_6$  (4) $K_2O$

9. What is the empirical formula of a compound with the molecular formula $C_6H_{12}O_6$?

   (1) $C_4H_8O_4$          (3) $C_2H_4O_2$
   (2) $C_3H_6O_3$          (4) $CH_2O$

10. Which compound has the same empirical and molecular formula?

    (1) $H_2O_2$  (2) $NH_3$  (3) $C_2H_6$  (4) $Hg_2Cl_2$

11. The empirical formula of a compound is $CH_2$. The molecular formula of this compound could be

    (1) $CH_4$  (2) $C_2H_2$  (3) $C_2H_4$  (4) $C_3H_3$

**Answer each of the following using complete sentences.**

12. What is the qualitative and quantitative information given by the formula $Ca_3(PO_4)_2$?

13. For each of the following formulas, write the name of each element and the number of atoms of that element that are in the formula.

    (a) $K_3PO_4$    (b) $Al(OH)_3$    (c) $Fe_2(SO_4)_3$

14. For each of the following formulas, write the name of each element and the number of atoms of that element that are in the formula.

    (a) $2K_3PO_4$    (b) $3Al(OH)_3$    (c) $5Fe_2(SO_4)_3$

15. What are the formulas and names of the polyatomic ions present in the compounds in question 14?

# Writing Formulas and Naming Compounds

All compounds must be electrically neutral, that is, the sum of the charges must equal zero. Common oxidation states for each element are listed in the upper right hand corner of each element's box in the periodic table. For many elements, the oxidation state is equal to the charge on the ion. Elements from Group 1 have an oxidation number of +1 and always have a charge of 1+ in compounds. All Group 2 elements have 2+ charges in compounds. Group 3 elements usually have a 3+ charge.

## Equalizing Charges

Compounds achieve neutrality by having an equal number of positive and negative charges. When a sodium ion ($Na^+$) and a chloride ion ($Cl^-$) combine, they will do so in a 1:1 ratio. The resulting formula will be NaCl, as such a ratio produces a neutral compound. Figure 2-3 shows the formulas of three compounds in which the charges of the ions are equal, but opposite.

In the case of a combination of $Mg^{2+}$ with $Cl^-$, a 1:1 ratio would not produce a neutral compound. To achieve neutrality there must be two $Cl^-$ ions for each $Mg^{2+}$. The correct formula will be $MgCl_2$. When ions have unequal and opposite charges, a simple technique will produce the correct formula. Simply write the charge of one ion as the subscript of the other. Transfer the number only, not the sign. Notice that this procedure automatically balances the positive and negative charges, producing neutral formulas.

Polyatomic ions form compounds with oppositely charged ions in the same way as single ions. The formula for $Na^+$ combining with $NO_3^-$ is simply $NaNO_3$. How would calcium ($Ca^{2+}$) combine with the nitrate ion ($NO_3^-$)? Because two nitrate ions are needed, enclose the nitrate ion in parentheses and write the subscript 2 after it, forming $Ca(NO_3)_2$.

| Ion formula | Compound formula |
|---|---|
| $K^+$ $Cl^-$ | KCl |
| $Mg^{2+}$ $S^{2-}$ | MgS |
| $Al^{3+}$ $N^{3-}$ | AlN |

**Figure 2-3. Examples of compounds with a 1:1 ion ratio:** The three compounds shown are potassium chloride, magnesium sulfide, and aluminum nitride.

## Naming Compounds

Compounds are named according to the types of elements that form them. Ionic compounds, whether they are binary (contain only two elements) or contain polyatomic ions, are named by one method. Covalent compounds that contain only nonmetals are named by a different method.

**Binary Ionic Compounds** The name of a binary ionic compound comes from the names of the elements in the compound. The positively charged particle, often a metallic ion, is placed first. The negatively charged ion will end the formula. A compound containing the sodium ion and the ion of chlorine will begin as *sodium*. The name of the negative ion is slightly changed from the element to end in *-ide*, making the negative ion of chlorine *chloride*. Hence, the compound containing the sodium and chloride ions is simply sodium chloride. Figure 2-5 summarizes naming binary compounds.

**Figure 2-4. Examples of ions with unequal charges:** To obtain the correct formula, write the absolute value of the ion charge as the subscript of the other ion.

**Figure 2-5. Naming binary compounds**

**Other Ionic Compounds** Naming compounds containing polyatomic ions is simple. When the positive portion is a metal, use the unmodified metal name plus the name of the negative polyatomic ion. For example, the name of $KNO_3$ is potassium nitrate.

Most polyatomic ions are negatively charged. Ammonium ($NH_4^+$) is an important exception. In a compound containing the ammonium ion, if the negative ion is a nonmetal, the ending is -ide. If the ammonium ion is combined with another polyatomic ion, they each retain their names.

Examples:     $NH_4Cl$        ammonium chloride
              $NH_4NO_3$      ammonium nitrate

**Binary Covalent Compounds** If a binary compound contains two nonmetals rather than a metal and a nonmetal, it is a molecular substance not composed of ions. The order in which the elements are arranged in the formula can be determined by considering the <u>electronegativity</u> values of the elements (See the *Reference Tables for Physical Setting/Chemistry*). The element with the lower electronegativity value is written first. For example, consider a compound containing carbon and oxygen. Because carbon has an electronegativity value of 2.6 while oxygen has a value of 3.4, carbon is written first. As in other binary compounds, the name of the compound will end in -ide. Because these two elements often can form more than one compound, a prefix is used to tell the reader how many atoms of each element are present. CO is named carbon monoxide, while $CO_2$ is named carbon dioxide. If only one atom of the first element is present, the prefix *mono-* is not used. If the element name starts with a vowel, any final *a* or *o* in the prefix is not used. For example, NO is named nitrogen monoxide, while $N_2O_4$ is dinitrogen tetroxide. Table 2-4 shows common prefixes used to name these compounds.

| Table 2-4. Common Prefixes | |
| --- | --- |
| Number of Atoms | Prefix |
| 1 | mono- |
| 2 | di- |
| 3 | tri- |
| 4 | tetra- |
| 5 | penta- |
| 6 | hexa- |
| 7 | hepta- |
| 8 | octo- |

**The Stock System** Some metals have more than one common oxidation state. For example, iron can have an oxidation number of either +2 or +3, which leads to a potential difficulty in naming compounds of iron. Which oxidation number is implied in the name iron chloride, the +2 or +3? The stock system solves this problem by simply stating the oxidation number by using Roman numerals after the name of the metal. Iron(II) chloride tells the reader that the iron has an oxidation number of +2, and the formula is $FeCl_2$. In iron(III) chloride, the iron has an oxidation number of +3, and the formula is $FeCl_3$.

# Review Questions

16. Pure nitrogen combines directly with an active metal to form a
    (1) nitrate
    (2) nitride
    (3) nitrite
    (4) permanganate

17. In a sample of solid $Al(NO_3)_3$, the ratio of aluminum ions to nitrate ions is
    (1) 1:1     (2) 1:2     (3) 1:3     (4) 1:6

18. In a sample of solid calcium phosphate $Ca_3(PO_4)_2$, the ratio of calcium ions to phosphate ions is
    (1) 1:1     (2) 2:3     (3) 3:2     (4) 3:4

19. What is the total number of atoms in $(NH_4)_2SO_4$?
    (1) 10     (2) 11     (3) 14     (4) 15

20. What is the total number of oxygen atoms present in one unit of $Mg(ClO_3)_2$?

    (1) 5     (2) 2     (3) 3     (4) 6

21. What is the total number of atoms of oxygen in the formula $Al(ClO_3)_3 \cdot 6H_2O$?

    (1) 6     (2) 9     (3) 10     (4) 15

22. Write the correct formulas for the following binary ionic compounds.

    (a) lithium fluoride     (d) beryllium chloride
    (b) calcium oxide     (e) potassium iodide
    (c) aluminum nitride     (f) aluminum oxide

23. Write the correct formulas for the following binary molecular compounds.

    (a) carbon monoxide     (d) carbon dioxide
    (b) boron tribromide     (e) carbon tetrabromide
    (c) sulfur hexafluoride     (f) nitrogen dioxide

24. Write the correct formulas for the following compounds that contain polyatomic ions.

    (a) sodium hydroxide     (d) aluminum phosphate
    (b) potassium nitrate     (e) aluminum nitrate
    (c) magnesium sulfate     (f) ammonium nitrate

25. Name each of the following binary ionic compounds.

    (a) NaBr     (d) $MgCl_2$
    (b) MgS     (e) $AlF_3$
    (c) CaO     (f) $CaI_2$

26. Name each of the following binary molecular compounds.

    (a) $O_2F_2$     (d) $SF_2$
    (b) $SiF_4$     (e) $H_2S$
    (c) $S_4N_4$     (f) $P_4O_{10}$

27. Name each of the following compounds.

    (a) $Ca(NO_3)_2$     (d) $Na_3PO_4$
    (b) KOH     (e) $LiNO_3$
    (c) $MgCO_3$     (f) $Mg(C_2H_3O_2)_2$

28. Write formulas for each of the following compounds.

    (a) iron(II) oxide     (d) mercury(II) iodide
    (b) tin(II) sulfide     (e) lead(II) nitrate
    (c) copper(I) chloride     (f) iron(III) oxide

29. Write the names of each of the following using stock nomenclature.

    (a) CuCl     (d) $Pb(NO_3)_2$
    (b) FeS     (e) $Sn(OH)_2$
    (c) $HgI_2$     (f) $Fe_2O_3$

30. How many metallic elements are present in the formula $NaKSO_4$?

31. When sulfur and oxygen combine to form a compound, which element should be written first? What values are considered in making this choice?

32. A student named $KClO_3$ potassium chlorine(V) oxide. Explain to her why the use of the stock system is not correct in this case, and write the correct name of the substance.

33. Vanadium has several oxidation states. Write correct formulas for vanadium(III) oxide and vanadium(V) oxide.

34. What incorrect information is given by the formula $MgOH_2$, instead of the correct formula, $Mg(OH)_2$?

# Chemical Reactions and Equations

The world around us is constantly changing. Some of these changes result from substances undergoing phase changes, such as ice melting or water boiling. In these cases, the **physical changes** that have taken place have not resulted in the formation of a new substance, but rather only a change in appearance of the starting material.

Other changes are more dramatic. When a substance is burned, whether it is a piece of paper or gasoline, the substances produced are quite different from the starting materials. These changes in which the identity of the products differs from the identity of the reactants are called **chemical changes.** In this section you will learn how to use chemical symbols to form equations that represent these chemical changes. A well-defined chemical change is called a <u>chemical reaction.</u>

**Burning of Carbon Dioxide**

carbon + oxygen $\longrightarrow$ carbon dioxide

$C(s) + O_2(g) \longrightarrow CO_2(g)$

**Figure 2-6. Word equation and formulaic equation**

## Chemical Equations

A chemical equation shows what takes place during a chemical reaction. It is similar to an algebraic equation in that what is written on one side of the equation equals what is written on the other side. A plus sign is used to separate each of the reactants and each of the products. The arrow is read *produces* or *yields*.

A substance that enters into a reaction is called a **reactant** and is written to the left of the arrow. A substance that is produced by a reaction is called a **product** and is written to the right of the arrow.

In the equation shown in Figure 2-6, carbon and oxygen are reactants, and carbon dioxide is a product. Plus signs separate reactants and products. Notice that in the equation, the atoms of the reactants and products are the same, but the manner in which they are combined is different. This figure shows how using models of the reactants and products can be used in an equation.

### Endothermic and Exothermic Processes

Chemical and physical changes involve the loss or gain of energy, most often expressed as heat. It takes heat to cook an egg. Heat is released when fuel is burned. Photosynthesis requires the energy of the sun in order to occur. When sodium hydroxide dissolves in water, the water warms up. Based on whether energy is absorbed or released, you can classify these energy changes into the two major groups in Table 2-5. Because of this classification, energy is often included as either a reactant or a product in an equation.

| Table 2-5. Summary of Endothermic and Exothermic Reactions | | | | |
|---|---|---|---|---|
| Type of Reaction | Surrounding Temperature | Potential Energy of Reactants | Potential Energy of Products | Value of Delta H |
| Endothermic | decreases | less | more | positive |
| Exothermic | increases | more | less | negative |

**Endothermic Processes** Processes that require energy in order to occur are called **endothermic** processes. The physical change of ice melting is endothermic. Chemical changes that occur as food cooks are endothermic. The energy required is absorbed from the surroundings, thus lowering the surrounding temperature. In endothermic processes, the reactants absorb energy as they become products. Hence, the products have more potential energy than the reactants.

$$H_2O(s) + energy \rightarrow H_2O(\ell)$$
$$6CO_2 + 6H_2O + energy \rightarrow C_6H_{12}O_6 + 6O_2$$

**Exothermic Processes** Processes that release thermal energy when they occur are **exothermic**. The burning of carbon in oxygen is an example of an exothermic reaction. Freezing of water is exothermic. The energy released from these processes is given off to the surroundings, thus raising the surrounding temperature. In exothermic reactions, the products have less potential energy than the reactants.

$$CH_4 + 3O_2 \rightarrow CO_2 + 2H_2O + energy$$
$$C_6H_{12}O_6 + 6O_2 \rightarrow 6CO_2 + 6H_2O + energy$$

## Balancing Chemical Equations

You can see by examining a correctly written chemical equation that the number of each type of atom is the same on both sides of the equation. This observation confirms the <u>law of conservation of mass</u>, which states that matter is neither created nor destroyed in chemical reactions. In any chemical reaction, the numbers and kinds of atoms must remain unchanged in the reaction.

Look at Figure 2-7. In the first equation there is conservation of atoms. There is one carbon atom shown on both the reactant and product side and two atoms of oxygen on either side. This equation agrees with the law of conservation of mass and is called a balanced equation.

| | | | |
|---|---|---|---|
| Balanced chemical equation: | C + O$_2$ One carbon atom, two oxygen atoms | $\longrightarrow$ | CO$_2$ One carbon atom, two oxygen atoms |
| Unbalanced chemical equation: | H$_2$ + O$_2$ Two hydrogen atoms, two oxygen atoms | $\longrightarrow$ | H$_2$O Two hydrogen atoms, one oxygen atom |

**Figure 2-7. A balanced and an unbalanced equation**

The second equation is different. While there are two atoms of hydrogen on both sides of the arrow, there are two atoms of oxygen on the reactant side but only one atom of oxygen on the product side. This equation is not balanced. As it is written, one atom of oxygen has been lost, or not conserved.

The equation must be changed so that it is balanced. How is this done? Remember that subscripts show the ratio of different types of atoms, and subscripts cannot be changed in a correctly written formula. The formula of oxygen gas is O$_2$ and cannot be changed. The only way to balance an equation, once correct formulas have been written, is to change the coefficients in the equation. Remember that coefficients are the numbers written before a formula.

You may want to think of balancing an equation as being similar to balancing a seesaw. In the second example the unbalanced equation is heavy with oxygen atoms on the reactant side. Because none of the reactant oxygen atoms can be removed, the only way to correct the imbalance is to add more oxygen atoms to the product side. This is done by placing a coefficient of 2 in front of the formula of water.

$$H_2(g) + O_2(g) \rightarrow 2H_2O(g)$$

The coefficient applies to both the hydrogen and oxygen in water. The equation is now balanced in terms of oxygen atoms, as there are two on both sides. The hydrogen atoms are now unbalanced because there are four hydrogen atoms on the product side but only two on the reactant side. This can be remedied by placing a 2 in front of the formula of hydrogen.

$$2H_2(g) + O_2(g) \rightarrow 2H_2O(g)$$

Inspection of the equation shows that there now is a conservation of atoms. Four atoms of hydrogen and two atoms of oxygen are now on both sides of the equation. The equation is now balanced.

If you examine equations that involve polyatomic ions, you will notice that sometimes the ions are the same in the reactants and products, and sometimes they are not. If polyatomic ions remain the same, they can be balanced as a unit. For example, in the following unbalanced equation, the nitrate ion can be balanced as a unit because it stays a nitrate ion on the product side of the equation.

$$AgNO_3 + MgCl_2 \rightarrow Mg(NO_3)_2 + AgCl$$

However, in the following unbalanced equation, the phosphite ($PO_3^{3-}$) and nitrate ions are changed during the reaction. They do not appear unchanged on the product side of the equation. In such a case, each type of atom must be balanced separately, and the polyatomic ions cannot be balanced as a unit.

$$HNO_3 + H_3PO_3 \rightarrow NO + H_3PO_4 + H_2O$$

You may have noticed that some symbols have appeared in parentheses after the formulas. It is often important to indicate the physical state of the substances in an equation. The symbol ($s$) is used to show that the substance is a solid, ($\ell$) indicates that it is a liquid, and ($g$) shows the substance to be a gas. In addition, ($aq$) means that the material is dissolved in water; that is, it is in an aqueous solution. Table 2-6 summarizes some common symbols used in equations.

## Table 2-6. Common Notation Used in Equations

| Symbol | Meaning |
|--------|---------|
| + | Separates two reactants or two products |
| → | Separates reactants from products; read as *yields* or *produces* |
| ($s$) | Identifies the substance as a solid |
| ($\ell$) | Identifies the substance as a liquid |
| ($g$) | Identifies the substance as a gas |
| ($aq$) | Identifies the substance as being dissolved in aqueous (water) solution |

# Review Questions

**35.** Consider the following unbalanced equation.

$$C_3H_8(g) + O_2(g) \rightarrow H_2O(g) + CO_2(g)$$

When the equation is completely balanced using smallest whole numbers, the coefficient of $O_2$ is

(1) 5　　(2) 2　　(3) 3　　(4) 7

**36.** When the equation $Al(s) + O_2(g) \rightarrow Al_2O_3(s)$ is correctly balanced using smallest whole numbers, the sum of the coefficients will be

(1) 9　　(2) 7　　(3) 3　　(4) 12

**37.** Consider the following unbalanced equation.

$$Ca(OH)_2 + (NH_4)_2SO_4 \rightarrow CaSO_4 + NH_3 + H_2O$$

What is the sum of the coefficients when the equation is completely balanced using the smallest whole-number coefficients?

(1) 5　　(2) 7　　(3) 9　　(4) 11

**38.** When the equation $Al_2(SO_4)_3 + ZnCl_2 \rightarrow AlCl_3 + ZnSO_4$ is correctly balanced using smallest whole numbers, the sum of the coefficients is

(1) 9　　(2) 8　　(3) 5　　(4) 4

**39.** Consider the following unbalanced equation.

$$C_8H_{16}(g) + O_2(g) \rightarrow H_2O(g) + CO_2(g)$$

When the equation is completely balanced using smallest whole numbers, the coefficient of $CO_2$ is

(1) 1　　(2) 8　　(3) 12　　(4) 16

**40.** Consider the following unbalanced equation.

$$FeCl_2 + Na_2CO_3 \rightarrow FeCO_3 + NaCl$$

When the equation is completely balanced using smallest whole numbers, the coefficient of NaCl is

(1) 6　　(2) 2　　(3) 3　　(4) 4

**41.** Consider the following unbalanced equation.

$$Ag + H_2S \rightarrow Ag_2S + H_2$$

What is the sum of the coefficients when the equation is completely balanced using the smallest whole-number coefficients?

(1) 5　　(2) 8　　(3) 10　　(4) 4

**42.** Consider the following unbalanced equation.

$$Li + N_2 \rightarrow Li_3N$$

When the equation is completely balanced using smallest whole numbers, the coefficient of lithium is

(1) 1      (2) 2      (3) 3      (4) 6

**43.** Consider the following unbalanced equation.

$$N_2(g) + O_2(g) \rightarrow N_2O_5(g)$$

When the equation is completely balanced using smallest whole numbers, the coefficient of $N_2(g)$ is

(1) 1      (2) 2      (3) 5      (4) 4

## Types of Reactions

While it would be difficult, if not impossible, to put all chemical reactions into distinct categories, there are four major types of reactions that you should know. It is important to be able to recognize these types and write equations to represent them.

**Synthesis (Combination) Reactions** When two or more reactants combine to form a single product, the reaction is a **synthesis,** or combination, reaction. The combination of hydrogen and oxygen to form water that was shown earlier is an example.

$$2H_2(g) + O_2(g) \rightarrow 2H_2O(g)$$

Many synthesis reactions are commonplace, such as the rusting of iron.

$$4Fe(s) + 3O_2(g) \rightarrow 2Fe_2O_3(s)$$

Synthesis reactions not only take place between elements, but they may also involve compounds.

$$CO_2(g) + H_2O(\ell) \rightarrow H_2CO_3(aq)$$

It is convenient to write this type of equation in a general form such as

$$A + B \rightarrow AB$$

A and B represent either elements or compounds, and AB represents a compound that is made of A and B. See Figure 2-8.

**Decomposition (Analysis) Reactions** A **decomposition,** or **analysis,** reaction is the reverse of a synthesis reaction in that a single compound is broken down (decomposed) into two or more simpler substances. All decomposition reactions begin with a single reactant.

$$H_2O(\ell) \rightarrow H_2(g) + O_2(g)$$

Although many decomposition reactions produce elements as the products, Figure 2-9 shows the breaking down of one compound into two compounds.

$$CaCO_3(s) \rightarrow CaO(s) + CO_2(g)$$

The general form of this reaction is the exact opposite of the equation for a synthesis reaction.

$$AB \rightarrow A + B$$

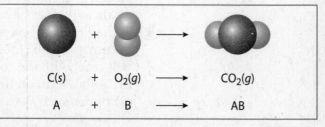

**Figure 2-8. Equation of a synthesis reaction:** In this example, two elements combine to form a compound.

**Figure 2-9. Equation of a decomposition reaction:** The models for $CaCO_3$ and $CaO$ show that the compounds are ionic and do not form molecules. They are compounds that exist as ions.

| Fe | + | CuSO$_4$ (aq) | → | FeSO$_4$ (aq) | + | Cu |
| A | + | BX | → | AX | + | B |

**Figure 2-10. Equation of a single replacement reaction:** The copper and iron ions are part of the compounds that are in solution, but the iron and copper atoms are solid metals.

**Single Replacement Reactions** When a piece of copper wire is placed into a solution of silver nitrate, a chemical reaction takes place. In a short period of time shiny crystals form on the copper wire, and the solution gradually becomes blue. Analysis of the crystals shows them to be silver metal. The blue color is caused by copper ions in solution. In this reaction the copper metal has replaced silver ions in silver nitrate, producing silver metal and copper ions.

$$Cu(s) + 2AgNO_3(aq) \rightarrow Cu(NO_3)_2(aq) + 2Ag(s)$$

This type of reaction where one element replaces another element in a compound is called a **single replacement** reaction (Figure 2-10). This type of reaction always involves an element and a compound. The general formula for this type of reaction where a metal replaces another metal in a compound is

$$A + BX \rightarrow B + AX$$

Will the reverse reaction take place, that is, will silver metal react with copper nitrate to produce copper and silver nitrate? If silver is placed into copper nitrate solution, no copper is formed. How can we predict whether or not a reaction will take place? The Activity Series Ⓡ in the *Reference Tables for Physical Setting/Chemistry* will provide the information. The table is arranged so that a metal listed on the table will react with the compound of a metal that is below it. For example, Zn is above Cu on the table. Therefore, Zn will react with a compound of copper such as Cu(NO$_3$)$_2$.

$$Zn + Cu(NO_3)_2 \rightarrow Cu + Zn(NO_3)_2$$

Because Cu is below Zn, it will not react with compounds of Zn.

$$Cu + Zn(NO_3)_2 \rightarrow \text{no reaction.}$$

It is worth noting that there is one element that is not a metal in the left column of the Activity Series, H$_2$. All metals above hydrogen will react with acids to release hydrogen gas and produce a salt. For example,

$$Mg + 2HCl \rightarrow H_2 + MgCl_2$$

AgNO₃(aq)  +  KCl(aq) ⟶ AgCl(s)  +  KNO₃(aq)

AB  +  CD ⟶ AD  +  CB

**Figure 2-11. An equation for a double replacement reaction:** Although all the compounds are ionic, AgCl is an ionic compound that is not soluble in water. Crystals of AgCl form a precipitate.v

Silver (Ag) is below hydrogen on the table, so it will not react with acids.

In the second column of the Activity Series is a short list of nonmetals. A nonmetal will replace a less active nonmetal in a compound according to the equation

$$A + XB \rightarrow B + XA$$

Fluorine is listed as the most active nonmetal, and it will replace chlorine, bromine, and iodine from their binary compounds.

$$F_2 + 2NaCl \rightarrow Cl_2 + 2NaF$$

Because chlorine is below fluorine on the list, it will not replace fluorine in a compound.

$$Cl_2 + NaF \rightarrow \text{no reaction}$$

When given a possible reaction between an element and an ionic compound, consult the Activity Series to determine whether or not a reaction will occur.

**Double Replacement Reactions** **Double replacement** reactions generally involve two soluble ionic compounds that react in solution to produce a precipitate, a gas, or a molecular compound such as water. Figure 2-11 shows that when aqueous solutions of silver nitrate and sodium chloride are mixed, a white precipitate of silver chloride is produced according to the following equation.

$$AgNO_3(aq) + NaCl(aq) \rightarrow AgCl(s) + NaNO_3(aq)$$

Double replacement equations can be represented by the general equation

$$AB + CD \rightarrow AD + CB$$

Just as not all combinations of single replacement reactants will produce a reaction, so too with double replacement reactions.

How can you determine if two ionic compounds will react? There are three situations that might cause a double replacement to occur.

1. A reaction will occur if one of the products is a solid (precipitate). Consult the Solubility Guidelines in the *Reference Tables for Physical Setting/Chemistry*. Check the solubility of the two ionic products. For example, in

$$AgNO_3(aq) + NaCl(aq) \rightarrow AgCl(s) + NaNO_3(aq)$$

silver chloride is listed as insoluble, and sodium nitrate is listed as soluble. Because one of the products is insoluble, the reaction will occur.

2. A reaction will occur if one of the products is a gas. For example,

$$Na_2S(aq) + 2HCl(aq) \rightarrow H_2S(g) + 2NaCl(aq)$$

3. A reaction will occur if a molecular substance such as water is formed. For example,

$$NaOH(aq) + HCl(aq) \rightarrow H_2O(\ell) + NaCl(aq)$$

# Review Questions

**Write and balance equations for the following synthesis reactions.**

44. hydrogen and bromine forming hydrogen bromide

45. fluorine and argon forming argon trifluoride

46. sulfur and oxygen forming sulfur dioxide

47. calcium and chlorine forming calcium chloride

48. nickel and oxygen forming nickel(II) oxide

**Write and balance equations for the following decomposition reactions.**

49. decomposition of water into hydrogen and oxygen

50. decomposition of aluminum oxide into aluminum and oxygen

51. decomposition of sodium chloride into sodium and chlorine

52. decomposition of ammonia into hydrogen and nitrogen

53. decomposition of mercury(II) oxide into mercury and oxygen

**For each of the following, indicate whether or not a single replacement reaction will occur.**

54. aluminum and hydrochloric acid

55. silver and magnesium chloride

56. chromium and lead(II) nitrate

57. silver and gold(III) chloride

58. chlorine and sodium iodide

59. Identify each of the following as equations for a synthesis (*S*), decomposition (*D*), single replacement (*SR*), or double replacement (*DR*) reactions.

(a) $Zn + HCl \rightarrow ZnCl_2 + H_2$

(b) $NaClO_3 \rightarrow NaCl + O_2$

(c) $P_4 + Cl_2 \rightarrow PCl_3$

(d) $HCl + Mg(OH)_2 \rightarrow MgCl_2 + H_2O$

(e) $BaO + SO_3 \rightarrow BaSO_4$

(f) $Pb + AgNO_3 \rightarrow Ag + Pb(NO_3)_2$

(g) $AgNO_3 + Na_2CrO_4 \rightarrow Ag_2CrO_4 + NaNO_3$

(h) $Al + Fe_3O_4 \rightarrow Al_2O_3 + Fe$

(i) $HNO_3 + Mg(OH)_2 \rightarrow Mg(NO_3)_2 + H_2O$

(j) $Ba(NO_3)_2 + Na_2SO_4 \rightarrow BaSO_4 + NaNO_3$

For the following, write a balanced chemical equation to show how the ions would combine in a double replacement equation.

60. sodium bromide and silver nitrate form sodium nitrate and silver bromide

61. potassium carbonate and calcium nitrate form potassium nitrate and calcium carbonate

62. ammonium sulfate and barium chloride form ammonium chloride and barium sulfate

63. barium nitrate and potassium chromate form barium chromate and potassium nitrate

64. sodium hydroxide and calcium chloride form sodium chloride and calcium hydroxide

## Unknown Reactants and Products

The law of conservation of mass requires that chemical reactions neither create nor destroy matter. When given a balanced equation in which either a reactant or a product is missing, you should be able to determine the formula of the missing substance. To do so, count the atoms in the formulas on both sides of the arrow. Subtract the atoms on the side with the missing formula from the side with the known substances. Any missing element must be present in the unknown.

As an example, look at the following equation.

$$2Na + 2H_2O \rightarrow X + 2NaOH$$

The reactant side is complete and contains two sodium atoms, four hydrogen atoms, and two oxygen atoms. One product is missing from the right side of the equation. There are two hydrogen atoms, two oxygen atoms, and two sodium atoms present in the other product. For the equation to balance, the missing substance must contain only two hydrogen atoms. What is the formula of a substance that contains two hydrogen atoms? $H_2$, hydrogen gas.

## Determining Missing Mass in Equations

Just as the formula of a missing reactant or product can be determined, the mass of a missing substance can also be found. The law of conservation of mass again is the guiding principle. Matter can be neither created nor destroyed in a chemical reaction. The total mass of the reactants must equal the total mass of the products.

### SAMPLE PROBLEM

If 103.0 g of potassium chlorate are decomposed to form 62.7 g of potassium chloride and oxygen gas according to the equation $2KClO_3 \rightarrow 2KCl + 3O_2$, how many grams of oxygen are formed?

**SOLUTION:** Identify the known and unknown values.

*Known*
mass of $KClO_3$ = 103.0 g
mass of KCl = 62.7 g

*Unknown*
mass of $O_2$ = ? g

Find the total mass of the reactants.
$KClO_3$ is the only reactant; it has a mass of 103.0 g.

The total mass of the reactants and products must be equal.

mass of $KClO_3$ = mass of KCl + mass of $O_2$
103.0 g = 62.7 g + mass of $O_2$
mass of $O_2$ = 103.0 g − 62.7 g
mass of $O_2$ = 40.3 g

**65.** Identify the missing reactant or product in each of the following equations. Include any coefficient needed to balance the equation.

(a) $2NaHCO_3 \rightarrow Na_2CO_3 + H_2O +$ _____

(b) $BaCl_2 + K_2CO_3 \rightarrow$ _____ $+ BaCO_3$

(c) $2C_6H_6 +$ _____ $\rightarrow 12CO_2 + 6H_2O$

(d) $CaCO_3 \rightarrow CaO +$ _____

**66.** Identify the missing reactant or product in each of the following equations. Include any coefficient needed to balance the equation.

(a) $2Al +$ _____ $\rightarrow 2AlCl_3 + 3H_2$

(b) _____ $+ H_2O \rightarrow H_2CO_3$

(c) $2NaOH +$ _____ $\rightarrow NaOCl + NaCl + H_2O$

(d) $Cr_2O_3 + 2Al \rightarrow$ _____ $+ 2Cr$

**67.** Identify the missing reactant or product in each of the following equations. Include any coefficient needed to balance the equation.

(a) $2HNO_3 +$ _____ $\rightarrow Mg(NO_3)_2 + 2H_2O$

(b) $2NH_4NO_3 \rightarrow$ _____ $+ 4H_2O + O_2$

(c) $H_2SO_4 + 2NaOH \rightarrow Na_2SO_4 +$ _____

(d) $3PbO +$ _____ $\rightarrow 3Pb + N_2 + 3H_2O$

**68.** Identify the missing reactant or product in each of the following equations. Include any coefficient needed to balance the equation.

(a) $3Cu + 8 HNO3 \rightarrow 3Cu(NO_3)_2 + 4H_2O +$ _____

(b) $C_6H_{11}OH \rightarrow C_6H_{10} +$ _____

(c) $4NH_3 + 5O_2 \rightarrow$ _____ $+ 6H_2O$

(d) $Ca(OH)_2 +$ _____ $\rightarrow CaCl_2 + H_2O$

**69.** Identify the missing reactant or product in each of the following equations. Include any coefficient needed to balance the equation.

(a) $2AgNO_3 +$ _____ $\rightarrow Ag_2S + 2NaNO_3$

(b) $H_2C_2O_4 + 2NaOH \rightarrow$ _____ $+ 2H_2O$

(c) $CCl_4 + 2HF \rightarrow CCl_2F_2 +$ _____

(d) _____ $+ CO_2 \rightarrow K_2CO_3$

**70.** What mass of carbon dioxide will be produced if 144 g of carbon react with 384 g of oxygen gas according to the equation $C + O_2 \rightarrow CO_2$?

**71.** How many grams of HCl are produced when 16.0 g of $CH_4$ react with 71.0 g of $Cl_2$ to produce 50.5 g of $CH_3Cl$ and HCl according to the equation $CH_4 + Cl_2 \rightarrow CH_3Cl + HCl$?

**72.** Consider the following equation.

$$3C_2H_4O_2 + PCl_3 \rightarrow 3C_2H_3OCl + H_3PO_3$$

How many grams of products will be produced if 90 g of $C_2H_4O_2$ completely react with 68 g of $PCl_3$?

**73.** How many grams of silver nitrate are needed to react with 156.2 g of sodium sulfide to produce 595.8 g of silver sulfide and 340.0 g of sodium nitrate?

$$2AgNO_3 + Na_2S \rightarrow Ag_2S + 2NaNO_3$$

**74.** Given the equation $PbO_2 \rightarrow PbO + O_2$, how many grams of oxygen will be produced if 47.8 g of lead(IV) oxide decompose to form 44.6 g of lead(II) oxide and oxygen gas?

**75.** Consider the following equation.

$$2Al + 3CuSO_4 \rightarrow Al_2(SO_4)_3 + 3Cu$$

Copper metal is produced when aluminum metal is reacted with copper(II) sulfate. How many grams of copper metal will be produced if 10.8 g of aluminum react with 95.8 g of copper sulfate to produce copper metal and 68.5 g of aluminum sulfate?

**76.** How many grams of Fe are needed to react with 8.0 g of $O_2$ to produce 28.9 g of $Fe_3O_4$ according to the equation $3Fe + 2O_2 \rightarrow Fe_3O_4$?

**77.** How many metric tons of nitric acid are produced from the reaction of 10.8 metric tons of $N_2O_5$ reacting with 1.8 metric tons of water according to the equation $N_2O_5 + H_2O \rightarrow 2HNO_3$?

**78.** How many pounds of sulfur will be produced from the decomposition of 318.2 pounds of copper(I) sulfide to produce 254.0 pounds of copper metal and sulfur according to the equation $Cu_2S \rightarrow 2Cu + S$?

**79.** Given the equation $2HgO \rightarrow 2Hg + O_2$, how many grams of mercury(II) oxide are needed to produce 12.7 g of mercury and 3.2 g of oxygen?

## Directions

Review the Test-Taking Strategies section of this book. Then answer the following questions. Read each question carefully and answer with a correct choice or response.

## Part A

1  A chemical formula is an expression used to represent
   (1) mixtures only
   (2) elements only
   (3) compounds only
   (4) compounds and elements

2  Two molecules of hydrogen are represented by
   (1) $H_2$     (2) $2H_2$     (3) $2H^+$     (4) $2H$

3  Which of the following is a polyatomic ion?
   (1) $CH_3COOH$          (3) $Na^+$
   (2) $Cr_2O_7^{2-}$          (4) $H_2$

4  Pure oxygen reacts with metals to form
   (1) oxalates          (3) oxides
   (2) oxalites          (4) oxygenates

5  Which of the following is the formula of a compound?
   (1) Fr          (3) LiH
   (2) Mn          (4) $O_3$

6  A chemical formula represents
   (1) qualitative information only
   (2) quantitative information only
   (3) both quantitative and qualitative information
   (4) neither qualitative nor quantitative information

7  An empirical formula represents
   (1) qualitative information only
   (2) only the metallic elements in the compound
   (3) the lowest integer ratio of the elements in a compound
   (4) a multiple of the simplest ratio of the elements in a compound

8  In an endothermic reaction
   (1) energy is a product and the surrounding temperature decreases
   (2) energy is a product and the surrounding temperature increases
   (3) energy is a reactant and the surrounding temperature increases
   (4) energy is a reactant and the surrounding temperature decreases

9  A reaction in which two substances combine to form a single product is called a
   (1) decomposition
   (2) synthesis
   (3) single replacement
   (4) double replacement

10  As an endothermic reaction occurs, the potential energy of the reactants
   (1) decreases
   (2) increases
   (3) remains the same
   (4) depends on the reaction

## Part B

11  What is the total number of atoms of oxygen in the formula $Al(ClO_3)_3 \cdot 6H_2O$?
   (1) 6          (2) 9          (3) 10          (4) 15

12  Which formula is correctly paired with its name?
   (1) $MgCl_2$, magnesium chlorine
   (2) $K_2O$, diphosphorus oxide
   (3) $CuCl_2$, copper(II) chloride
   (4) $FeO$, iron(III) oxide

13  Which of the following is an empirical formula?
   (1) $S_2H_2$          (3) $C_2Cl_2$
   (2) $H_2O_2$          (4) $CaCl_2$

14  What is the empirical formula of a compound with a molecular formula of $C_6H_{12}O_6$?
   (1) $C_6H_{12}O_6$          (3) $C_2H_4O_2$
   (2) $C_3H_6O_3$          (4) $CH_2O$

15  What is the correct formula of nickel(II) oxide?
   (1) NiO          (3) $NiO_2$
   (2) $Ni_2O$          (4) $Ni_2O_2$

16  What is the name of the compound whose formula is $N_2O_5$?
   (1) nitrogen oxide
   (2) dinitrogen pentoxide
   (3) pentanitrogen dioxide
   (4) dinitrogen oxide

17  Which is the correct formula of dichlorine monoxide?
   (1) ClO     (2) $Cl_2O$     (3) $ClO_2$     (4) OCl

18 Which of the following is a synthesis reaction?
   (1) $Cu + 2AgNO_3 \rightarrow Cu(NO_3)_2 + 2Ag$
   (2) $2Cu + O_2 \rightarrow 2CuO$
   (3) $CuCO_3 \rightarrow CuO + CO_2$
   (4) $CuO + H_2 \rightarrow Cu + H_2O$

19 Which of the following reactions will *not* take place spontaneously?
   (1) $Ca + AgNO_3$
   (2) $Pb + Al(NO_3)_3$
   (3) $Cr + Pb(NO_3)_2$
   (4) $Co + HCl$

20 Consider the following unbalanced equation.
   $$Mg_2Si + HCl \rightarrow MgCl_2 + SiH_4$$
   When the equation is balanced using the smallest whole-number coefficients, the coefficient of HCl is
   (1) 1        (2) 2        (3) 3        (4) 4

21 Consider the following unbalanced equation.
   $$Fe + H_2O \rightarrow Fe_3O_4 + H_2$$
   When correctly balanced using smallest whole numbers, the sum of the coefficients is
   (1) 4        (2) 7        (3) 11        (4) 12

# Part C

22 Write the correct formulas for iron(II) chloride and iron(III)nitrate. Why are the Roman numerals used in the names? [3]

23 What are polyatomic ions? Why do they have a charge? [2]

24 Given the formula: $Al_2(SO_4)_3$. Write the name of each element in the compound and the number of atoms of each element in the formula. [3]

25 How many grams of water are produced when 80. g of NaOH react with 73 g of HCl to form 117 g of NaCl and water? Show your work. [2]

26 What is the name of a metal found on Table J that will react with hydrochloric acid? What is the name of an element that will not react with compounds of aluminum? [2]

27 Write the chemical formula of a negative polyatomic ion present in an aqueous nitric acid solution.

**Use the following information to answer questions 28 and 29.**

In an investigation, a dripless wax candle is massed and then lighted. As the candle burns, a small amount of liquid wax forms near the flame. After 10 minutes, the candle's flame is extinguished and the candle is allowed to cool. The cooled candle is massed.

28 Identify one physical change that takes place in this investigation.

29 State one observation that indicates that a chemical change has taken place.

_____

30 Balance this equation using the lowest whole-number coefficients.
   _____ $C_6H_{12}O_6 \rightarrow$ _____ $C_2H_5OH +$ _____ $CO_2$

31 Identify the type of reaction represented in the equation in question 30.

32 Acid rain contains droplets of oxides of sulfur and nitrogen that combine with water to form acids that lower the pH of the soil. Calcium hydroxide will neutralize these acids and raise the pH. Balance the equation to show the neutralization of nitric acid by calcium hydroxide.
   _____ $HNO_3 +$ _____ $Ca(OH)_2 \rightarrow$ _____ $Ca(NO_3)_2 +$ _____ $H_2O$

33 The decomposition of sodium azide, $NaN_3$, is used to inflate airbags. In the reaction begun with an electrical spark, $N_2$ (g) and Na (s) are produced. Write a balanced equation for the decomposition using the smallest whole-number coefficients.
   _____ $NaN_3 \rightarrow$ _____$N_2 +$ _____ Na

**Use the following information to answer questions 34 and 35.**

Magnesium metal reacts with hydrochloric acid to produce hydrogen. Balance the equation for the reaction using the lowest whole-number integers.

34 _____ Mg (s) + _____ HCl (aq) $\rightarrow MgCl_2$ (aq) + $H_2$(g)

35 What type of chemical reaction occurs during this reaction?

_____

**Use the following information to answer questions 36 and 37.**

Rust contains $Fe_2O_3$. Given the balanced equation representing the formation of rust:
   _____ Fe (s) + _____ $O_2$ (g) $\rightarrow$ _____ $Fe_2O_3$ (s).

36 Balance the equation using the smallest whole-number coefficients.

37 Identify the type of reaction represented by this equation.

# The Mathematics of Formulas and Equations

## How Scientists Use Math to Solve Problems

**?** **Why do you think chemists celebrate Mole Day on October 23?** **?**

Every October 23, chemists celebrate Mole Day! Avogadro's Number or $6.02 \times 10^{23}$, is the number of particles in a mole. Look at the "molely" math problem below.

72 g carbon

12 g hydrogen

+ 96 g oxygen

_____

$6.02 \times 10^{23}$ molecules of glucose

**How many molecules of glucose is this?**

If each molecule were one kilogram, they would equal over 20 times the mass of Earth! Calculate how many years it would take to count 1 mole of glucose atoms at the rate of 1 molecule per second. Hint: there are about 31.5 million seconds ($3.15 \times 10^7$) in a year.

# The Mathematics of Formulas and Equations

## Vocabulary

formula mass

gram formula mass

mole

percentage composition

## Topic Overview

Math is the language of chemistry. It enables us to easily determine the amount of a chemical needed for a reaction or the amount that will be produced. In this topic you will learn how to apply simple math relations to the solving of chemical problems.

### SAMPLE PROBLEM

What is the formula mass of $K_2CO_3$?

**SOLUTION:** Identify the known and unknown values.

*Known*
formula = $K_2CO_3$
atomic masses from the periodic table

*Unknown*
formula mass = ? amu

1. Determine the number of atoms of each element from the formula.

| Element: | Number of atoms: |
|----------|------------------|
| K | 2 |
| C | 1 |
| O | 3 |

2. Consult the table of the elements for the atomic mass of each element, and multiply it by the number of atoms to determine the total mass for each element.

For K:  2 atoms × 39.1 amu/atom = 78.2 amu
For C:   1 atom × 12.0 amu/atom = 12.0 amu
For O:  3 atoms × 16.0 amu/atom = 48.0 amu

3. Add the total mass for each element to determine the formula mass.

$$
\begin{array}{r}
78.2 \text{ amu} \\
12.0 \text{ amu} \\
+\ 48.0 \text{ amu} \\
\hline
\end{array}
$$

Formula mass    138.2 amu

## The Mathematics of Formulas

Recall that the mass of an atom is a relative value based on the mass of a carbon-12 atom. All atoms are compared to this standard. Thus, a magnesium atom with an atomic mass of 24 amu is twice as massive as the standard carbon atom with an atomic mass of 12. This relationship will remain the same in any system of weights or masses. As long as there is a mass ratio of 12 parts of carbon to 24 parts of magnesium, equal numbers of carbon and magnesium atoms are present. Twelve grams of carbon contain the same number of atoms as 24 grams of magnesium. These mass relationships of atoms are the basis for mass relationships in compounds.

### Formula Mass

Remember that compounds are represented by formulas that show the type and number of atoms present in the compound. Because compounds are represented by formulas, the mass of the smallest unit of the compound is the **formula mass,** which is the sum of the atomic masses of all the atoms present. While the term *molecular mass* is often used to represent the mass of a unit of a compound, *formula mass* is preferred because ionic and network solids do not form discrete molecules. For example, sodium bromide (NaBr) is an ionic compound. No molecules of NaBr exist, so *molecular mass* does not apply to NaBr. However, formula mass can be calculated for a formula unit of the compound. The formula mass of NaBr is the mass of one atom of Na plus the mass of one atom of Br in amu.

**Gram Formula Mass** The **gram formula mass** of a substance is simply the formula mass expressed in grams instead of atomic mass units. Thus, the gram formula mass of $K_2CO_3$ is 138.2 g. Some substances, such as sucrose (table sugar), form molecules. It is common to express the gram formula masses of molecular substances as <u>gram molecular masses</u>.

# Review Questions

1. What is the gram formula mass of $Ca(OH)_2$?
   (1) 29 g
   (2) 34 g
   (3) 56 g
   (4) 74 g

2. Which substance has the greatest molecular mass?
   (1) $H_2O_2$
   (2) NO
   (3) $CF_4$
   (4) $I_2$

3. What is the gram formula mass of $C_3H_5(OH)_3$?
   (1) 48 g
   (2) 58 g
   (3) 74 g
   (4) 92 g

4. What is the gram formula mass of $Na_2CO_3$?
   (1) 51 g
   (2) 74 g
   (3) 106 g
   (4) 138 g

5. What is the gram formula mass of $(NH_4)_3PO_4$?
   (1) 113 g
   (2) 121 g
   (3) 149 g
   (4) 404 g

6. What is the gram formula mass of calcium nitrate $Ca(NO_3)_2$?
   (1) 70.0 g
   (2) 102 g
   (3) 150 g
   (4) 164 g

7. What is the gram formula mass of $Li_2SO_4$?
   (1) 54 g
   (2) 55 g
   (3) 110 g
   (4) 206 g

8. What is the gram formula mass of $Mg(ClO_3)_2$?
   (1) 107 g
   (2) 142 g
   (3) 174 g
   (4) 191 g

9. What is the gram molecular mass of the compound with the formula $CH_3COOH$?
   (1) 22.4 g   (2) 44.0 g   (3) 48.0 g   (4) 60.0 g

10. Determine the formula mass and the gram formula mass of each of the following compounds.
    (a) $NaHCO_3$
    (b) $MgCl_2$
    (c) $NH_4Cl$
    (d) $FeCl_3$
    (e) $Al_2O_3$
    (f) $Mg(NO_3)_2$
    (g) $Al_2(SO_4)_3$
    (h) $(NH_4)_2SO_4$
    (i) $C_5H_{10}(OH)_2$
    (j) $C_{12}H_{22}O_{11}$

**For each of the following, compute the answer, showing your work.**

11. What is the formula mass of $Al(OH)_3$?

12. What is the formula mass of $C_6H_{12}O_6$?

13. What is the formula mass of $MgBr_2 \cdot 6H_2O$?

## Percentage Composition

Formulas represent the composition of a substance. Using the subscripts and atomic masses of the elements, the percent by mass of a substance can be calculated. The **percentage composition** of a substance represents the composition as a percentage of each element compared with the total mass of the compound.

**Hydrates** Ionic substances often include definite amounts of water as part of the crystal structure. The water molecules are shown as part of the formula, such as $CuSO_4 \cdot 5H_2O$. Crystals that contain attached water molecules are called <u>hydrates</u>, while substances without water are termed <u>anhydrous</u>. If it is necessary to calculate the percentage of water in such a crystal, treat the water molecule as a single unit.

## SAMPLE PROBLEM

What is the percentage of oxygen in potassium chlorate ($KClO_3$)?

**SOLUTION:** Identify the known and unknown values.

*Known*
formula = $KClO_3$
atomic masses from
  the periodic table

*Unknown*
%O = ? %

**1.** Determine the formula mass of potassium chlorate.

For K:  1 atom × 39.1 amu/atom = 39.1 amu
For Cl:  1 atom × 35.5 amu/atom = 35.5 amu
For O:  3 atoms × 16.0 amu/atom = 48.0 amu
                   Formula mass = 122.6 amu

**2.** Calculate the percent of oxygen in the compound by dividing the mass of oxygen by the formula mass and multiplying by 100%.

$$\%O = \frac{48.0 \text{ amu}}{122.6 \text{ amu}} \times 100\%$$

$$\%O = 39.2\%$$

## SAMPLE PROBLEM

What is the percentage, by mass, of water in sodium carbonate crystals, $Na_2CO_3 \cdot 10H_2O$?

**SOLUTION:** Identify the known and unknown values.

*Known*
formula = $Na_2CO_3 \cdot 10H_2O$
atomic masses from
  the periodic table

*Unknown*
$\%H_2O$ = ? %

**1.** Determine the formula mass of the crystal. (Hint: Treat the water as a unit.)

For Na: 2 atoms × 23.0 amu/atom = 46.0 amu
For C:  1 atom × 12.0 amu/atom = 12.0 amu
For O:  3 atoms × 16.0 amu/atom =  48.0 amu
For $H_2O$: 10 units × 18.0 amu/unit = 180.0 amu
                Formula mass = 286.0 amu

**2.** Calculate the percent of water in the compound by dividing the mass of water by the formula mass and multiplying by 100%.

$$\%H_2O = \frac{180.0 \text{ amu}}{286.6 \text{ amu}} \times 100\%$$

$$\%H_2O = 62.9\%$$

# Review Questions

**14.** The percent by mass of nitrogen in $NH_4NO_3$ is closest to

(1)  15%
(2)  20%
(3)  35%
(4)  60%

**15.** What is the percent by mass of carbon in $CO_2$?

(1)  12%
(2)  27%
(3)  44%
(4)  73%

**16.** What is the percent by mass of water present in $CaSO_4 \cdot 2H_2O$?

(1)  10.%
(2)  12%
(3)  21%
(4)  79%

**17.** What is the percent by mass of oxygen in magnesium oxide (MgO)?

(1)  20%
(2)  40%
(3)  50%
(4)  60%

**18.** The percent by mass of oxygen in $H_2C_2O_4$ is equal to

(1) $\dfrac{90 \text{ amu}}{64 \text{ amu}} \times 100\%$   (3) $\dfrac{8 \text{ amu}}{4 \text{ amu}} \times 100\%$

(2) $\dfrac{64 \text{ amu}}{90 \text{ amu}} \times 100\%$   (4) $\dfrac{4 \text{ amu}}{8 \text{ amu}} \times 100\%$

**19.** What is the percent by mass of oxygen in $Fe_2O_3$? The formula mass of $Fe_2O_3 = 160$ amu.

(1) 16%   (2) 30.%   (3) 56%   (4) 70.%

**20.** What is the percent by mass of sulfur in sulfur dioxide?

(1) 32 %   (2) 33%   (3) 50.%   (4) 67%

**21.** The percent by mass of Ca in $CaCl_2$ is equal to

(1) $\dfrac{40 \text{ amu}}{111 \text{ amu}} \times 100\%$   (3) $\dfrac{3 \text{ amu}}{1 \text{ amu}} \times 100\%$

(2) $\dfrac{111 \text{ amu}}{40 \text{ amu}} \times 100\%$   (4) $\dfrac{1 \text{ amu}}{3 \text{ amu}} \times 100\%$

**22.** Which species contains the greatest percent by mass of hydrogen?

(1) $OH^-$   (2) $H_2O$   (3) $H_3O^+$   (4) $H_2O_2$

**23.** The percent by mass of water in $BaCl_2 \cdot 2H_2O$ (formula mass = 243 amu) is equal to

(1) $\dfrac{18 \text{ amu}}{243 \text{ amu}} \times 100\%$   (3) $\dfrac{243 \text{ amu}}{18 \text{ amu}} \times 100\%$

(2) $\dfrac{36 \text{ amu}}{243 \text{ amu}} \times 100\%$   (4) $\dfrac{243 \text{ amu}}{36 \text{ amu}} \times 100\%$

**Answer each of the following questions in complete sentences.**

**24.** A crystalline material containing 30.0 g of barium chloride crystals was placed into an oven at 400°C and heated for two hours. It was then cooled and weighed. The new mass was less than before it was heated, containing 20.0 g of barium chloride. How is this possible?

**25.** Copper(II) sulfate is a hydrated crystal with the formula $CuSO_4 \cdot 5H_2O$ and a deep blue color. When it is heated the crystals crumble and turn white.

(a) Propose an explanation for this change of color.

(b) What would you do to restore the blue color?

**26.** A chemist needs to order $Na_2B_4O_7$. One supplier offers it in an anhydrous (without water) form, while another offers it as a hydrated crystal, $Na_2B_4O_7 \cdot 10H_2O$. If the prices from the two suppliers are the same for a 500.0-g bottle, which one would supply more of the desired $Na_2B_4O_7$? Explain your answer.

---

## The Mole

We are quite familiar with collective nouns in our everyday life. *Dozen* is a convenient word to describe 12 of something. A gross of paper contains 144 sheets, while a ream contains 500. These units enable you to count by collective units of items instead of by individual items.

Chemists use a specific collective noun to define a particularly usable number of particles. A **mole** is defined as the number of atoms of carbon present in 12.000 grams of C-12. The number of particles in a mole of a substance is $6.022 \times 10^{23}$, which is called <u>Avogadro's number</u>. While it would be impossible to individually count a mole of particles, the mass of one mole of a substance can be found by determining its gram formula mass. This quantity contains $6.02 \times 10^{23}$ particles of that substance. Therefore, the gram formula mass of any substance is the mass of one mole of that substance. The accepted abbreviation for mole is mol.

**Converting Grams to Moles**  To convert grams to moles:

$$\text{moles} = \text{number of grams} \times \frac{1 \text{ mol}}{\text{gram formula mass}}$$

**Converting Moles to Grams**  To convert moles to grams:

$$\text{grams} = \text{number of moles} \times \frac{\text{gram formula mass}}{1 \text{ mol}}$$

## SAMPLE PROBLEM

How many grams are present in 40.5 mol of sulfuric acid ($H_2SO_4$)?

**SOLUTION:** Identify the known and unknown values.

*Known*
moles $H_2SO_4$ = 40.5 mol

*Unknown*
mass $H_2SO_4$ = ? g

1. Calculate the formula mass of sulfuric acid.

   For H:  2 atoms × 1.0 amu/atom =  2.0 amu
   For S:  1 atom × 32.1 amu/atom = 32.1 amu
   For O: 4 atoms × 16.0 amu/atom = 64.0 amu
            Formula mass $H_2SO_4$ = 98.1 amu

2. Calculate the gram formula mass of sulfuric acid.

   gram formula mass = formula mass in grams
   gram formula mass of $H_2SO_4$ = 98.1 g

3. Use the gram formula mass to convert the given number of moles to grams.

   $$\text{number of grams} = \text{moles} \times \frac{\text{gram formula mass}}{1\ \text{mol}}$$

   $$\text{grams } H_2SO_4 = 40.5\ \text{mol} \times \frac{98.1\ \text{g}}{1\ \text{mol}}$$

   grams $H_2SO_4$ = 3970 g

## SAMPLE PROBLEM

How many moles are equivalent to 4.75 g of sodium hydroxide (NaOH)?

**SOLUTION:** Identify the known and unknown values.

*Known*
mass NaOH = 4.75 g

*Unknown*
moles NaOH = ? mol

1. Calculate the formula mass of sodium hydroxide.

   For Na: 1 atom × 23.0 amu/atom  = 23.0 amu
   For O:  1 atom × 16.0 amu/atom  = 16.0 amu
   For H:  1 atom ×  1.0 amu/atom  =  1.0 amu
            Formula mass NaOH = 40.0 amu

2. Calculate the gram formula mass of sodium hydroxide.

   gram formula mass = formula mass in grams
   gram formula mass of NaOH = 40.0 g

3. Use the gram formula mass to convert the given mass to moles.

   $$\text{moles} = \text{number of grams} \times \frac{1\ \text{mol}}{\text{gram formula mass}}$$

   $$\text{moles NaOH} = 4.74\ \text{g} \times \frac{1\ \text{mol}}{40.0\ \text{g}}$$

   moles NaOH = 0.119 mol

# Review Questions

27. Which quantity is equivalent to 39 g of LiF?

    (1)  0.50 mol
    (2)  1.0 mol
    (3)  1.5 mol
    (4)  2.0 mol

28. What is the total mass of 0.75 mol of $SO_2$?

    (1) 16 g    (2) 24 g    (3) 32 g    (4) 48 g

29. The mass in grams of 2 mol of sulfuric acid is

    (1) $\dfrac{98\ g}{2}$

    (2) 2(98 g)

    (3) $\dfrac{196\ g}{2}$

    (4) 2(196 g)

30. The mass of 1 mol of $NaNO_3$ is

    (1) 42 g    (2) 53 g    (3) 85 g    (4) 116 g

31. The mass of a mole of nitrogen gas is

    (1) 7 g    (2) 14 g    (3) 28 g    (4) 56 g

32. What is the number of moles of potassium chloride (gram formula mass = 74 g) present in 148 g of KCl?

    (1) 2.0 mol
    (2) 2.5 mol
    (3) 3.0 mol
    (4) 3.5 mol

**33.** How many moles are in 168 g of KOH? (gram formula mass = 56 g)

(1) 0.3 mol      (3) 1.0 mol

(2) 0.5 mol      (4) 3.0 mol

**34.** How many moles of oxygen atoms are in one mole of $Mg_3(PO_4)_2$?

(1) 1      (2) 4      (3) 6      (4) 8

**35.** What is the mass of 4.5 mol of KOH?

(1) 0.080 g      (3) 56 g

(2) 36 g      (4) 252 g

**36.** What is the mass of 0.50 mol of $CuSO_4 \cdot 5H_2O$?

(1) 47.8 g      (3) 125 g

(2) 95.6 g      (4) 250 g

## Finding Molecular Formulas from Empirical Formulas

When the molecular mass of a compound and its empirical formula are known, it is possible to determine the correct molecular formula. For example, the molecular mass of propene is 42 amu. The empirical formula of propene is $CH_2$, and the molecular mass of $CH_2$ is 14 amu. Divide the mass of the compound by the mass of the empirical formula. The result will be an integer. In this case it is 3. This tells you that the molecular formula is three times the empirical formula. Simply multiply each subscript by three to find the molecular formula, $C_3H_6$.

**Memory Jogger**

Recall the difference between an empirical formula and a molecular formula. The empirical formula shows the simplest integer ratio of elements in a compound. $C_3H_6$ is the molecular formula of a substance named propene. Its empirical formula is $CH_2$.

### SAMPLE PROBLEM

A compound has a molecular mass of 180 amu and an empirical formula of $CH_2O$. What is its molecular formula?

**SOLUTION:** Identify the known and unknown values.

*Known*
molecular mass = 180 amu
empirical formula = $CH_2O$

*Unknown*
molecular formula = ?

**1.** Determine the molecular mass of $CH_2O$:

For C: 1 atom × 12.0 amu/atom = 12.0 amu
For H: 2 atoms × 1.0 amu/atom = 2.0 amu
For O: 1 atom × 16.0 amu/atom = 16.0 amu
Molecular mass of $CH_2O$ = 30.0 amu

**2.** Divide the molecular mass of the compound by the mass of the empirical formula.

$$\frac{180 \text{ amu}}{30 \text{ amu}} = 6$$

**3.** Multiply the subscripts in the empirical formula by 6.

$$C_{1\times6}H_{2\times6}O_{1\times6} = C_6H_{12}O_6$$

The molecular formula of the compound is $C_6H_{12}O_6$.

## Review Questions

**37.** The empirical formula of a compound is $CH_4$. The molecular formula of the compound could be

(1) $CH_4$    (2) $C_2H_6$    (3) $C_3H_8$    (4) $C_4H_{10}$

**38.** A compound with an empirical formula of $CH_2$ has a molecular mass of 70 amu. What is its molecular formula?

(1) $CH_2$    (2) $C_2H_4$    (3) $C_4H_8$    (4) $C_5H_{10}$

**39.** A compound has an empirical formula of CH and a molecular mass of 78 amu. What is the molecular formula of the compound?

(1) $C_2H_2$    (2) $C_3H_3$    (3) $C_4H_4$    (4) $C_6H_6$

**40.** A compound has an empirical formula of $CH_2$ and a molecular mass of 28 amu. What is its molecular formula?

**41.** A compound has an empirical formula of $CH_2$ and a molecular mass of 56 amu. What is its molecular formula?

**42.** Vitamin C has an empirical formula of $C_3H_4O_3$ and a molecular mass of 176 amu. What is its molecular formula?

**43.** A compound has a molecular mass of 30 amu and an empirical formula of $CH_3$. What is its molecular formula?

**44.** Why can't a substance have an empirical formula of NO and a gram-formula mass of 45 g?

---

# Mole Relations in Balanced Equations

Chemical equations include both qualitative and quantitative information about the reaction. The formulas of the compounds give qualitative information about the nature of the reactants and products, along with some quantitative information. The coefficients represent quantitative information that relates specifically to that reaction.

In problems involving chemical reactions, the relative amounts of reactants and products are represented by the coefficients. Coefficients represent both the basic unit and mole ratios in balanced equations.

Consider the equation for the combustion of ethane, $C_2H_6$, as shown in Figure 3-1. The coefficients tell you that 2 mol of ethane combines with 7 mol of oxygen to produce 4 mol of carbon dioxide and 6 mol of water. These ratios will remain constant for any amounts of the substances involved, as shown in the figure.

Balanced chemical equation:

$$2C_2H_6 + 7O_2 \rightarrow 4CO_2 + 6H_2O$$

| Moles $C_2H_6$ | Moles $O_2$ | Moles $CO_2$ | Moles $H_2O$ |
|---|---|---|---|
| 2 | 7 | 4 | 6 |
| 4 | 14 | 8 | 12 |
| 1 | 3.5 | 2 | 3 |

**Figure 3-1. Mole ratios from a balanced equation:** Regardless of the number of moles of any of the reactants or products, the ratio must remain 2:7:4:6 for this reaction.

## Volume Relationships of Gases in Balanced Equations

Not only do coefficients represent mole ratios in balance equations, they also represent volume relations of gases. Using the same equation in the previous sample problem, we can solve for unknown quantities of gases.

> ### SAMPLE PROBLEM
>
> How many liters of carbon dioxide gas will be produced from the complete combustion of 30.0 liters of ethane according to the following equation?
>
> $$2C_2H_6(g) + 7O_2(g) \rightarrow 4CO_2(g) + 6H_2O(g)$$
>
> **SOLUTION:** Identify the known and unknown values.
>
> *Known*
> Volume of $C_2H_6(g)$ = 30.0 L
> Ratio of $C_2H_6(g)$: $CO_2$ = 2:4
>
> *Unknown*
> Vol of $CO_2(g)$ = ? liters
>
> Set up proportion and solve:
>
> $$\frac{30.0\ L}{2} = \frac{x}{4}$$
>
> $$x = 60\ liters$$

How many moles of water will be produced from the complete combustion of 3.0 mol of ethane according to the following equation?

$$2C_2H_6(g) + 7O_2(g) \rightarrow 4CO_2(g) + 6H_2O(g)$$

**SOLUTION:** Identify the known and unknown values.

*Known*
moles $C_2H_6$ = 3.0 mol balanced equation

*Unknown*
moles water = ? mol

1. Use the balanced equation to determine the mole ratio between ethane and water.

   moles ethane: moles water = 2:6

2. Set up a proportion between the known moles of ethane (3.0 mol) and the coefficient of ethane, and moles of water ($x$) and the coefficient of water

$$\frac{3.0 \text{ mol } C_2H_6}{2 \text{ mol } C_2H_6} = \frac{x}{6 \text{ mol } H_2O}$$

3. Solve for the number of moles of $H_2O$ ($x$).

$$x = \frac{(3.0 \text{ mol } C_2H_6)(6 \text{ mol } H_2O)}{2 \text{ mol } C_2H_6}$$

$$x = 9.0 \text{ mol } H_2O$$

# Review Questions

**45.** Given the reaction $4Al(s) + 3O_2(g) \rightarrow 2Al_2O_3(s)$, what is the minimum number of moles of oxygen gas required to produce 1.00 mol of aluminum oxide?

(1) 1.0 mol      (3) 3.0 mol
(2) 1.5 mol      (4) 6.0 mol

**46.** Given the reaction $4NH_3 + 5O_2 \rightarrow 4NO + 6H_2O$, what is the maximum number of moles of $H_2O$ that can be produced when 2.0 mol of $NH_3$ are completely reacted?

(1) 1.0 mol      (3) 3.0 mol
(2) 2.0 mol      (4) 6.0 mol

**47.** Given the reaction $2KClO_3(s) \rightarrow 2KCl(s) + 3O_2(g)$, what is the total number of moles of $KClO_3$ needed to produce 6 mol of $O_2$?

(1) 1 mol    (2) 2 mol    (3) 3 mol    (4) 4 mol

**48.** Given the reaction $CH_4 + 2O_2 \rightarrow CO_2 + 2H_2O$, what amount of oxygen is needed to completely react with 1 mol of $CH_4$?

(1) 2 mol      (3) 2 g
(2) 2 atoms      (4) 2 molecules

**49.** Given the reaction $4NH_3 + 5O_2 \rightarrow 4NO + 6H_2O$, what is the total number of moles of $O_2$ required to produce 40 mol of NO?

(1) 5 mol    (2) 9 mol    (3) 32 mol    (4) 50 mol

**50.** Given the reaction $2CH_3OH(l) + 3O_2(g) \rightarrow 2CO_2(g) + 4H_2O(g)$, how many moles of $O_2(g)$ are needed to produce exactly 20. mol of $CO_2(g)$?

(1) 10. mol      (3) 30. mol
(2) 20. mol      (4) 40. mol

**51.** Given the reaction $4Na + O_2 \rightarrow 2Na_2O$, how many moles of oxygen are completely consumed in the production of 1.00 mol of $Na_2O$?

(1) 0.50 mol      (3) 2 mol
(2) 1 mol      (4) 4.0 mol

**52.** Given the reaction $Ca + 2H_2O \rightarrow Ca(OH)_2 + H_2$, what is the total number of moles of Ca needed to react completely with 4.0 mol of $H_2O$?

(1) 0.50 mol      (3) 2.0 mol
(2) 1.0 mol      (4) 4.0 mol

**53.** Consider the following equation.
$$CH_4(g) + 2O_2(g) \rightarrow CO_2(g) + 2H_2O(g)$$
How many moles of oxygen are needed for the complete combustion of 3.0 mol of $CH_4(g)$?

(1) 2.0 mol
(2) 3.0 mol
(3) 4.0 mol
(4) 6.0 mol

54. According to the reaction $2Al + 3H_2SO_4 \rightarrow 3H_2 + Al_2(SO_4)_3$, the total number of moles of $H_2SO_4$ needed to react completely with 5.0 mol of Al is

(1) 2.5 mol      (3) 7.5 mol
(2) 5.0 mol      (4) 9.0 mol

55. Given the equation $N_2(g) + 3H_2(g) \rightarrow 2NH_3(g)$, what is the total number of moles of $NH_3$ produced when 10. mol of $H_2$ reacts completely with $N_2$?

(1) 2.0 mol      (3) 6.7 mol
(2) 3.0 mol      (4) 15 mol

56. According to the equation $2K(s) + Cl_2(g) \rightarrow 2KCl(s)$, potassium reacts with chlorine to form potassium chloride. If 100 atoms of potassium react with chlorine gas, how many chlorine molecules will be needed to completely react?

57. What do coefficients represent in a balanced equation?

58. A student is given the equation $N_2 + H_2 \rightarrow NH_3$ to balance. She answers with $N_2 + 2H_2 \rightarrow 2NH_2$. Explain why her answer is not correct. Balance the equation correctly.

59. Consider the equation $H_2 + Cl_2 \rightarrow 2HCl$. A student suggests that according to the ratio shown by the coefficients, 20 g of hydrogen will react with 20 g of chlorine to form 40 g of HCl. Is the student correct? Explain.

60. The process of photosynthesis can be represented by the following equation.
$6CO_2(g) + 6H_2O(\ell) + energy \rightarrow C_6H_{12}O_6(s) + 6O_2(g)$
If 4 mol of $C_6H_{12}O_6$ is produced by the process, how many moles of $CO_2(g)$ and $H_2O(\ell)$ were used?

61. How many molecules of water are needed to produce 6 molecules of $C_6H_{12}O_6$ according to the equation in the previous question?

62. How many moles of oxygen gas are produced when 6 mol of $CO_2$ are consumed in the process of photosynthesis? (See problem 59 for the equation.)

63. Hydrogen gas and chlorine gas react to form hydrogen chloride.

$$H_2(g) + Cl_2(g) \rightarrow 2HCl(g)$$

If 2 mol of hydrogen gas are mixed with 4 mol of chlorine gas, how many moles of hydrogen chloride will be produced?

64. In the previous question, one of the reactants will not be completely used up. Which one will not be completely used, and how many moles will not react?

65. Make a drawing of 6 molecules of hydrogen gas ($H_2$) in a container. Using a different symbol, add the correct number of nitrogen gas ($N_2$) molecules to form ammonia according to the following equation.

$$N_2(g) + 3H_2(g) \rightarrow 2NH_3$$

In a second drawing, show the number and composition of ammonia molecules in the container after the reaction has been completed.

66. In the reaction $4NH_3(g) + 5O_2(g) \rightarrow 4NO(g)$ and $6H_2O(g)$, what volume of oxygen is required if 20 liters of $NH_3$ is consumed?

(1) 5 liters
(2) 25 liters
(3) 47 liters
(4) 125 liters

67. Given the balanced equation:
$$C_2H_4(g) + 3O_2(g) \rightarrow 2CO_2(g) + 2H_2O(g)$$

How many liters of $CO_2$ are produced when 15 liters of $O_2$ are consumed?

(1) 10      (2) 15      (3) 30      (4) 45

68. Given the reaction: $H_2(g) + Cl_2(g) \rightarrow 2HCl(g)$

What is the total volume of $H_2(g)$ consumed when 22.4 liters of $Cl_2(g)$ completely reacts?

(1) 11.2 L    (2) 22.4 L    (3) 44.8 L    (4) 89.6 L

69. Given the reaction:
$$2C_8H_{18}(g) + 25 O_2(g) \rightarrow 16CO_2(g) + 18 H_2O(g)$$

What is the total number of liters of oxygen required for the complete combustion of 4.00 liters of $C_8H_{18}$?

(1) 25.0     (2) 50.0     (3) 100.     (4) 200.

70. Given the reaction:
$$C_3H_8(g) + 5O_2(g) \rightarrow 4H_2O(g) + 3CO_2(g)$$

What is the total number of liters of $CO_2(g)$ produced when 150. liters of $O_2(g)$ reacts with $C_3H_8$?

(1) 90.      (2) 150.      (3) 3.0      (4) 250.

71. Given the reaction:
$$2SO_2(g) + O_2(g) \rightarrow 2SO_3(g)$$

What is the total number of liters of $SO_3(g)$ produced when 32.0 liters of $SO_2(g)$ reacts completely?

(1) 11.2 L
(2) 32.0 L
(3) 40.0 L
(4) 44.8 L

# Practice Questions
## for the New York Regents Exam

TOPIC **3**

## Directions

Review the Test-Taking Strategies section of this book. Then answer the following questions. Read each question carefully and answer with a correct choice or response.

## Part A

1 The term *mole* is a unit used to represent
   (1) density of particles    (3) numbers of particles
   (2) kinds of particles    (4) reactivity of particles

2 One mole of carbon and one mole of neon both have the same
   (1) mass    (3) number of particles
   (2) volume    (4) number of protons

3 The mass of a mole of a substance is equal to
   (1) the atomic number in grams
   (2) the mass of the most common isotope in grams
   (3) the gram formula mass
   (4) the mass of 22.4 L of any substance

4 A hydrated crystal is one in which
   (1) water molecules are part of the crystal
   (2) water molecules have been removed
   (3) hydrogen molecules are part of the crystal
   (4) hydrogen molecules have been removed

5 To find the percent of an element in a compound
   (1) divide the atomic mass of the element by its atomic number × 100%
   (2) divide the total mass of an element by the total mass of the compound × 100%
   (3) multiply the atomic mass of the element by the total mass of the compound × 100%
   (4) multiply the atomic mass of the elements by their subscripts × 100%

6 In a balanced equation, coefficients always represent
   (1) the number of atoms present
   (2) the ratio of volumes of substances
   (3) the mole ratios of reactants and products
   (4) the volume ratios of reactants and products

## Part B

7 What is the gram atomic mass of zinc?
   (1) 1.33 g    (2) 30. g    (3) 65 g    (4) 130. g

8 The mass of a mole of $O_2(g)$ is
   (1) 8.0 g    (2) 16.0 g    (3) 24.0 g    (4) 32.0 g

9 If the mass of a mole of $H_2X$ is 34 g, then X must represent
   (1) O    (2) Cl    (3) Kr    (4) S

10 The mass of a mole of $Ca(OH)_2$ is
   (1) 38 g    (2) 57 g    (3) 58 g    (4) 74 g

11 The mass of 4 moles of $CO_2$ is
   (1) 22 g    (2) 44 g    (3) 88 g    (4) 176 g

12 What is the total number of moles in 80.0 grams of $C_2H_5Cl$ (gram-formula mass = 64.5 grams/mole)?
   (1) 0.806    (2) 1.24    (3) 2.48    (4) 5.16

13 Consider the following equation.

$$2C_2H_6 + O_2 \rightarrow 4CO_2 + 6H_2O$$

When 4 mol of $C_2H_6$ are burned the number of moles of $CO_2$ produced will be
   (1) 2 mol    (2) 6 mol    (3) 7 mol    (4) 8 mol

14 Given the equation $Mg + 2HCl \rightarrow MgCl_2 + H_2$, how many moles of hydrochloric acid are needed to react with 0.50 mol of magnesium?
   (1) 0.5 mol    (3) 2.0 mol
   (2) 1.0 mol    (4) 4.0 mol

15 Given the balanced equation representing a reaction:
   $2CO(g) + O_2(g) \rightarrow 2CO_2(g)$

What is the mole ratio of $CO(g)$ to $CO_2(g)$ in this reaction?
   (1) 1:1    (2) 1:2    (3) 2:1    (4) 3:2

## Part C

16 What is the gram formula mass of $CaSO_4 \cdot 2H_2O$? [1]

17 What is the formula mass of glucose, $C_6H_{12}O_6$? [1]

18 What is the gram-formula mass of ethylene glycol, $C_2H_4(OH)_2$? [1]

19 What is the percent by mass of nitrogen in $(NH_4)_2CO_3$? [1]

20 What is the percent by mass of oxygen in $NO_2$? [1]

Topic 3: The Mathematics of Formulas and Equations **55**

21 What is the percent by mass of oxygen in propanal, $CH_3CH_2CHO$? [1]

22 Calculate the percent composition, by mass, of carbon in $Na_2CO_3$. [1]

23 Explain the difference between a molecular and an empirical formula. [2]

24 What is the empirical formula of aspirin, $C_9H_8O_4$? [1]

25 What is the mass in grams present in a 0.80 mol sample of $NaN_3(s)$ (gram formula mass = 65.0 grams/mole)? [1]

26 Given the reaction:

$$2H_2O \rightarrow 2H_2 + O_2$$

What is the total number of moles of $O_2$ produced when 8 moles of $H_2O$ is completely consumed? [1]

27 Given the balanced equation:

$$4Al(s) + 3O_2(g) \rightarrow 2Al_2O_3(s)$$

What is the total number of moles of $O_2$ that must react completely with 8.0 moles of $Al(s)$ in order to form $Al_2O_3$? [1]

28 Given the balanced equation:

$$\rightarrow 2Al_2O_3(s) \rightarrow 4Al(s) + 3O_2(g)$$

What is the total number of moles of $O_2$ that are produced when 8.0 mol of $Al_2O_3(s)$ are totally decomposed? [1]

**Base your answers on questions 29 through 31 on the following information.**

A student places a 2.50 gram sample of magnesium metal in a bottle and adds hydrochloric acid. The acid reacts with The magnesium to produce hydrogen gas and $MgCl_2$.

29 Balance the equation for this reaction of magnesium and hydrochloric acid, using the smallest whole-number coefficients. [1]

_____$Mg$ + _____$HCl \rightarrow$ _____$MgCl_2$ + _____$H_2$

30 How many moles of magnesium were used in this reaction? [1]

31 How many moles of hydrogen gas were produced if all of the magnesium reacted? [1]

32 Some dry chemicals can be used to put out forest fires. One of these chemicals is $NaHCO_3$. When $NaHCO_3(s)$ is heated, one of the products is $CO_2(g)$, as shown in the following equation:

$$NaHCO_3(s) + heat \rightarrow Na_2CO_3(s) + H_2O(l) + CO_2(g)$$

Determine the number of moles of $CO_2(g)$ produced when 7.0 moles of $NaHCO_3(s)$ is completely reacted. [1]

33 Given the balanced equation representing a reaction:

$$4NH_3 + 5O_2 \rightarrow 4NO + 6H_2O$$

What is the minimum number of moles of $O_2$ that are needed to completely react with 16 moles of $NH_3$? [1]

(1) 16 mol
(2) 20. mol
(3) 64 mol
(4) 80. mol

# Physical Behavior of Matter

## How Scientists Study Phases of Matter

### Water, water everywhere. What makes it so unique?

The glaciers of the world hold quantities of solid water, which, if melted, would raise the oceans and change the face of the continents. Vast quantities of gaseous water—water vapor—swirl around our heads, produced by the evaporation of liquid water and sublimation of solid water. Water vapor condenses and falls as rain. Liquid water is, well, everywhere.

So why is water so unique? It's a combination of structure and bonding that gives $H_2O$ its unusual properties.

Learn more about phases of matter in this topic.

# Physical Behavior of Matter

## Vocabulary

| | | |
|---|---|---|
| condensation | heat | solid phase |
| deposition | heat of fusion | sublimation |
| freezing | heat of vaporization | temperature |
| fusion | kinetic molecular theory | vaporization |
| gaseous phase | liquid phase | |

## Digging Deeper

Glass is a common substance that appears to be a solid. However, careful analysis shows that glass does not have a true crystalline structure and is not a true solid. Over time, the particles making up glass are able to slowly flow past one another. Substances like glass are called <u>supercooled liquids</u>.

There is a fourth phase of matter, plasma. A plasma is a gas or vapor in which some or all of the electrons have been removed from the atoms.

## Topic Overview

In this chapter you will first examine the solid, liquid, and gaseous phases of matter. Next, you will study how to calculate the heat exchanged during heating, cooling, and phase changes. The kinetic molecular theory will then be presented to explain the behavior of gases. Finally, you'll learn about the various means of separating mixtures.

## Phases of Matter

An element, compound or mixture may exist in the form of a solid, liquid, or a gas. These three forms are called the phases of matter.

The **solid phase** contains matter that is held in a rigid form. Because of this rigid form, a substance in the solid phase has a definite volume and shape. Strong attractive forces among the particles in a solid hold the particles in fixed locations. True solids have a crystalline structure.

Particles in the **liquid phase** are not held together as rigidly as those in the solid phase. Liquid phase particles are able to move past one another. The mobility of the particles prevents liquids from having a definite shape. The particles, however, are held together with sufficient attractive force to give a liquid a definite volume.

Particles in the **gaseous phase** have minimal attractive forces holding them together. Due to this lack of attraction among particles, gases have neither a definite shape nor a definite volume. Gases spread out indefinitely unless they are confined in a container. In a closed container, the gaseous particles always expand to fill the volume of the container. A vapor is the gaseous phase of a substance that is a liquid or a solid at normal conditions. Figure 4-1 summarizes the three phases of matter.

## Heating and Cooling Curves

Figure 4-2 shows the heating of a hypothetical substance from the solid phase to the gaseous phase. At time = 0,

| Solid NaCl | Liquid H$_2$O | Gaseous O$_2$ |
|---|---|---|
| Particles are arranged in a regular pattern. The solid is rigid. | Particles are less ordered and are able to flow over one another. | Particles are at much greater distances from one another and are far less ordered. |

**Figure 4-1. Particles of matter in three phases**

shown as point A on the graph, the temperature of the solid is 10°C. Heat is then added to the substance at a constant rate. From time = 0 to time = 2 minutes, the temperature rises at a constant rate until the temperature of the solid reaches its melting point (B). During this portion of the process (AB), the kinetic energy of the substance is increasing.

Eventually some of the particles in the substance possess enough kinetic energy to break the bonds holding them in the solid phase; melting, also known as **fusion**, begins (B). During the melting process (BC), the temperature remains constant even though heat is still being added at a constant rate. During this time, the heat is absorbed by the substance in the form of potential energy. Both solid and liquid phases of the substance are present during the melting process. As time goes on, the amount of liquid continually increases and the amount of solid continually decreases. Because the liquid phase of a substance has more potential energy than the solid phase, the potential energy of the substance increases during the melting process. The unchanging temperature during melting is evidence of the fact that the substance's kinetic energy remains constant during the process. The amount of heat needed to convert a solid at its melting point to a liquid is called the heat of fusion.

**Figure 4-2. A typical heating curve:** The heating of a solid (AB), liquid (CD), and gas (EF) results in an increase in the substance's temperature. Phase changes that occur during melting (BC) and boiling (DE) are not accompanied by temperature changes.

When all of the solid has melted (C) and only the liquid phase is present, the temperature once again begins to rise. This temperature rise is due to the increase in kinetic energy of the substance. The temperature continues to rise until the boiling point is reached (D). Boiling, also known as **vaporization,** begins as some of the particles in the liquid have enough kinetic energy to break free from the attractive forces holding them in the liquid phase. These particles escape the liquid and enter the gas phase. Once boiling begins, the temperature remains constant as the substance's potential energy increases. During this phase change, both the liquid and gaseous (vapor) phases are present. Because the gaseous phase of a substance has more potential energy than the liquid phase, the potential energy of the substance increases as heat is absorbed during the boiling process. If heat is added to the substance in its gas phase, the temperature of the gas begins to rise (EF).

**Heating Curve Summary** All of the steps (AB, BC, CD, DE, and EF) shown in Figure 4-2 are endothermic.

AB: heating of a solid, one phase present, kinetic energy increases
BC: melting of a solid, two phases present, potential energy increases, kinetic energy remains constant
CD: heating of a liquid, one phase present, kinetic energy increases
DE: boiling of a liquid, two phases present, potential energy increases, kinetic energy remains constant
EF: heating of a gas, one phase present, kinetic energy increases

Endothermic reactions absorb heat energy (heat is a reactant). Exothermic reactions release heat energy (heat is a product).

**Cooling Curve Summary** If a gas at high temperature is allowed to cool at a constant rate, a cooling curve results. See Figure 4-3. Note that the reverse of boiling is called **condensation,** and the reverse of melting is called **freezing.** Freezing is also called solidification. All of the steps shown in Figure 4-3 are exothermic.

AB: cooling of a gas (vapor), one phase present, kinetic energy decreases
BC: condensation of the gas (vapor) to liquid, two phases present, potential energy decreases, kinetic energy remains constant
CD: cooling of a liquid, one phase present, kinetic energy decreases
DE: solidification (freezing) of a liquid, two phases present, potential energy decreases, kinetic energy remains the same
EF: cooling of a solid, one phase present, kinetic energy decreases

## Sublimation and Deposition

Heating and cooling curves show the normal transitions between phases. Some substances, however, change directly from a solid to a gas without passing through a noticeable liquid phase. An example is solid carbon dioxide ($CO_2$), which changes from a solid to a gas at normal atmospheric pressure. This process, in which a solid changes directly into a gas, is called **sublimation.** A substance that undergoes sublimation is said to sublime. The reverse of the sublimation process, in which a gas changes directly into a solid, is called **deposition.**

**Figure 4-3. A typical cooling curve:** The cooling of a gas (AB), liquid (CD), and solid (EF) results in a decrease in the substance's temperature. Phase changes occurring during condensation (BC) and freezing (DE) are not accompanied by temperature changes.

# Review Questions

1. Which substance has a definite shape and a definite volume at STP?

   (1) NaCl(aq)       (3) $CCl_4(\ell)$
   (2) $Cl_2(g)$       (4) $AlCl_3(s)$

2. At STP, which element has a definite shape and volume?

   (1) Ag    (2) Hg    (3) Ne    (4) Xe

3. Which sample is most likely to take the shape of and occupy the total volume of its container?

   (1) $CO_2(g)$
   (2) $CO_2(\ell)$
   (3) $CO_2(aq)$
   (4) $CO_2(s)$

4. As a substance changes from a liquid to a gas, the average distance between molecules

   (1) decreases
   (2) increases
   (3) remains the same

5. Which substance takes the shape of and fills the volume of any container into which it is placed?

   (1) $H_2O(\ell)$       (3) $I_2(s)$
   (2) $CO_2(g)$       (4) Hg($\ell$)

6. In which phase are the particles the most random?

   (1) solid    (2) liquid    (3) gas

7. Which phase change represents sublimation?

   (1) $H_2O(\ell) \rightarrow H_2O(s)$    (3) $I_2(s) \rightarrow I_2(g)$
   (2) $H_2O(\ell) \rightarrow H_2O(g)$    (4) $I_2(s) \rightarrow I_2(\ell)$

8. Which phase change represents sublimation?

   (1) $NH_3(\ell) \rightarrow NH_3(g)$    (3) $KI(s) \rightarrow KI(\ell)$
   (2) $CO_2(s) \rightarrow CO_2(g)$    (4) $H_2O(\ell) \rightarrow H_2O(s)$

9. As ice cools from 273 K to 263 K, the average kinetic energy of its molecules

   (1) decreases
   (2) increases
   (3) remains the same

**10.** A solid substance initially at a temperature below its melting point is heated at a constant rate. The heating curve for the substance is shown in the graph below.

Which portions of the graph represent times when heat is absorbed and potential energy increases while kinetic energy remains constant?

(1) A and B          (3) A and C
(2) B and D          (4) C and D

**11.** A solid substance initially at a temperature below its melting point is heated at a constant rate. The heating curve for the substance is shown in the graph below.

Which segment of the graph represents a time when both the solid and liquid phases are present?

(1) AB     (2) BC     (3) DE     (4) EF

**12.** A gaseous substance initially at a temperature above its boiling point is cooled at a constant rate. The cooling curve for the substance is shown below.

How much time passes between the first appearance of the liquid phase of the substance and the presence of the substance completely in its solid phase?

(1) 5 minutes          (3) 7 minutes
(2) 2 minutes          (4) 4 minutes

**13.** The heat of fusion is defined as the energy required (at constant temperature) to change a

(1) gas to a liquid       (3) solid to a gas
(2) gas to a solid        (4) solid to a liquid

**14.** Which occurs as a substance melts?

(1) It changes from a solid to a liquid and heat is absorbed.
(2) It changes from a solid to a liquid and heat is released.
(3) It changes from a liquid to a solid and heat is absorbed.
(4) It changes from a liquid to a solid and heat is released.

**15.** Which phase change is endothermic?

(1) gas → solid        (3) liquid → solid
(2) gas → liquid       (4) liquid → gas

**16.** Which phase change is exothermic?

(1) $H_2O(s) \rightarrow H_2O(\ell)$     (3) $H_2O(s) \rightarrow H_2O(g)$
(2) $H_2O(\ell) \rightarrow H_2O(s)$     (4) $H_2O(\ell) \rightarrow H_2O(g)$

# Temperature Scales

The **temperature** of a substance is a measure of the average kinetic energy of its particles. The particles of all substances at the same temperature have the same average kinetic energy. The temperature difference between two bodies indicates the direction of heat flow. That is, whenever two objects with different temperatures are in contact, heat flows from the object at the higher temperature to the object at the lower temperature. The heat flow continues until the two objects are at the same temperature.

The average kinetic energy depends only on the temperature of the substance, and not on the nature or amount of the material. Thus, 10 g of $H_2O$ at 50°C has greater average kinetic energy than 500 g of Fe(s) at 20°C.

| | Celsius | | Kelvin |
|---|---|---|---|
| Boiling point of water | ⎯⎯⎯ 100°C | 100 kelvins | 373 K ⎯⎯⎯ |
| | 100 Celsius degrees | | |
| Freezing point of water | ⎯⎯⎯ 0°C | | 273 K ⎯⎯⎯ |
| Absolute zero | ⎯⎯⎯ −273°C | | 0 K ⎯⎯⎯ |

Converting between °C and K
K = °C + 273

**Figure 4-4. Comparison of Celsius and Kelvin temperature scales**

Temperature is measured using a thermometer. Thermometers are calibrated by establishing two fixed reference points; the distance between them is then divided into the desired number of units. The fixed points on common thermometers are the freezing and boiling points of water. The freezing point of water is the ice–water (solid–liquid) equilibrium temperature at normal atmospheric pressure (101.3 kPa). The boiling point of water is the water–steam (liquid–gas) equilibrium temperature at normal atmospheric pressure.

As shown in Figure 4-4, the boiling and freezing reference points are used on both the Celsius and Kelvin temperature scales. Note that there are 100 units between the two reference points on both the Celsius and Kelvin scales.

Because there are an equal number of divisions between the fixed reference points of both the Celsius and Kelvin scales, a change of one degree Celsius is equal to a change of one Kelvin. A change of 50°C represents the same temperature change as 50 Kelvins. The Celsius and Kelvin scales are related by the following equation:

$$K = °C + 273$$

Although often confused, heat and temperature are not the same. **Heat** is a measure of the amount of energy transferred from one substance to another. Heat is measured in units of calories or joules. Temperature is a measure of the average kinetic energy of a substance's particles, and is measured in degrees Celsius or in Kelvins. An example of the difference between heat and temperature involves the melting of ice. It requires more energy to melt 10 g of ice than it does to melt 1 g of ice, yet in both cases the temperature of the ice does not change.

## SAMPLE PROBLEM

What Kelvin temperature is equivalent to 35°C?

**SOLUTION:** Identify the known and unknown values.

| *Known* | *Unknown* |
|---|---|
| temperature = 35°C | temperature = ? K |

Substitute the known temperature into the equation relating Kelvin and Celsius, and solve.

K = °C + 273
K = 35 + 273
K = 308

308 K is equivalent to 35°C.

**17.** Which is not a form of energy?

   (1) light         (3) electricity

   (2) temperature    (4) heat

**18.** Which unit is used to express the amount of energy absorbed or released during a chemical reaction?

   (1) degree       (3) gram

   (2) torr         (4) joule

**19.** Which term represents a form of energy?

   (1) heat        (3) kilojoule

   (2) degree     (4) temperature

**20.** The minimum number of fixed reference points required to establish the Celsius temperature scale for a thermometer is

   (1) 1      (2) 2      (3) 3      (4) 4

**21.** What are the fixed reference points on the Celsius thermometer?

   (1) 32 and 100    (3) 32 and 212

   (2) 0 and 212     (4) 0 and 100

**22.** The difference between the boiling point and the freezing point of pure water at standard pressure is

   (1) 32 K   (2) 273 K   (3) 100 K   (4) 373 K

**23.** What is the freezing point of water on the Kelvin scale at standard pressure?

   (1) 0 K   (2) 32 K   (3) 100 K   (4) 273 K

**24.** When the temperature of an object changes by 100°C, the same temperature change in Kelvins would be

   (1) 100 K   (2) 173 K   (3) 273 K   (4) 373 K

**25.** Energy is added to a substance. Compared to the Celsius temperature of the substance, the Kelvin temperature

   (1) will always be 273 greater

   (2) will always be 273 lower

   (3) will have the same reading at 0

   (4) will have the same reading at 273

**26.** What Kelvin temperature is equal to −73°C?

   (1) 100 K   (2) 173 K   (3) 200 K   (4) 346 K

**27.** Which temperature is equal to 20 K?

   (1) −253°C  (2) −293°C  (3) 253°C  (4) 293°C

**28.** Different masses of copper and iron have the same temperature. Compared to the average kinetic energy of the copper atoms, the average kinetic energy of the iron atoms is

   (1) less     (2) greater     (3) the same

**29.** The average kinetic energy of water molecules increases when

   (1) $H_2O(s)$ changes to $H_2O(\ell)$ at 0°C

   (2) $H_2O(\ell)$ changes to $H_2O(s)$ at 0°C

   (3) $H_2O(\ell)$ at 10°C changes to $H_2O(\ell)$ at 20°C

   (4) $H_2O(\ell)$ at 20°C changes to $H_2O(s)$ at 10°C

## Measurement of Heat Energy

The amount of heat given off or absorbed in a reaction can be calculated using the following equation:

$$q = mC\Delta T$$

$q$ = heat (in joules)      $C$ = specific heat capacity of substance

$m$ = mass of the substance   $\Delta T$ = (Temperature$_{initial}$ − Temperature$_{final}$)

### SAMPLE PROBLEM

How many joules are absorbed when 50.0 g of water are heated from 30.2°C to 58.6°C?

**SOLUTION:** Identify the known and unknown values.

*Known*

$m$ = 50.0 g

$C_{water}$ = 4.18 J/g•°C

$\Delta T$ = (58.6°C − 30.2°C) = 28.4°C

*Unknown*

$q$ = ? J

Substitute the known values into the formula $q = mC\Delta T$ and solve for $q$.

$q = (50.0 \text{ g})(4.18 \text{ J/g•°C})(28.4°C)$

$q = 5936 \text{ J} = 5.94 \times 10^3 \text{ J}$

Stirrer

Source of
direct current

Thermometer

Insulation

Water

Reaction
chamber

Wire coil for
igniting charge

**Figure 4-5.** Cutaway drawing showing the components of a calorimeter

As shown in Figure 4-5, a device known as a calorimeter can be used to measure the amount of heat given off in a reaction. The reaction takes place in the reaction chamber, and the heat released by the reaction is absorbed by the surrounding water. By measuring the temperature increase of the water, the heat given off in the reaction can be calculated.

Whenever a substance undergoes a temperature change, the equation $q = mc\Delta T$ can be used to calculate the heat involved. However, this equation cannot be used to determine the amount of heat required to melt or boil a substance. Why? Temperature remains constant during a phase change, so there is no $\Delta T$, and the equation cannot be used. Recall from Figure 4-2 that the line segment BC represents the melting of a substance. To determine the heat required for a phase change such as this, you must use an equation involving the substance's heat of fusion.

## Heat of Fusion

The amount of heat needed to convert a unit mass of a substance from solid to liquid at its melting point is called the **heat of fusion.** The heat of fusion of solid water (ice) at 0°C and 1 atmosphere is 334 J/g. The heat absorbed by the substance during the melting process increases the potential energy of the substance without increasing the average kinetic energy of the substance's particles. Becausethere is no change in kinetic energy, there is no temperature change during the process.

---

**SAMPLE PROBLEM**

How many joules are required to melt 255 g of ice at 0°C?

**SOLUTION:** Identify the known and unknown values.

_Known_
$m = 255$ g
heat of fusion = 334 J/g

_Unknown_
$q = ?$ J

Multiply the heat of fusion by the total mass of ice to determine the heat required.

$q = (255 \cancel{g})(334 \text{ J/}\cancel{g}) = 85{,}170$ J $= 85.2$ kJ

---

The process of melting is an endothermic process, that is, it requires heat. Therefore, the reverse process of freezing (also called solidification) must be exothermic. During the freezing process, water releases 334 J/g of heat and its potential energy decreases.

## Heat of Vaporization

During the boiling process, a substance in the liquid phase is converted to the gaseous (vapor) phase. The temperature remains constant during the boiling process even though energy is constantly added. The heat energy increases the potential energy of the particles in the gaseous phase. The amount of heat needed to convert a unit mass of a substance from its liquid phase to its vapor phase at constant temperature is called its **heat of vaporization.** As heat is added, the particles absorb sufficient energy to overcome the attractive forces holding them in the liquid phase. The potential energy of the system increases as the temperature remains constant. The heat of vaporization of water at 100°C and 1 atmosphere is 2260 J/g.

The condensation process is the reverse of boiling process. Therefore the heat of condensation is also 2260 J/g. Condensation is an exothermic process.

---

## SAMPLE PROBLEM

How many joules of energy are required to vaporize 423 g of water at 100°C and 1 atm?

**SOLUTION:** Identify the known and unknown values.

*Known*  
m = 423 g  
heat of fusion = 2260 J/g

*Unknown*  
q = ? J

Multiply the heat of vaporization by the total mass of water to determine the heat required.

q = (423 g)(2260 J/g) = 955,980 J = 956 kJ

---

# Review Questions

**30.** When 25.0 grams of water are cooled from 20.0°C to 10.0°C, the number of joules of heat energy released is

(1) 42  
(2) 105  
(3) 840  
(4) 1050

**31.** How many joules of heat energy are released when 50.0 g of water are cooled from 70.0°C to 60.0°C?

(1) 41.8 J  
(2) $2.09 \times 10^3$ J  
(3) 209 J  
(4) $4.18 \times 10^3$ J

**32.** What is the total number of joules of heat energy absorbed when the temperature of 200.0 g of water is raised from 10.0°C to 40.0°C?

(1) 126 J  
(2) 840. J  
(3) $2.51 \times 10^4$ J  
(4) $3.36 \times 10^4$ J

**33.** How many kilojoules of heat energy are absorbed when 100.0 g of water are heated from 20.0°C to 30.0°C?

(1) 4.18 kJ  
(2) 41.8 kJ  
(3) 418 kJ  
(4) 0.418 kJ

**34.** The temperature of a sample of water in the liquid phase is raised 30.0°C by the addition of 3762 J. What is the mass of the water?

(1) 0.03 g  
(2) 0.30 g  
(3) 30.0 g  
(4) 300.0 g

**35.** When 418. joules of heat energy are added to 10.0 grams of water at 20.0°C, the final temperature of the water will be

(1) 10.0°C  
(2) 30.0°C  
(3) 40.0°C  
(4) 100.0°C

**36.** When 20.0 g of a substance are completely melted at its melting point, 3444 J are absorbed. What is the heat of fusion of this substance?

(1) 41 J/g  
(2) 172 J/g  
(3) 16,400 J/g  
(4) 68,900 J/g

**37.** The heat of vaporization of a liquid is 1344 J/g. What is the minimum number of joules needed to change 40.0 g of the liquid to vapor at the boiling point?

(1) 33.6 J  
(2) 1344 J  
(3) 13,776 J  
(4) 53,800 J

For each of the following problems, be sure to show your work, use the proper units, and express your answer to the correct number of significant figures.

38. A sample of water is heated from 10.0°C to 15.0°C by the addition of 125 J of heat. What is the mass of the water?

39. What is the total number of joules absorbed by 65.0 g of water when the temperature of the water is raised from 25.0°C to 40.0°C?

40. If 100.0 J are added to 20.0 g of water at 30.0°C, what will be the final temperature of the water?

41. The temperature of 50.0 g of water was raised to 50.0°C by the addition of 1.0 kJ of heat energy. What was the initial temperature of the water?

42. What would be the temperature change if 3.0 g of water absorbed 15 J of heat?

43. What is the total number of kilojoules of heat needed to change 150. g of ice to water at 0°C?

44. What is the total number of kilojoules required to completely boil 100.0 g of water at 100.0°C and 1 atmosphere?

45. How much energy is required to vaporize 10.00 g of water at its boiling point?

46. At 1 atmosphere of pressure, 25.0 g of a compound at its normal boiling point are converted to a gas by the addition of 34,400 J. What is the heat of vaporization for this compound in J/g?

# Behavior of Gases

Scientists construct models to explain the behavior of substances. While the gas laws describe how gases behave, they do not explain why gases behave the way they do. The **kinetic molecular theory** (KMT) is a model or theory that is used to explain the behavior of gases. This theory describes the relationships among pressure, volume, temperature, velocity, frequency, and force of collisions.

## Kinetic Molecular Theory

The major ideas of kinetic molecular theory are summarized in the following statements:

- Gases contain particles (usually molecules or atoms) that are in constant, random, straight-line motion.
- Gas particles collide with each other and with the walls of the container. These collisions may result in a transfer of energy among the particles, but there is no net loss of energy as the result of these collisions. The collisions are said to be perfectly elastic.
- Gas particles are separated by relatively great distances. Because of this, the volume occupied by the particles themselves is negligible and need not be accounted for.
- Gas particles do not attract each other.

**Relationship of Pressure and Numbers of Gas Particles** The kinetic molecular theory easily explains why gases exert pressure. Not only do gas molecules collide with each other, but they also collide with the walls of their container. These collisions with the container wall exert a force over the surface area of the wall—the particles exert pressure on the wall. For example, if you add more air to a bicycle tire, the pressure is increased. The greater the number of air particles, the greater the pressure. Pressure and the number of gas molecules are directly proportional.

Figure 4-6. **Pressure-volume relationship:** (A) **At constant temperature, as the volume of a gas decreases, the pressure it exerts increases.** (B) **This graph shows the variation of gas volume with changing pressure at constant temperature. PV = constant**

**Relationship of Pressure and Volume of a Gas** Picture a cylinder with a piston at one end. If the piston can be pushed in, the volume will decrease. The molecules of the gas become more concentrated and hit the walls of the container more often. The pressure increases. If the piston is moved outward so as to increase the volume, the molecules hit the walls less often, causing a decrease in pressure. Thus volume and pressure are indirectly, or inversely, related. If one of the variables (volume or pressure) increases, the other must decrease.

**Relationship of Temperature and Pressure of a Gas** You may recall that the temperature of a substance is defined as a measure of the average kinetic energy of its particles. The kinetic energy (KE) is given by the formula $KE = (\frac{1}{2})mv^2$. As the temperature rises, the kinetic energy increases. This increase is due not to an increase in the mass of the particles, but rather to an increase in their velocity. As the temperature rises, the velocity of the particles increases, causing them to hit the walls of the container more often and with greater force. Thus an increase in temperature causes the pressure to increase. Pressure and temperature are directly related.

**Relationship of Temperature and Volume of a Gas** If the volume of a container could change while the pressure remained constant, how would volume and temperature be related? As the temperature increases, the molecules push harder on the piston of the container. When the internal pressure of the container exceeds the pressure pushing from the outside, the piston is pushed upward and the volume increases. The piston continues to move until the internal and external pressures are equal. Thus volume and temperature are directly related.

**Relationship of Temperature and Velocity** You know that as the temperature of a substance increases, its kinetic energy increases. What is the cause of this increase in temperature? Obviously, the masses of the particles do not increase; therefore, it must be the velocity of the particles that increases. The higher the temperature, the greater the average velocity of the particles.

**Combined Gas Law Equation** The relationships among pressure, temperature, and volume can be mathematically represented by an equation known as the combined gas law.

$$\frac{P_1 V_1}{T_1} = \frac{P_2 V_2}{T_2}$$

This law can be used to solve problems involving the gas properties of temperature (*T*), volume (*V*), and pressure (*P*) whenever two or more of these properties are involved. For problems in which two of the properties are involved and the third property remains constant, simply cancel out the variable representing the constant property and then solve for the remaining unknown.

**Figure 4-7. Temperature-pressure relationship:** At constant volume, as the temperature of a gas increases, the pressure it exerts increases.

**Figure 4-8. Temperature-volume relationship:** (A) At constant pressure, as the temperature of a gas increases, the volume it occupies increases. (B) This graph shows the variation of gas volume with changing Kelvin temperature at constant pressure. *V/T* = a constant

## SAMPLE PROBLEM

What volume will a gas occupy if the pressure on 244 cm$^3$ gas at 4.0 atm is increased to 6.0 atm? Assume the temperature remains constant.

**SOLUTION:** Identify the known and unknown values.

*Known*
$V_1 = 244$ cm$^3$
$P_1 = 4.0$ atm
$P_2 = 6.0$ atm
$T = $ constant

*Unknown*
$V_2 = ?$ cm$^3$

1. Since temperature remains constant, delete the $T$ variable from the combined gas law equation.
$$\frac{P_1V_1}{T_1} = \frac{P_2V_2}{T_2} \quad \text{yields} \quad P_1V_1 = P_2V_2$$

2. Rearrange the equation to solve for $V_2$.
$$V_2 = (P_1V_1)/P_2$$

3. Substitute the known values and solve.
$$V_2 = (244 \text{ cm}^3)(4.0 \text{ atm})/(6.0 \text{ atm}) = 160 \text{ cm}^3$$

## SAMPLE PROBLEM

If 75 cm$^3$ of a gas is at STP, what volume will the gas occupy if the temperature is raised to 75°C and the pressure is increased to 945 torr?

**SOLUTION:** Identify the known and unknown values:

*Known*
$P_1 = 760$ torr
$V_1 = 75$ cm$^3$
$T_1 = 0°C$
$P_2 = 945$ torr
$T_2 = 75°C$

*Unknown*
$V_2 = ?$ cm$^3$

1. Convert the known temperatures into Kelvin.
$$T_1 = 0 + 273 = 273 \text{ K}$$
$$T_2 = 75 + 273 = 348 \text{ K}$$

2. Solve the combined gas law equation for $V_2$.
$$V_2 = \frac{P_1V_1T_2}{P_2T_1}$$

3. Substitute the known values and solve for $V_2$.
$$V_2 = \frac{(760 \text{ torr})(75 \text{ cm}^3)(348 \text{ K})}{(945 \text{ torr})(273 \text{ K})}$$
$$V_2 = 77 \text{ cm}^3$$

### Ideal Versus Real Gases

Kinetic molecular theory explains the behavior of gases by using a model gas called an "ideal" gas. When the gas laws are used to solve problems involving "real" gases, the answers obtained often do not exactly match the results obtained in the lab. This is because the ideal gas model does not exactly match the behavior of real gases. These discrepancies arise from the fact that two of the assumptions made by kinetic molecular theory are not exactly correct.

- **Gas particles do not attract one another.** In most cases, the attractive forces between gas particles are so small that they can be disregarded. However, when conditions become extreme, these small forces become important. For example, water molecules in the atmosphere attract each other when temperatures become cold enough. The water molecules combine to form snow or rain.

- **Gas particles do not occupy volume.** Although gas particles themselves occupy a small volume of space under normal conditions, as pressure increases the volume occupied by the particles can no longer be ignored. At high pressures, the increased concentration of particles leads to more frequent collisions and far greater chances of combining.

A gas is said to be "ideal" if it behaves exactly as predicted. Although no gas is truly "ideal," hydrogen and helium are nearly ideal in behavior. In general, gases vary from ideal behavior because of two factors: increasing mass and increasing polarity. These factors become important as pressure is increased and temperature is decreased. Gases are most ideal at low pressures and high temperatures.

## Avogadro's Hypothesis

Avogadro proposed a rather startling theory about equal volumes of gases. He stated that when the volume, temperature, and pressure of two gases were the same, they contained the same number of molecules. Thus, 12 liters of nitrogen at STP would contain the same number of molecules as 12 liters of oxygen at STP, or for that matter, the same number of molecules as any gas at those conditions. Today, we believe that 22.4 liters of any gas at STP contains one mole of the gas. For example, 22.4 liters of neon contains one mole of neon—10g. One mole of any substance contains $6.02 \times 10^{23}$ molecules, a number called Avogadro's number.

**Memory Jogger**

Standard temperature and pressure (STP) is defined as one atmosphere of pressure and a temperature of 0°C (273 K).

Pressure is defined as force per unit area. In chemistry, pressure is often expressed in units of torr, millimeters of mercury (mm Hg), atmospheres (atm), and kilopascals (kPa). Normal atmospheric pressure is 760 torr, 760 mm Hg, 1 atm, and 101.3 kPa.

# Review Questions

**47.** What volume will a 300.0 mL sample of a gas at STP occupy when the pressure is doubled at constant temperature?

(1) 150.0 mL     (3) 2000. mL
(2) 600.0 mL     (4) 4000. mL

**48.** The volume of a sample of a gas at 273°C is 200.0 L. If the volume is decreased to 100.0 L at constant pressure, what will be the new temperature of the gas?

(1) 0 K    (2) 100 K    (3) 273 K    (4) 546 K

**49.** At constant pressure, how does the volume of 1 mole of an ideal gas vary?

(1) directly with the Kelvin temperature
(2) indirectly with the Kelvin temperature
(3) directly with the mass of the gas
(4) indirectly with the mass of the gas

**50.** Which graph best shows the change in the volume of 1 mole of nitrogen gas as pressure increases and temperature remains constant?

**51.** Which graph best shows the relationship between Kelvin temperature and average kinetic energy?

**52.** Under which conditions will the volume of a given sample of a gas always decrease?

(1) decreased pressure and decreased temperature
(2) decreased pressure and increased temperature
(3) increased pressure and decreased temperature
(4) increased pressure and increased temperature

53. At constant temperature, the relationship between the volume (V) of a gas and its pressure (P) is
    (1) $V = $ (constant)$P$
    (2) $P = $ (constant)$V$
    (3) $PV = $ constant
    (4) $V/P = $ constant

54. Which changes in pressure and temperature occur as a given mass of gas at 380 torr and 546 K is changed to STP?
    (1) The pressure is doubled and the temperature is halved.
    (2) The pressure is doubled and the temperature is doubled.
    (3) The pressure is halved and the temperature is halved.
    (4) The pressure is halved and the temperature is doubled.

55. As the temperature of a gas is increased from 0°C to 10°C at constant pressure, the volume of the gas
    (1) increases by $\frac{1}{273}$
    (2) increases by $\frac{10}{273}$
    (3) decreases by $\frac{1}{273}$
    (4) decreases by $\frac{10}{273}$

56. The table below shows the changes in the volume of a gas as the pressure changes at constant temperature.

| Pressure (atm) | Volume (mL) |
| --- | --- |
| 0.5 | 1000 |
| 1.0 | 500 |
| 2.0 | 250 |

Which equation best expresses the relationship between pressure and volume for the gas?
    (1) $\frac{P}{V} = 500$ atm•mL
    (2) $PV = 500$ atm•mL
    (3) $\frac{V}{P} = 500$ atm•mL
    (4) $PV = 1/500$ atm•mL

57. A cylinder with a tightly fitted piston is shown in the diagram below.

Air at constant temperature

As the piston moves downward, the number of molecules of air in the cylinder
    (1) decreases
    (2) increases
    (3) remains the same

58. A gas has a volume of 1000 mL at a temperature of 20. K and a pressure of 760 mm Hg. What will be the new volume when the temperature is changed to 40.0 K and the pressure is changed to 380 mm Hg?
    (1) 250 mL
    (2) 1000 mL
    (3) 4000 mL
    (4) 5600 mL

59. The graph below represents the relationship between pressure and volume of a gas at constant temperature. The product of pressure and volume is constant.

According to the graph, what is the product of pressure and volume (in atm•mL)?
    (1) 20.     (2) 40.     (3) 60.     (4) 80.

60. A sample of gas has a volume of 12 liters at 0°C and 380 torr. What will be its volume when the pressure is changed to 760 torr at a constant temperature?
    (1) 24 L     (2) 18 L     (3) 12 L     (4) 6.0 L

61. A 2.5 liter sample of gas is at STP. When the temperature is raised to 273°C and the pressure remains constant, the new volume of the gas will be
    (1) 1.25 L     (2) 2.5 L     (3) 5.0 L     (4) 10.0 L

62. A gas occupies a volume of 500. mL at a pressure of 380. torr and a temperature of 298 K. At what temperature will the gas occupy a volume of 250. mL and have a pressure of 760. torr?
    (1) 149 K
    (2) 298 K
    (3) 447 K
    (4) 596 K

63. A gas at STP has a volume of 1.0 liter. If the pressure is doubled and the temperature remains constant, the new volume of the gas will be
    (1) 0.25 L     (2) 2.0 L     (3) 0.5 L     (4) 4.0 L

For each of the following problems, be sure to show your work, use the proper units, and express your answer to the correct number of significant figures.

64. A gas has a volume of 2 liters at 323 K and 3 atmospheres. What will be the new volume if the temperature is changed to 273 K and the pressure is changed to 1 atmosphere?

65. What will be the new volume of 100. mL of gas if the Kelvin temperature and the pressure are both doubled?

66. The pressure exerted on 200. mL of a gas is decreased from 900. torr to 800. torr. What is the new volume of the gas if the temperature remains constant?

## Separation of Mixtures

The properties of a mixture's components often provide a means by which they can be separated. Density, molecular polarity, freezing point, and boiling point are a few of the properties that can be used to separate the components of mixtures. In this section you will learn some techniques that can be used to separate the components of mixtures.

### Filtration

Many mixtures are made up of solids in a liquid. The solids are not dissolved in the liquid, but may be suspended. When allowed to stand undisturbed, the solids will settle to the bottom of the liquid. In some cases, you can separate the two components of the mixture by carefully pouring off the liquid without disturbing the solid. This method, though inefficient, can sometimes be used.

A filter is a material that allows small particles to pass through while trapping larger particles on or in the filter material. In essence, the filter is a material containing holes. Particles that are smaller than the holes pass through, while larger particles cannot pass through the holes and are trapped. A mixture of a solid in a liquid can often be separated by filtration. As the mixture passes through the filter, the solid is retained on the filter paper, while the liquid passes through. The substance that passes through the filter is called the filtrate, while the substance remaining on the filter is called the residue.

Filters are also commonly used to separate mixtures of solids and gases. Air conditioners have filters that allow the air to pass through while trapping solids such as lint and dust. Cars and trucks have similar filters.

Some mixtures are composed of two liquids. Two liquids that are not soluble in each other are termed <u>immiscible</u>. Oil and water is an example of such a mixture. Because the oil has a density less than water, the oil rises to the top when the mixture is allowed to stand. In some cases, it is possible to simply pour off the upper layer into a separate container. Figure 4-9 shows a separatory funnel that can be used to separate two liquids that do not dissolve in each other. After the two liquids have been allowed to separate, the valve is opened and the more dense liquid flows from the bottom of the funnel.

Oil

Water

**Figure 4-9. Separatory funnel:** Two immiscible liquids can be separated with a separatory funnel. When the valve is opened, the denser liquid flows from the funnel.

Thermometer

Distilling flask

Mixture

Water outlet

Condenser

Cold water inlet

Distillate

**Figure 4-10. A simple distillation apparatus**

## Distillation

When solids are dissolved in liquids, making a homogeneous solution, they may be separated by distillation. Figure 4-10 shows a typical distillation apparatus. In the case of a salt and water mixture, the solution is heated and the water begins to boil. The steam passes from the distilling flask into the condensing tube. A water jacket lowers the temperature of the steam. The steam condenses and is collected. The salt remains in the distillation flask.

Liquids that mix with each other are called <u>miscible</u>. If miscible liquids have different boiling points, they may also be separated by the process of distillation. Alcohol and water are miscible liquids that form a solution. Alcohol has a lower boiling point than the water, and it vaporizes first. The alcohol vapors escape the distillation flask and are converted back to a liquid in the condenser. Water, with its higher boiling point, remains in the distillation flask.

Gasoline is obtained from crude oil by the process of distillation. Crude oil is a mixture of many different carbon compounds having different boiling points. The parts of the crude oil are separated into various parts, called fractions, by distillation. Gasoline is one of the lighter fractions. It has a relatively low boiling point when compared with other fractions such as diesel oil or home heating oil.

# Chromatography

The process known as chromatography can also be used to separate the components of a mixture. The different components of a mixture often have different attractions for substances not in the mixture. For example, when a piece of paper is dipped into some inks, the water in the ink begins to rise by capillary action. The other components of the ink are drawn up along with the water, but they move up the paper at different rates. Because the components of the ink move at different rates, they begin to separate from each other as they move up the paper.

There are many types of chromatography. Gas chromatography allows gases to pass through a medium separating the components of the gaseous mixture. In all chromatography techniques, the principle remains the same—the components of the mixture have different attractions with the transporting medium. Figure 4-11 shows two common chromatography techniques.

**A**
**Paper Chromatography**

Chromatography paper

Ink dot

Liquid

**B**
**Column Chromatography**

Solvent added

Funnel

Ink layer

Glass column packed with a stationary phase

Erlenmeyer flask

**Figure 4-11. Chromatography techniques:** (A) A strip of chromatography paper suspended in a liquid can be used to separate the components of the ink. (B) In a column chromatography apparatus, the material to be separated is added at the top and separates as it flows to the bottom.

# Review Questions

67. By using a paper filter, which of the following can be separated?

   (1) two immiscible liquids
   (2) two heterogeneous solids
   (3) a solid in a liquid
   (4) two miscible liquids

68. Distillation can be used to separate

   (1) two solids
   (2) two miscible liquids with different boiling points
   (3) solids suspended in a gas
   (4) gases with different densities

69. Gasoline is separated into its components by

   (1) fractional distillation
   (2) filtration
   (3) paper chromatography
   (4) column chromatography

70. The principle that allows paper chromatography to separate mixtures depends on the different components having

   (1) different boiling points
   (2) different attractions to the paper
   (3) different densities
   (4) similar solubility in water

## Directions

Review the Test-Taking Strategies section of this book. Then answer the following questions. Read each question carefully and answer with a correct choice or response.

## Part A

1   Which set of properties does a substance such as $CO_2(g)$ have?
    (1) definite shape and definite volume
    (2) definite shape but no definite volume
    (3) no definite shape but definite volume
    (4) no definite shape and no definite volume

2   A liquid is poured from a volumetric flask into a beaker. Which of the following is true?
    (1) It retains its original volume and shape.
    (2) It retains its original volume, but its shape changes.
    (3) It retains its original shape, but its volume changes.
    (4) Both the volume and shape change.

3   The heat required to change 1 gram of a solid at its normal melting point to a liquid at the same temperature is called the heat of
    (1) vaporization          (3) reaction
    (2) fusion                (4) formation

4   Which statement best describes the molecules of $H_2O$ in the solid phase?
    (1) They move slowly in straight lines.
    (2) They move rapidly in straight lines.
    (3) They are arranged in a regular geometric pattern.
    (4) They are arranged in a random pattern.

5   As the temperature of a substance rises, the average kinetic energy of the particles making up the substance
    (1) increases
    (2) decreases
    (3) remains the same

6   When a substance melts, it undergoes a process known as
    (1) condensation         (3) sublimation
    (2) fusion               (4) vaporization

7   Which phase change is accompanied by the release of heat?
    (1) $H_2O(s) \rightarrow H_2O(\ell)$   (3) $H_2O(s) \rightarrow H_2O(g)$
    (2) $H_2O(\ell) \rightarrow H_2O(s)$   (4) $H_2O(\ell) \rightarrow H_2O(g)$

8   Which of the following is a unit of heat?
    (1) torr                 (3) gram
    (2) degree               (4) joule

9   Which energy transfer occurs when ice cubes are placed in water that has a temperature of 45°C?
    (1) Chemical energy is transferred from the ice to the water.
    (2) Chemical energy is transferred from the water to the ice.
    (3) Thermal energy is transferred from the ice to the water.
    (4) Thermal energy is transferred from the water to the ice.

## Part B

10  The graph below represents the uniform heating of a substance, starting below its melting point, when the substance is solid.

    Which line segments represent an increase in average kinetic energy?

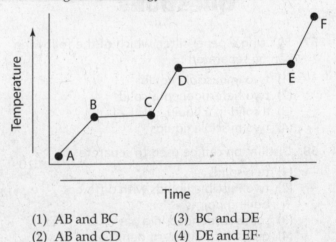

    (1) AB and BC            (3) BC and DE
    (2) AB and CD            (4) DE and EF

11  A liquid's freezing point is −38°C and its boiling point is 357°C. How many Kelvins are there between the boiling point and the freezing point of the liquid?
    (1) 319                  (3) 592
    (2) 395                  (4) 668

**12** As a solid is heated at a constant rate, its temperature increases from 10°C to 25°C, remains at 25°C for 5 minutes, and then increases to beyond 45°C. Based on this information, what conclusion can be drawn about the substance?
(1) Its melting point is 45°C.
(2) Its boiling point is 45°C.
(3) Its melting point is 25°C.
(4) Its boiling point is 25°C.

**13** Which Celsius temperature is equivalent to 323 K?
(1) 50°C       (3) 273°C
(2) 212°C      (4) 596°C

**14** When steam condenses to water, the surrounding temperature
(1) decreases
(2) increases
(3) remains the same

**15** Which grouping of the three phases of bromine is listed in order from left to right for increasing distance between bromine molecules?
(1) gas, liquid, solid
(2) liquid, solid, gas
(3) solid, gas, liquid
(4) solid, liquid, gas

**16** How many joules of energy are needed to convert 50.0 g of water at 50°C to 65°C?

**17** Which graph best represents a change of phase from a gas to a solid?

**18** What volume will 250. mL of gas at STP occupy if the pressure changes to 2.0 atmospheres and the temperature changes to 30°C?

**19** How many joules are needed to completely boil 40.0 g of water at 100°C?

**20** A substance has a specific heat capacity of 2.0 J/g•°C. How many joules are needed to raise the temperature of 30.0 g of this substance by 15°C?

## Part C

**Use the following information to answer questions 21 through 24.**

Cylinder A contains 22.0 grams of $CO_2(g)$ and cylinder B contains $N_2(g)$. The volumes, pressures, and temperatures of the two gases are indicated under each cylinder. The cylinders are fitted with moveable pistons.

| Cylinder A | Cylinder B |
|---|---|
| $CO_2(g)$ | $N_2(g)$ |
| V = 12.3 L | V = 12.3 L |
| P = 1.0 atm | P = 1.0 atm |
| T = 300. K | T = 300. K |

**21** What is the total number of moles of $CO_2(g)$ in cylinder A? [1]

**22** Explain why the number of molecules of $N_2(g)$ in cylinder B is the same as the number of molecules of $CO_2(g)$ in cylinder A. [1]

**23** The temperature of the $CO_2(g)$ is increased to 450 K and the volume of the cylinder remains constant. What is the new pressure of the $CO_2(g)$ in cylinder A? [1]

**24** The piston on cylinder B is pushed in until the volume is 6.0 liters. If the temperature remains constant, what is the new pressure of the $N_2(g)$? [1]

25 A light bulb contains argon gas at a temperature of 295 K and at a pressure of 75 kilopascals. The light bulb is switched on and after 30 minutes, the temperature is 418 K. If the volume of the bulb remains constant, what is the pressure at 418 K? [1]

**Use the following information and graph to answer questions 26 through 28.**

The graph below shows a compound being cooled at a constant rate starting in the liquid phase at 75°C and ending at 15°C.

26 What is the freezing point of the compound in degrees Celsius? [1]

27 State what is happening to the average kinetic energy of the particles of the sample between minutes 2 and 6.

28 A different experiment was conducted with another sample of the same compound starting in the solid phase. The sample was heated at a resulting heating curve. Complete the graph.

**Use the following information to answer questions 29 and 30.**

A gas sample is held at a constant temperature in a closed system. The volume of the gas is changed, which causes the pressure of the gas to change. Volume and pressure data are shown in the table. below.

**Volume and Pressure of a Gas Sample**

| Volume (mL) | Pressure (atm) |
| --- | --- |
| 1200 | 0.5 |
| 600 | 1.0 |
| 300 | 2.0 |
| 150 | 4.0 |
| 100 | 6.0 |

29 Mark an appropriate scale on the axis labeled "Volume (mL)", plot the data and connect the points. [2]

30 Based on your graph, what is the pressure of the gas when the volume of the gas is 200 milliliters? [1]

# The Periodic Table

## How Scientists Use the Periodic Table

**?** **Is a Russian periodic table the same as an American periodic table?** **?**

The first periodic table was developed in Russia almost 150 years ago. Look at part of the original periodic table in the picture below. Even though you might not be able to read Russian, think about what you know about the periodic table. See if you can answer these questions:

- **What portion of the table is shown? How do you know?**
- **What information is given about each element?**
- **What seems to be different from a modern periodic table?**

77

# TOPIC 5

# The Periodic Table

## Vocabulary

| | | |
|---|---|---|
| atomic radius | ionic radius | noble gas |
| electronegativity | ionization energy | nonmetal |
| family | metal | periodic law |
| group | metalloid | period |

## Topic Overview

Look in almost any chemistry classroom or lab here in the United States, or for that matter, almost anywhere in the world, and you will find a periodic table. The table is a brilliant arrangement of the elements used by chemists everywhere. Just finding a given element in the periodic table tells you much about an element.

Currently, more than 100 elements are known. Most of them occur naturally, while others are made artificially. These elements vary greatly in their physical and chemical properties as well as in the characteristics of their compounds. It has long been recognized that if the elements could be classified, it would simplify their study. In this topic we will present the arrangement of the periodic table. Next, we will examine different types of elements. Finally, trends of important properties will be considered.

## Classifying Elements

While there were early attempts to classify and arrange the elements in some orderly fashion, it was Dmitri Mendeleev, a Russian chemist, who is given credit for first arranging elements in a usable manner. Mendeleev observed that when the elements were arranged in order of increasing atomic mass, similar chemical and physical properties appeared at regular, or periodic, intervals. Mendeleev's work in the middle of the nineteenth century laid the basis for the periodic table as we know it today.

However, in Mendeleev's periodic table, the properties of several pairs of elements, such as iodine and tellurium, seemed out of order. If they were switched on the table, the properties would match better, but they would not be in order of increasing atomic mass.

The modern periodic table is not arranged by increasing atomic mass, but rather by increasing atomic number. Henry Moseley, an English scientist, used X rays to identify the atomic number of the elements. If the elements were listed by increasing atomic number, the properties repeated periodically. Modern **periodic law** states: *The properties of the elements are periodic functions of their atomic numbers.*

# Table Information about the Elements

The periodic table is an arrangement of the elements, from left to right across each descending row, in order of increasing atomic number. The periodic table used in the *Reference Tables for Physical Setting/Chemistry* displays some properties of each of the elements. To fully understand some of the information the periodic table provides, refer to Figure 5-1 as the boxes on the periodic table are discussed.

Figure 5-1. **Sample information from the periodic table:** Although the information about the elements can differ from one periodic table to another, some information, such as atomic mass, atomic number, and symbol, are common to almost all tables.

## Chemical Symbols

The symbol of each element is usually found in the center of the box. With over 100 elements to refer to, a symbol is a short and easy way to indicate what element you're talking about, and scientists all over the world can identify an element by its symbol.

Each symbol has one, two, or three letters. The first letter is capitalized, and any other letters present are lower case.

The symbol is related to the name of the element, although sometimes the relationship is not obvious. For example, carbon has an obvious symbol of C. Sodium, however, has the symbol Na, which comes from its Latin name of *natrium*.

Symbols are assigned by an organization known as IUPAC after agreement on the name of a newly discovered element. Agreement has now been reached for the first 111 elements with Ds (110) and Rg (111) having been recently added. Discovery of elements beyond # 111 have been reported, but are unconfirmed. Systematic names are assigned to identify these elements as shown in Fig. 5-2. For example # 118 has the systematic symbol of Ununoctium.

| Roots Used for Naming Elements | | | |
|---|---|---|---|
| Digit | Root | Digit | Root |
| 0 | nil | 5 | pent |
| 1 | un | 6 | hex |
| 2 | bi | 7 | sept |
| 3 | tri | 8 | oct |
| 4 | quad | 9 | enn |

Figure 5-2. **Prefixes used in systematic names:** To name elements with atomic numbers greater than 108, use the prefix for each digit, then add *-ium* to the end of the third prefix. For example, Element 118 would have the systematic symbol of Ununoctium.

## Other Information about the Elements

In the boxes on the periodic table in this book, the atomic number is located below and to the left of the symbol. Below the atomic number is the electron configuration showing how the electrons are arranged according to their energy levels. The atomic mass is above the symbol and to the left. Selected oxidation states are in the upper right-hand corner of the box.

Often, a periodic table will include the name of the element and its state at room temperature. Not all tables include electron configuration and common oxidation states. The information provided by a periodic table will often depend on what information is needed. A periodic table used to

The decimal atomic masses given for each element on the periodic table are the weighted average of the masses of the isotopes of that element.

determine bonding types, for example, might just include the symbols and electronegativities of the elements.

## Arrangement of the Periodic Table

You now know that the elements on the periodic table are listed according to increasing atomic number. But how does this arrangement allow periodic properties to be seen? As you will learn, the columns and rows of the table have special significance.

### Periods

The horizontal rows of the table are called **periods.** The number at the beginning of the period indicates the principal energy level in which the valence electrons are located for the atoms of that period. Potassium (K) and bromine (Br) are members of Period 4, so they have valence electrons in the fourth principal energy level.

In each period, the number of valence electrons increases from left to right, and the properties of the elements change systematically across a period. For example, the elements on the left side of the table have common properties that are described in the next section; these elements are called **metals.** Metals comprise about 75% of all the elements. To the right of the middle of the table are elements called **metalloids,** which have some properties of both metals and nonmetals. On most periodic tables, the metalloids are located adjacent to a diagonal, stair-step line. To the right of

**Figure 5-3. A trend from left to right across a period:** Metals are found on the left of the periodic table; metalloids, on the staircase; and nonmetals and noble gases on the right side.

the metalloids, each period contains one or more elements with properties also described in the next section; these elements are known as **nonmetals**. Each period of the table ends with a noble gas. The metals and metalloids are all solid with the exception of mercury, a liquid. Nonmetals include solids, a liquid (bromine), and gases. Figure 5-3 summarizes this trend on the periodic table.

## Groups, or Families

The vertical columns of the periodic table are called **groups**, or **families**. With a few exceptions, each member of a given group contains the same number of valence electrons. The number of valence electrons for each element is shown as the last number in the electron configuration. Phosphorus, in Group 15, has an electron configuration of 2-8-5. Thus, phosphorus has five valence electrons. All the members of Group 15 have five valence electrons. The elements in Group 18 have eight valence electrons. Helium, in Group 18, is an exception, having only two valence electrons. Because it is the number of valence electrons that determines much of the chemical reactivity of the element, the members of a given group have similar chemical properties.

## Types of Elements

You've just seen that most elements are metals, and some are metalloids or nonmetals. An element can be classified as one of these types according to where it is located on the periodic table. The properties of each type of element are quite important in determining how it can be used.

### Metals

Remember that most known elements are metals. The most active metals are located in Groups 1 and 2. In any group of the periodic table, the metallic properties of the elements increase from the top to the bottom of the group.

#### General Properties of Metals

- Metals are solids at room temperature, with the exception of mercury, which is a liquid.
- Most of the metals have densities greater than water, but the alkali metals (Group 1) will float.
- Metals are <u>malleable</u>, which means that they can be hammered into a shape.
- Metals are <u>ductile</u>, which means that they can be drawn or pulled into a wire.
- Metals have <u>luster</u>, which means that they are shiny.
- Metals are good conductors of heat and electricity. This property stems from the mobility of their valence electrons.
- Metals have relatively low ionization energy and electronegativity values.
- Metals tend to lose electrons to form positive ions with smaller radii. (See Figure 5-4A.)

**Transition Elements** The elements of Groups 3 through 12 are called the transition elements, or sometimes the transition metals. The transition elements in each period represent a series of elements in which the outermost $d$ orbitals are being filled. For example, in Period 4, the transition elements proceed from scandium to zinc. Going from left to right across these elements, the $3d$ orbitals are being filled.

Transition elements are typically hard solids with high melting points, with the notable exception of mercury.

Transition elements are characterized by multiple oxidation states. When the transition elements react, they may use electrons from both $s$ and $d$ sublevels. The ionization energies of the $d$-orbital electrons have values close to those of their $s$ electrons, and different numbers of electrons can be removed, resulting in different oxidation states. In general, the transition elements are far less reactive than the metals of Groups 1 and 2.

Another rather unique property of transition elements is that they often form ions that have color. The transition elements have several empty or half-filled $d$ orbitals of nearly equal energy content. White light shining on these elements can excite electrons to slightly higher orbitals by the absorption of energy. When the electrons return to their ground state, they emit energy with the frequencies of visible colors.

## Metalloids

The metalloids (B, Si, Ge, As, Sb, and Te), sometimes called semimetals, are sandwiched between the metals and the nonmetals. They can be found adjacent to the diagonal, stair-step line on the periodic table used in this book. Metalloids represent an intermediate type of element, displaying both metallic and nonmetallic properties.

## Nonmetals

Although the properties of nonmetals vary more than those of metals, some standard properties can be observed.

**General Properties of Nonmetals**

- Many nonmetals are gases or molecular or network solids at room temperature. Bromine is an exception, being a liquid at room temperature.
- Nonmetals are not malleable or ductile; they tend to be brittle in the solid phase.
- Solid nonmetals lack luster, and their surface appears dull.
- Nonmetals have high ionization energy and high electronegativity values.
- Nonmetals are poor conductors of heat and electricity.
- Nonmetals tend to gain electrons to become negative ions with radii larger than their atoms. (See Figure 5-4B.)

**Figure 5-4. Ion formation:** (A) Metals have three or fewer valence electrons. They tend to lose these electrons during chemical reactions, forming positive ions. (B) Nonmetals have four or more valence electrons. The more valence electrons a nonmetal has, up to seven, the more likely it is to gain electrons, forming a negative ion.

## Noble Gases

The elements in Group 18 are called the **noble gases.** Noble gases don't have all the properties of nonmetals because they are generally unreactive. Only a few stable compounds containing noble gases have been formed.

Each of these elements has a completely filled outer energy level (valence level) of electrons. The valence level of helium is filled with only two electrons, whereas the rest of the noble gases have a complete <u>octet</u> (eight electrons), which is an extremely stable electron configuration.

**Allotropes** Some nonmetals can exist in two or more forms in the same phase. These forms are called <u>allotropes</u>. Oxygen ($O_2(g)$) and ozone ($O_3(g)$) are examples of allotropes. Table 5-1 compares some physical properties of oxygen and ozone.

| Table 5-1. Properties of Oxygen and Ozone | | |
|---|---|---|
| Property | Oxygen ($O_2$) | Ozone ($O_3$) |
| Molecular mass (amu) | 32 | 48 |
| Melting point (K) | 54.3 | 80.5 |
| Boiling point (K) | 90.2 | 161.7 |
| Density (g/cm$^3$) | 1.14 | 1.61 |

The table shows that allotropes have different physical properties. They also differ chemically. Ozone is a much stronger oxidizing agent than molecular oxygen and can cause serious damage to organic molecules. In the upper layers of the atmosphere, ozone absorbs harmful ultraviolet rays preventing them from reaching ground level.

Other nonmetals also show allotropy. Carbon is found as graphite, diamond, and buckminsterfullerene, which has a formula of $C_{60}$. Phosphorus can be found as yellow (white), red, and black allotropes.

# Review Questions

**1.** The observed regularities in the properties of the elements are periodic functions of their

(1) atomic numbers
(2) mass numbers
(3) oxidation states
(4) nonvalence electrons

**2.** Elements in Mendeleev's periodic table were arranged according to their

(1) atomic number
(2) atomic mass
(3) relative activity
(4) relative size

**3.** Most of the groups in the periodic table of the elements contain

(1) nonmetals only
(2) metals only
(3) nonmetals and metals
(4) metals and metalloids

**4.** An element is a gas at room temperature. It could be

(1) a metal or a metalloid
(2) a metal or a nonmetal
(3) a metalloid or a nonmetal
(4) a nonmetal only

5. Atoms of metals tend to

    (1) lose electrons and form negative ions
    (2) lose electrons and form positive ions
    (3) gain electrons and form negative ions
    (4) gain electrons and form positive ions

6. Which property is generally characteristic of metallic elements?

    (1) low electrical conductivity
    (2) high heat conductivity
    (3) existence as brittle solids
    (4) existence as molecular solids

7. When a metal atom combines with a nonmetal atom, the nonmetal atom will

    (1) lose electrons and decrease in size
    (2) lose electrons and increase in size
    (3) gain electrons and decrease in size
    (4) gain electrons and increase in size

8. A Mg atom differs from a $Mg^{2+}$ ion in that the atom has a

    (1) smaller radius     (3) smaller nucleus
    (2) larger radius     (4) larger nucleus

9. Which of the following elements has an ionic radius smaller than its atomic radius?

    (1) neon     (3) sodium
    (2) nitrogen     (4) sulfur

10. When a potassium atom reacts with a bromine atom, the potassium atom will

    (1) lose only 1 electron   (3) gain only 1 electron
    (2) lose 2 electrons     (4) gain 2 electrons

11. At room temperature, potassium is classified as

    (1) a metallic solid     (3) a network solid
    (2) a molecular solid   (4) an ionic solid

12. At room temperature, which substance is the best conductor of electricity?

    (1) nitrogen     (3) sulfur
    (2) neon     (4) silver

13. The element arsenic has the properties of

    (1) metals only
    (2) nonmetals only
    (3) both metals and nonmetals
    (4) neither metals nor nonmetals

14. Which list of elements contains two metalloids?

    (1) Ga, Ge, Sn     (3) C, Si, Ge
    (2) Si, P, S     (4) B, C, N

15. Which set of elements contains a metalloid?

    (1) K, Mn, As, Ar     (3) Ba, Ag, Sn, Xe
    (2) Li, Mg, Ca, Kr     (4) Fr, F, O, Rn

16. On the periodic table, an element classified as a metalloid can be found in

    (1) Period 6, Group 5   (3) Period 3, Group 16
    (2) Period 2, Group 14  (4) Period 4, Group 15

17. Which element in Period 4 is classified as an active nonmetal?

    (1) Ga     (3) Br
    (2) Ge     (4) Kr

18. A property of most nonmetals in the solid state is that they are

    (1) good conductors of heat
    (2) good conductors of electricity
    (3) brittle
    (4) malleable

19. Which properties are characteristic of nonmetals?

    (1) low thermal conductivity and low electrical conductivity
    (2) low thermal conductivity and high electrical conductivity
    (3) high thermal conductivity and low electrical conductivity
    (4) high thermal conductivity and high electrical conductivity

20. Which element in Period 2 of the periodic table is the most reactive nonmetal?

    (1) carbon     (3) oxygen
    (2) nitrogen     (4) fluorine

21. Which element is brittle in the solid phase and is a poor conductor of heat and electricity?

    (1) calcium     (3) sulfur
    (2) strontium     (4) copper

22. Which element in Period 4 is classified as an active metal?

    (1) Ca     (3) Br
    (2) V     (4) Ge

23. The presence of which ion usually produces a colored solution?

    (1) $K^+$     (3) $Fe^{2+}$
    (2) $F^-$     (4) $S^{2-}$

24. Which set of properties is most characteristic of transition elements?

    (1) colorless ions in solution, multiple positive oxidation states
    (2) colorless ions in solution, multiple negative oxidation states
    (3) colored ions in solution, multiple positive oxidation states
    (4) colored ions in solution, multiple negative oxidation states

**25.** Which salt contains an ion that forms a colored solution?

(1) $Mg(NO_3)_2$      (3) $Ni(NO_3)_3$

(2) $Ca(NO_3)_2$      (4) $Al(NO_3)_3$

**26.** Which group in the periodic table contains an element that can form a blue sulfate compound?

(1) 1      (3) 11

(2) 2      (4) 17

**27.** Aqueous solutions of compounds containing element X are blue. Element X could be

(1) carbon      (3) sodium

(2) copper      (4) potassium

**28.** Pure silicon is chemically classified as a metalloid because silicon

(1) is malleable and ductile

(2) is an excellent conductor of heat and electricity

(3) exhibits hydrogen bonding

(4) exhibits metallic and nonmetallic properties

**29.** Which compound forms a colored aqueous solution?

(1) $CaCl_2$

(2) $CrCl_3$

(3) $NaOH$

(4) $KBr$

# Properties of Elements

Some periodic properties of elements, such as metallic character, already have been discussed. However, many other properties of elements can be predicted based on the period or group the element belongs to.

## Ionization Energy

The amount of energy needed to remove the most loosely bound electron from a neutral gaseous atom is called the **ionization energy** of the element.

$$X + energy \rightarrow X^+ + e-$$

Atoms with more than one electron have more than one ionization energy, but this first ionization energy is most significant.

**Trends in a Period** Figure 5-5 illustrates the periodic function of ionization energy. Values from left to right across a period generally increase. Notice that the same pattern is seen in the two periods shown. As the atoms are considered from left to right of the table, an increase in the number of protons is revealed. As the nuclear charge increases, the electrons are more strongly attracted, and hence more energy is needed to remove them from the atom.

**Trends in a Group** Figure 5-6 shows the ionization energy from the top to the bottom of Group 2. The ionization energy decreases because valence electrons in each successive element are at a higher energy level and, thus, farther from the nucleus. It is easier to remove them when they are farther from the positive charge of the nucleus and shielded from it by other levels of electrons.

## Atomic Radii

The radius of an atom is a good measure of the size of the atom. The **atomic radius** is defined as half the distance between two adjacent atoms in a crystal or half the distance between nuclei of identical atoms that are bonded together. Several methods can be used to determine the atomic radius of an element. No matter how the radius is measured, certain trends remain constant.

**Figure 5-5. Ionization energy of Periods 2 and 3:** In general, ionization energy increases from left to right across a period. The peaks in the lines result from the increased stability of filled and half-filled sublevels of electrons.

**Figure 5-6. Ionization energy of Group 2:**
Ionization energy is less in larger atoms that
have the same valence electron configuration as
smaller atoms.

**Figure 5-7. Atomic radii for Periods 2 and 3:**
From left to right, atomic radius decreases across a
period.

**Trends in a Period** From left to right in a period, there is a
repeating pattern of decreasing atomic radii. See Figure 5.7.
In each period, metals have larger radii than nonmetals.
The valence electrons of all the members of a period are at
the same general energy level, but the number of protons in
the nucleus attracting them increases, causing the radii to
decrease.

**Trends in a Group** In any given group, each successive member
has more inner-level electrons than the preceding member.
These electrons shield the valence electrons from the nucleus,
reducing the attractive force of the nucleus. Additionally, the
valence electrons are more energetic than those of elements
higher in the group. Thus, the atomic radius increases from
top to bottom of a group. The atomic radii are shown in
Table S of Appendix 1, *Reference Tables for Physical Setting/* Ⓡ
*Chemistry*. Atomic radii are often measured in picometers
($10^{-12}$ m).

## Other Properties and Trends

You can easily see from the properties discussed so far that
properties of elements follow predictable trends. Other
properties of the elements also follow patterns.

**Ionic Radii** Atoms gain or lose electrons to become charged
particles called ions. Metals tend to lose their valence
electrons in chemical reactions to become positive ions.
Nonmetals tend to gain electrons in chemical reactions and
become negative ions. As these atoms gain or lose electrons,
they complete an octet of valence electrons.

One way to compare an ion to the original atom is to compare
the atomic radius to the ionic radius. **Ionic radius** is the
distance from the nucleus to the outer energy level of the ion.
As you might expect, when an atom loses its valence electrons
and becomes positively charged it loses an energy level and
its radius decreases. Therefore, the radius of a metallic ion is
smaller than the radius of the atom. When a nonmetal gains
electrons, the stable arrangement results in an increase in the
radius. Thus, the radii of nonmetallic ions are greater than
those of their atoms, as shown in Figure 5-4.

**Electronegativity** The **electronegativity** value of an atom is a
measure of its attraction for electrons when bonded to another
atom. Cesium, with an electronegativity value of 0.7, has the
lowest attraction for bonded electrons. Fluorine, with a value
of 4.0, has the highest. Electronegativity values are listed in
Table S of Appendix 1, *Reference Tables for Physical Setting/* Ⓡ
*Chemisty*.

Electronegativity values can be used to predict the type of bond that will
be formed between two atoms. The noble gases are not generally assigned
electronegativity values because they form very few stable chemical
compounds.

There is a regular increase in the electronegativity value of each element when a period is considered from left to right. Metals tend to have low values, while the nonmetals of each period are higher.

In each group, the highest electronegativity value is found at the top. Attraction for bonded electrons is less toward the bottom of the group.

**Reactivity of Elements** Some elements can be found uncombined in nature, that is, in the atomic state. Oxygen may be simply $O_2$. The noble gases are always found as free elements, as they rarely react. Other elements are so reactive that they are never found in the uncombined, or free, state. Such is the case for the elements of Groups 1, 2, and 17. Some of these elements can only be obtained by the electrolysis of their fused salts.

# Properties of Groups

The elements in any group of the periodic table have related chemical properties. Inspection of a group shows that all the members have the same number of valence electrons, and it is this similarity that accounts for the similarity in chemical properties. There is a regularity that can be seen quite clearly in the manner in which the members of a group react with elements of a different group.

Although each member of a group has the same number of valence electrons, there can be a change in the type of element from top to bottom. In Group 14, the top member, carbon, is clearly a nonmetal. Silicon and germanium are metalloids, while tin and lead are metals. As each group is considered from top to bottom, the metallic characteristics increase.

Examine the chemical properties of each group of the representative elements. Notice how these properties are based on the arrangements of the electrons in each group.

## Hydrogen

The vertical columns of the periodic table have been previously identified as "groups." Hydrogen is unique among all of the elements as the only element not belonging to a group. Although it seems to be placed in Group 1, notice that it is separated from the rest of the group. Hydrogen does not have physical or chemical properties similar to the Group 1 metals.

In a chemical reaction, hydrogen often loses its single valence electron to become $H^+$. Hydrogen also can combine with metals to form metallic hydrides, such as NaH. In these compounds the metals have a positive oxidation state, while the hydrogen is assigned $1- H^-$. Hydrogen will also share electrons with another atom to gain stability. An example of hydrogen and oxygen sharing electrons can be seen in water ($H_2O$).

## Groups 1 and 2

The elements of Group 1 (Figure 5-8), the <u>alkali metals</u>, and of Group 2 (Figure 5-9), the <u>alkaline earth metals</u>, show typical metallic characteristics. The members of both these groups easily lose their electrons and are never found in nature in their atomic state. That is, they are always found in

Figure 5-8. Group 1, the alkali metals.

Figure 5-9. Group 2, the alkaline earth metals.

Figure 5-10. Elements in Group 15.

compounds. They can be reduced to their free states by electrolysis of their compounds. All of these elements have low ionization energies and electronegativity values. They typically achieve stable octets by losing electrons to form ionic bonds.

In general, from top to bottom in both groups, reactivity increases. It should be noted that each Group 1 element is more reactive than the Group 2 element of the same period. Francium is the most reactive metal.

## Group 15

The members of Group 15 (Figure 5-10) show the change from nonmetallic to metallic properties from top to bottom of the group. Nitrogen and phosphorus are typical nonmetals and can accept three electrons to form 3− anions. Bismuth loses electrons to become a positive cation, which is typical of metals. Arsenic and antimony are generally classified as metalloids.

Nitrogen is a stable gas at room temperature, largely because it contains a triple bond between the two nitrogen atoms in $N_2$. Phosphorus forms $P_4$, which is far more reactive than $N_2$. Nitrogen is an essential component of protein synthesis and plant processes. Because atmospheric $N_2$ is so unreactive, it must be changed to a usable form. One way this is done is by nitrogen-fixing bacteria that release usable nitrogen compounds into the soil.

## Group 16

The elements in Group 16 (Figure 5-11) also show the expected progression from nonmetal to metal with increasing atomic number. Oxygen and sulfur are typical nonmetals, while the last member, polonium, is a metal. Selenium and tellurium are metalloids.

Oxygen may well be the most important element in the group. It is a diatomic molecule at room temperature, sharing two pairs of electrons between the two atoms. Oxygen is a reactive element, easily forming compounds with other elements. Were it not for the process of photosynthesis, all of the oxygen on Earth would be in the combined state.

In a compound, oxygen normally has an oxidation value of 2−. Its negative oxidation value results from its high electronegativity as it attracts shared electrons in a bond. Only when oxygen bonds to the only element more electronegative than itself (fluorine) does oxygen have a positive oxidation value.

## Group 17

The members of Group 17 (Figure 5-12) are also known as the <u>halogens</u> when they are in the free state. When atoms of elements in this group gain an electron, they become an ion with a 1– charge, and the salts formed are called <u>halides.</u> All the members of the group are nonmetals, but the normal trend of nonmetallic to metallic characteristics is seen even in this group. Iodine, the heaviest nonradioactive member, is a solid with some luster characteristic of metals.

The halogens are the only group of the table containing all three states of matter at room conditions. Fluorine and chlorine are gases; bromine is a liquid; and iodine, a solid. Astatine is a radioactive element with no practical uses. The half-life of At-210 is only 8.3 hours. Therefore, there are no sizeable amounts of astatine in nature.

As is the case with other nonpolar molecules, the halogens are held in the solid and liquid phases by weak van der Waals forces. Because these forces are the result of temporary dipoles caused by the movement of electrons, it follows that the more electrons a molecule possesses, the higher its melting and boiling points.

Because of their high reactivity, the halogens occur in nature only in their combined form. Fluorine, the most reactive halogen, can only be prepared from its fluoride compounds by electrolysis. The other halogens can be prepared by chemical means.

## Group 18

The elements of Group 18 (Figure 5-13) are called the noble gases. They do not combine to form diatomic molecules, but rather exist as monatomic molecules. Each of these atoms has a complete outer energy level of electrons and therefore is chemically unreactive. The outer energy level of helium has two electrons, while each of the remaining noble gases has eight.

**Figure 5-11. Elements in Group 16.**

**Figure 5-12. The halogens (Group 17).**

**Figure 5-13. The noble gases (Group 18).**

**Memory Jogger**

Recall how to use charges to write correct formulas. Remember that all compounds must be electrically neutral. When the charges in a compound formed from two ions are the same but of opposite sign, the ions combine in a 1:1 ratio. If the charges are different, write the charge of one as the subscript of the other to obtain the correct formula.

This group was once called the <u>inert gas group</u> because it was thought that the elements could not react to produce stable compounds. Because their valence levels are full, the noble gases normally would not add additional electrons. However, fluorine has such a high attraction for electrons that it can attract electrons from some of the noble gases, causing them to have a positive oxidation state. Thus, some reactivity is observed. Only argon and xenon have produced stable compounds, although even neon has been coaxed into reactions under severe conditions of temperature and pressure. Helium alone has not shown any reactivity at all.

Like the halogen group, the noble gases are nonpolar and are therefore held in the liquid and solid phases by van der Waals forces. As expected, helium, with the fewest electrons, has the lowest boiling point, and the boiling point increases from top to bottom in the group.

## Reactions Between Groups

Consider the reactions of Group 1 (the alkali metals) with the members of Group 17 (the halogens). The members of Group 1 each have one valence electron to lose and form ions with a 1+ charge. Group 17 elements each have seven valence electrons and can accept one electron from the alkali metal, forming an ion with a 1− charge. The general formula for the combining of a Group 1 element with a Group 17 element is MX, where M represents the Group 1 element, and X represents the Group 17 element. An example is KI.

Group 2 elements have two valence electrons and form compounds with Group 17 elements having the general formula $MX_2$. Examples include $BeCl_2$, $MgBr_2$, and $CaF_2$.

# Review Questions

**30.** Which value represents the first ionization energy of a nonmetal?

(1) 497.9 kJ      (3) 811.7 kJ
(2) 577.4 kJ      (4) 1000. kJ

**31.** As the elements of Group 1 are considered in order from top to bottom, the first ionization energy of each successive element will

(1) decrease
(2) increase
(3) remain the same
(4) follow an unpredictable pattern

**32.** Compared to an atom of potassium, an atom of calcium has a

(1) larger radius and lower reactivity
(2) larger radius and higher reactivity
(3) smaller radius and lower reactivity

**33.** Which statement describes the elements in Period 3?

(1) Each successive element has a greater atomic radius.
(2) Each successive element has a lower electronegativity.
(3) All elements have similar chemical properties.
(4) All elements have valence electrons in the same principal energy level.

**34.** As atoms of elements in Group 16 are considered in order from top to bottom, the electronegativity of each successive element

(1) decreases
(2) increases
(3) remains the same

**35.** A nonmetal could have an electronegativity of
   (1) 1.0
   (2) 2.0
   (3) 1.6
   (4) 2.6

**36.** Which properties are most common in nonmetals?
   (1) low ionization energy and low electronegativity
   (2) low ionization energy and high electronegativity
   (3) high ionization energy and low electronegativity
   (4) high ionization energy and high electronegativity

**37.** A diatomic element with a high first ionization energy would most likely be a
   (1) nonmetal with a high electronegativity
   (2) nonmetal with a low electronegativity
   (3) metal with a high electronegativity
   (4) metal with a low electronegativity

**38.** Which element at room temperature is a poor conductor of electricity and has a relatively high electronegativity?
   (1) Cu          (3) Mg
   (2) S           (4) Fe

**39.** Within Period 2 of the periodic table, as the atomic number increases, the atomic radius generally
   (1) decreases        (3) remains the same
   (2) increases        (4) follows no pattern

**40.** Atoms of which element have the smallest radius?
   (1) Si          (3) S
   (2) P           (4) Cl

**41.** Which statement best compares the atomic radius of a potassium atom and the atomic radius of a calcium atom?
   (1) The radius of the potassium atom is smaller because of its smaller nuclear charge.
   (2) The radius of the potassium atom is smaller because of its larger nuclear charge.
   (3) The radius of the potassium atom is larger because of its smaller nuclear charge.
   (4) The radius of the potassium atom is larger because of its larger nuclear charge.

**42.** According to the reference table, which of the following elements has the smallest radius?
   (1) nickel         (3) calcium
   (2) cobalt         (4) potassium

**43.** In which area of the periodic table are the elements with the strongest nonmetallic properties located?
   (1) lower left      (3) lower right
   (2) upper left      (4) upper right

**44.** At which location in the periodic table would the most active metallic element be found?
   (1) in Group 1 at the top
   (2) in Group 1 at the bottom
   (3) in Group 17 at the top
   (4) in Group 17 at the bottom

**45.** In which section of the periodic table are the most active nonmetals located?
   (1) upper right corner    (3) upper left corner
   (2) lower right corner    (4) lower left corner

**46.** What is the total number of elements in Group 17 that are gases at room temperature and standard pressure?
   (1) 1           (3) 3
   (2) 2           (4) 4

**47.** Which of the following groups in the periodic table contain elements so reactive that they are never found in the free state?
   (1) 1 and 2        (3) 2 and 15
   (2) 1 and 11       (4) 11 and 15

**48.** Which halogen can only be prepared from its fused compounds?
   (1) $I_2$          (3) $Br_2$
   (2) $Cl_2$         (4) $F_2$

**49.** As the elements in Group 15 are considered in order of increasing atomic number, which sequence in properties occurs?
   (1) nonmetal→metalloid→metal
   (2) metalloid→metal→nonmetal
   (3) metal→metalloid→nonmetal
   (4) metal→nonmetal→metalloid

**50.** Which elements have the most similar chemical properties?
   (1) K and Na       (3) K and Ca
   (2) K and Cl       (4) K and S

**51.** Because of its high reactivity, which element is normally obtained by the electrolysis of its fused salts?
   (1) sulfur         (3) argon
   (2) lithium        (4) gold

**52.** Which element in Group 17 is the most active nonmetal?
   (1) Br          (3) Cl
   (2) I           (4) F

53. Which of the following Group 15 elements has the most nonmetallic properties?

(1) Bi
(2) P
(3) Sb
(4) N

54. The elements calcium and strontium have similar chemical properties because they both have the same

(1) atomic number
(2) mass number
(3) number of valence electrons
(4) number of completely filled subshells

55. Which Group 15 element exists as a diatomic molecule at room temperature and pressure?

(1) phosphorus
(2) nitrogen
(3) bismuth
(4) arsenic

56. Which two elements have chemical properties that are most similar?

(1) Cl and Ar
(2) Li and Na
(3) K and Ca
(4) C and N

57. In which set do the elements exhibit the most similar chemical properties?

(1) N, O, and F
(2) Hg, Br, and Rn
(3) Li, Na, and K
(4) Al, Si, and P

58. Which of these metals loses electrons most readily?

(1) calcium
(2) magnesium
(3) potassium
(4) sodium

59. If M represents an element in Group 2, the formula of its chloride would be

(1) MCl
(2) $MCl_2$
(3) $M_2Cl$
(4) $M_2Cl_2$

60. Which group below contains elements with the greatest variation in chemical properties?

(1) Li, Be, B
(2) Li, Na, K
(3) B, Al, Ga
(4) Be, Mg, Ca

61. Which element in Group 15 would most likely have luster and good electrical conductivity?

(1) N
(2) P
(3) Bi
(4) As

62. Which statement best describes the Group 2 metals?

(1) They have one valence electron, and they form ions with a 1+ charge.
(2) They have one valence electron, and they form ions with a 1− charge.
(3) They have two valence electrons, and they form ions with a 2+ charge.
(4) They have two valence electrons, and they form ions with a 2− charge.

63. Which element in Group 15 has the strongest metallic character?

(1) Bi
(2) As
(3) P
(4) N

64. Which halogens are gases at room temperature and pressure?

(1) chlorine and fluorine
(2) chlorine and bromine
(3) iodine and fluorine
(4) iodine and bromine

65. In which group of elements do the atoms gain electrons most readily?

(1) 1
(2) 2
(3) 16
(4) 18

66. Which element is more reactive than strontium?

(1) potassium
(2) calcium
(3) iron
(4) copper

67. The oxide of metal X has the formula XO. Which group in the periodic table contains metal X?

(1) Group 1
(2) Group 2
(3) Group 13
(4) Group 17

68. As elements in a group of the periodic table are considered in order from top to bottom, the metallic character of each successive element generally

(1) decreases
(2) increases
(3) remains the same

69. As the elements in Period 3 are considered from left to right, they tend to

(1) lose electrons more readily and increase in metallic character
(2) lose electrons more readily and increase in nonmetallic character
(3) gain electrons more readily and increase in metallic character
(4) gain electrons more readily and increase in nonmetallic character

70. An atom of which element in the ground state has a complete outermost energy level?

(1) He
(2) Be
(3) Hg
(4) H

71. Which of the following Group 15 elements has the most metallic properties?

(1) Bi
(2) P
(3) Sb
(4) N

72. As the atoms of the elements in Group 1 of the periodic table are considered from top to bottom, the number of valence electrons in the atoms of each successive element

 (1) decreases
 (2) increases
 (3) remains the same

73. Which element attains the structure of a noble gas when it becomes a $1^+$ ion?

 (1) K          (3) F
 (2) Ca         (4) Ne

74. According to the reference table, which sequence correctly places the elements in order of increasing ionization energy?

 (1) H→Li→Na→K
 (2) I→Br→Cl→F
 (3) O→S→Se→Te
 (4) H→Be→Al→Ga

**Answer the following questions, using complete sentences when appropriate.**

75. The ionization energy of Na is 118 kcal, while the ionization energy of Mg to form $Mg^+$ is 175. While this is the expected result for an adjacent element, the ionization of $Na^+$ to $Na^{2+}$ is 1091 kcal, while only 345 kcal is needed to ionize $Mg^+$ to $Mg^{2+}$. Explain.

76. The $Na^+$ ion has a smaller radius than the Ne atom. Explain why this is so.

77. Chlorine reacts with water according to the equation:

$$Cl_2 + H_2O \rightarrow HClO + H^+ + Cl^-$$

 Write an equation to show how iodine reacts with water.

78. Why is the periodic table organized by increasing atomic number rather than by increasing atomic mass, as had been suggested by Mendeleev?

79. Explain why the members of Group 1 react by losing an electron, but the members of Group 17 react by gaining an electron.

80. Let the letter M stand for a member of Group 13. What is the formula of the combination of this element with bromine? With oxygen? Explain.

81. Why is hydrogen not considered to be a member of Group 1 (the alkali metals)?

82. Consider atoms of the elements boron, carbon and aluminum. Which is the largest? The smallest? Which has the highest ionization energy? The lowest?

83. Why do elements in a given group of the periodic table show similar chemical properties?

84. Why do the elements of a given period always follow the progression of metal to metalloid to nonmetal to noble gas?

85. What change in charge takes place as a metal loses one or more electrons?

86. Using the law of octets, explain why it is unlikely for sodium to form a $Na^{2-}$ ion.

87. What would be the general formula of a Group 2 element (represented by M) combined with chlorine of Group 17?

88. What would be the general formula of a Group 17 element (represented by X) combined with magnesium of Group 2?

89. What would be the general formula of a Group 1 element combined with an element of Group 16?

90. Mendeleev arranged the elements on the table in order of increasing atomic mass, but it was later learned that the correct order is by increasing atomic number. Study the periodic table and locate examples where the atomic number of two successive elements increases, but the atomic mass decreases.

## Directions

Review the Test-Taking Strategies section of this book. Then answer the following questions. Read each question carefully and answer with a correct choice or response.

## Part A

1  The elements in the modern periodic table are arranged according to their
   (1) atomic number
   (2) oxidation number
   (3) atomic mass
   (4) nuclear mass

2  Which characteristic describes most nonmetals in the solid phase?
   (1) good conductors of electricity
   (2) good conductors of heat
   (3) malleable
   (4) brittle

3  When combining with nonmetallic atoms, metallic atoms generally will
   (1) lose electrons and form negative ions
   (2) lose electrons and form positive ions
   (3) gain electrons and form negative ions
   (4) gain electrons and form positive ions

4  When metal atoms bond with nonmetal atoms, the nonmetal atoms will
   (1) lose electrons and the resulting ions are smaller
   (2) lose electrons and the resulting ions are larger
   (3) gain electrons and the resulting ions are smaller
   (4) gain electrons and the resulting ions are larger

5  Which characteristic describes most metals in the solid phase?
   (1) good conductors of electricity
   (2) poor conductors of heat
   (3) dull
   (4) brittle

6  Which element is a nonmetallic liquid at room temperature?
   (1) hydrogen
   (2) oxygen
   (3) mercury
   (4) bromine

7  Which physical characteristic of a solution may indicate the presence of a transition element?
   (1) its density
   (2) its color
   (3) its effect on litmus
   (4) its effect on phenolphthalein

8  Compared to atoms of metals, atoms of nonmetals generally
   (1) have higher electronegativity values
   (2) have lower first ionization energies
   (3) conduct electricity more readily
   (4) lose electrons more readily

9  Properties of metals include
   (1) low ionization energy and high electronegativity
   (2) low ionization energy and low electronegativity
   (3) high ionization energy and high electronegativity
   (4) high ionization energy and low electronegativity

10 Which part of the periodic table contains elements with the strongest metallic properties?
   (1) upper right          (3) lower right
   (2) upper left           (4) lower left

11 Which Group 17 element is a solid at room temperature and pressure?
   (1) $Br_2$               (3) $Cl_2$
   (2) $F_2$                (4) $I_2$

12 Which gas is monatomic at room temperature and pressure?
   (1) nitrogen             (3) fluorine
   (2) neon                 (4) chlorine

13 Atoms of elements in a group of the periodic table have similar chemical properties. This similarity is most closely related to the atoms'
   (1) number of principal energy levels
   (2) number of valence electrons
   (3) atomic numbers
   (4) atomic masses

14 In which group are all the elements found naturally only in compounds?
(1) 18                (3) 11
(2) 2                 (4) 14

## Part B

15 An element is a solid at room temperature. It can be a
(1) metal only
(2) metalloid only
(3) metal or a nonmetal only
(4) metal, a metalloid, or a nonmetal

16 How does the size of a barium ion compare to the size of a barium atom?
(1) The ion is smaller because it has fewer electrons.
(2) The ion is smaller because it has more electrons.
(3) The ion is larger because it has fewer electrons.
(4) The ion is larger because it has more electrons.

17 Which element is malleable and ductile?
(1) S                 (3) Ge
(2) Si                (4) Au

18 Which of the following Period 4 elements has the most metallic characteristics?
(1) Ca                (3) As
(2) Ge                (4) Br

19 Which three groups of the periodic table contain the most elements classified as metalloids?
(1) 1, 2, and 13
(2) 2, 13, and 14
(3) 14, 15, and 16
(4) 16, 17, and 18

20 An aqueous solution of $XCl_2$ contains colored ions. Element X could be
(1) Ba                (3) Ni
(2) Ca                (4) Bi

21 Which element has the highest first ionization energy?
(1) sodium
(2) aluminum
(3) calcium
(4) phosphorus

22 An element has a first ionization energy of 1314 kJ/mol and an electronegativity of 3.5. It is classified as a
(1) metal
(2) nonmetal
(3) metalloid
(4) halogen

23 Which sequence of elements is arranged in order of decreasing atomic radii?
(1) Al, Si, P
(2) Li, Na, K
(3) Cl, Br, I
(4) N, C, B

24 Which ion has the largest radius?
(1) $Na^+$            (3) $K^+$
(2) $Mg^{2+}$         (4) $Ca^{2+}$

25 In the ground state, atoms of the elements in Group 15 of the periodic table all have the same number of
(1) filled principal energy levels
(2) occupied principal energy levels
(3) neutrons in the nucleus
(4) electrons in the valence energy level

26 Which of the following Group 18 elements would be most likely to form a compound with fluorine?
(1) He                (3) Ar
(2) Ne                (4) Kr

27 The properties of carbon are expected to be most similar to those of
(1) boron
(2) aluminum
(3) silicon
(4) phosphorus

28 If M represents an alkali metal of Group 1, what is the formula for the compound formed by M and oxygen?
(1) $MO_2$            (3) $M_2O_3$
(2) $M_2O$            (4) $M_3O_2$

29 An atom of an element has 28 innermost electrons and 7 valence electrons. In which period of the periodic table is this element located?
(1) 5                 (3) 3
(2) 2                 (4) 4

## Part C

30 Mendeleev arranged the periodic table in order of increasing atomic masses. Locate iodine and tellurium on the table and note that they are not arranged by increasing mass, and yet Mendeleev placed iodine in Group 17 and tellurium in Group 16. What is the likely reason that he did not arrange them by increasing mass?

31 Ions are isoelectronic when they contain the same number of electrons. Which of the following ions are isoelectronic? $Mg^{2+}$, $Cl^-$, $Al^{3+}$, $K^+$, $S^{2-}$, $Ba^{2+}$. For each of the preceding ions, name the noble gas that it is isoelectronic with.

32 In the 19th century, Dmitri Mendeleev predicted the existence of a then unknown element $X$ with a mass of 68. He also predicted that an oxide of $X$ would have the formula $X_2O_3$. On the modern periodic table, what is the group number and period number of the element $X$? [1]

33 What are two metalloids that belong to the same period of the periodic table? [1]

34 Describe one chemical property of Group 1 metals that results from the atom of each metal having only one valence electron. [1]

**Base your answers to questions 35 through 38 on the information below.**

A metal, M, was obtained from a compound in a rock sample. Experiments have determined that the element is a member of Group 2 of the periodic table.

35 What is the phase of element $M$ at STP? [1]

36 Explain, in terms of electrons, why element $M$ is a good conductor of electricity. [1]

37 Explain why the radius of a positive ion of the element $M$ is smaller than an atom of element $M$. [1]

38 Using the symbol $M$ for the element, write the chemical formula for the compound that forms when element $M$ reacts with iodine. [1]

---

**Base your answers to questions 39 and 40 on the information below.**

Elements with atomic number 112 and 114 have been produced and their IUPAC names are pending approval. However, an element that would be put between these two elements on the periodic table has not yet been produced. If produced, this element will be identified by the symbol Uut until an IUPAC name is approved.

39 Determine the charge of an Uut nucleus. Include both the numerical value and the sign of the charge. [1]

40 Identify one element that would be chemically related to Uut. [1]

---

41 Using information from the periodic table, explain why radium forms chemical bonds in the same way as calcium does. [1]

42 Why does chemical reactivity increase from top to bottom of Group 1, while it decreases from top to bottom of Group 17?

43 Which of the following has the greater ionization energy, Na or $Na^+$? Explain your answer.

# Bonding

## What Scientists Know About Bonding

### How does the body get energy from food?

We have all learned that we get energy to live from oxidizing foods, often sugar, $C_6H_{12}O_6$. But where does the energy actually come from? The answer is not what most people expect. We don't get the energy from breaking the bonds of sugar, because breaking bonds is an endothermic process. Rather, the energy is released after the body has broken the sugar bonds and made the bonds of the products, carbon dioxide ($CO_2$) and water ($H_2O$). The bonds of water and carbon dioxide have less energy than the bonds of sugar, and the difference between the energy of the two is what is used to live.

# 6 Bonding

## Vocabulary

| | | |
|---|---|---|
| asymmetrical molecule | Lewis dot diagram | octet |
| covalent bond | malleability | octet rule |
| double covalent bond | metallic bond | polar covalent bond |
| hydrogen bond | multiple covalent bond | symmetrical molecule |
| ion | nonpolar covalent bond | triple covalent bond |
| ionic bond | | |

## Topic Overview

Chemical bonds provide the "glue" that holds all compounds together. There are different types of chemical bonds, and these different bond types account for the different properties of substances. In this section you will learn how the electron structure of atoms helps explain many aspects of chemical bonding. You will also use Lewis dot diagrams to aid in your understanding of electronic structure and its role in bonding.

## Energy and Chemical Bonds

Chemical bonds are the forces that hold atoms together in a compound. Energy is required to overcome these attractive forces and separate the atoms in a compound. Thus, the breaking of a chemical bond is an <u>endothermic</u> process. If energy is required to break a bond, then the opposite process of forming a bond must release energy. The formation of a bond is an <u>exothermic</u> process.

When a chemical bond is formed, the resulting compound has less potential energy than the substances from which it was formed. Why? Energy is always released when a bond is formed. The greater the energy released during the formation of a bond, the greater its stability. Consider the following two reactions.

Reaction 1     $B + C \rightarrow BC + 100$ joules
Reaction 2     $K + L \rightarrow KL + 400$ joules

**Memory Jogger**

In exothermic reactions, heat is a product and is released; in endothermic reactions, heat is a reactant and is absorbed.

The bond formed in reaction 2 is more stable than the bond formed in reaction 1. It takes 400 joules to break apart compound KL, but only 100 joules to break apart compound BC.

# Review Questions

1. As energy is released during the formation of a bond, the stability of the chemical system generally

   (1) decreases
   (2) increases
   (3) remains the same

2. Which kind of energy is stored in a chemical bond?

   (1) potential energy    (3) activation energy
   (2) kinetic energy    (4) ionization energy

3. Consider the reaction below.

   $$2Na(s) + Cl_2(g) \rightarrow 2NaCl(s)$$

   As the reactants form products, the stability of the chemical system

   (1) decreases
   (2) increases
   (3) remains the same

4. When a chemical bond forms between two hydrogen atoms, the potential energy of the atoms

   (1) decreases
   (2) increases
   (3) remains the same

5. Energy is released when the atoms of two elements bond together to form a compound. Compared to the total potential energy of the atoms before bonding, the total potential energy of the atoms after bonding is

   (1) higher and the compound formed is stable
   (2) higher and the compound formed is unstable
   (3) lower and the compound formed is stable
   (4) lower and the compound formed is unstable

## Lewis Electron Dot Structures

In the next sections you will study the two types of bonds that commonly form. These two bond types result from the transfer of electrons from one atom to another and from the sharing of valence electrons between atoms. A simple modeling technique known as a Lewis dot diagram provides an easy method for showing how electrons are transferred or shared during bond formation. Learning to draw and interpret these diagrams is an important skill.

A **Lewis dot diagram,** also called an electron dot diagram, consists of a chemical symbol surrounded by one to eight dots representing valence electrons. See Figure 6-1.

Figure 6-2 shows the Lewis dot diagram of a sodium atom. The symbol of the element (Na) represents the sodium atom's nucleus along with all of its nonvalence electrons; this portion of the diagram is called the <u>kernel</u>. The kernel of every atom is positively charged. The valence electrons surround the kernel and are usually represented by small dots, x's, or o's.

Figure 6-3 shows the relationship between the groups of the periodic table and the electron dot diagrams of the atoms and ions in those groups.

| Period | Group | | | | | | | |
|--------|-------|---|----|----|----|----|----|----|
|        | 1     | 2 | 13 | 14 | 15 | 16 | 17 | 18 |
| 1      | Ḣ     |   |    |    |    |    |    | He |
| 2      | Li    | Be | Be· | Ċ· | ·N· | :O· | :F· | :Ne: |
| 3      | Na    | Mg | Ai· | Si· | ·P· | :S· | :Cl· | :Ar: |
| 4      | K     | Ca | Ga· | Ge· | ·As· | :Se· | :Br· | :Kr: |

**Figure 6-1. Electron dot diagrams of elements in Periods 1 through 4**

Topic 6: Bonding **99**

The chemical symbol Na represents the kernel of the sodium atom.

**Na** •

This dot represents a sodium atom's single valence electron.

**Figure 6-2. The Lewis dot diagram of a sodium atom:** The kernel, represented by the symbol Na, contains 11 protons and 10 electrons; the kernel has a 1+ overall charge. The 1+ charge of the kernel is balanced by the 1− charge of the single valence electron. Overall, the sodium atom is neutral.

There are slight variations in how electrons are arranged around the kernel in an electron dot diagram. Often, the first two electrons are placed at the 12 o'clock position. As the next three electrons are added, they are placed singly at the 3, 6, and 9 o'clock positions. The last three electrons are added to make pairs in the same order, at the 3, 6, and 9 o'clock positions.

When atoms gain or lose electrons they become charged particles called **ions.** Notice in Figure 6-3 that ions are represented differently than atoms. When metals react, they do so by losing their valence electrons. Thus, there aren't any dots in the electron dot diagrams of the ions for sodium ($Na^+$), magnesium ($Mg^{2+}$), or aluminum ($Al^{3+}$). The square brackets around the kernel and the ionic charge written as a superscript outside the brackets indicate the diagram is that of an ion. Whereas metals lose electrons to form ions, nonmetals gain electrons to form ions. The valence electrons gained when a nonmetal ion forms are shown in its electron dot diagram. It is common to show the added valence electrons with a different symbol than that used to represent the atom's originally present valence electrons.

The number of valence electrons to use in an electron dot diagram can also be determined by consulting the periodic table. The periodic table often lists the electron configuration for the elements using a modified Bohr model. For example, the electron configuration for sodium (Na) is listed as 2-8-1. This notation indicates that there is only one outermost, or valence electron for a sodium atom. The other 10 electrons belong to the kernel of the atom. The corresponding electron dot diagram for the sodium atom would show this one valence electron as a single dot, outside the kernel.

## Lewis Electron-Dot Diagrams of Compounds

Lewis diagrams can also be used to show how atoms combine to form molecules. When atoms combine to form diatomic molecules, single, double, and triple covalent bonds can be shown.

The Lewis structure of a hydrogen atom is simply

H •

When two hydrogen atoms combine to form the hydrogen molecule ($H_2$), they share the two electrons between them in a nonpolar covalent bond:

H **:** H

Instead of using dots to show the pair of electrons, a single dash may be used to show the covalent bond.

H — H

| Group number | 1 | 2 |
|---|---|---|
| Atoms | Ṅa | M̈g |
| Ions | [Na]$^+$ | [Mg]$^{2+}$ |

| Group number | 13 | 14 | 15 | 16 | 17 | 18 |
|---|---|---|---|---|---|---|
| Atoms | Äl• | S̈i• | •P̈• | •S̈: | •C̈l: | :Är: |
| Ions | [Al]$^{3+}$ | * | [:P̈:]$^{3-}$ | [:S̈:]$^{2-}$ | [:C̈l:]$^-$ | * |

*Si and Ar do not ordinarily form ions.

**Figure 6-3. Electron dot diagrams of some Period 3 elements and ions**

The members of column 17, the halogens, also form single bonds between them in their diatomic molecules. In addition to the single covalent bond, each atom has 6 additional valence electrons for a complete octet of 8.

$$\ddot{:}\ddot{C}l - \ddot{C}l\ddot{:}$$

Oxygen has 6 valence electrons with two atoms combining to form $O_2$. In this case, the two oxygen atoms share two pairs of electrons

$$\ddot{:}O = O\ddot{:}$$

Notice that each oxygen atom has a total of 8 valence electrons.

Nitrogen has five valence electrons and forms the diatomic $N_2$ molecule by forming a triple covalent bond

$$:N \equiv N:$$

When drawing Lewis diagrams for compounds, a pair of electrons forming a covalent bond is usually represented by a dashed line, while any unpaired electrons are represented by a pair of dots.

In drawing Lewis diagrams for compounds it is helpful to remember that the octet rule calls for each atom to have 8 valence electrons. Hydrogen is an exception, having a maximum of 2 electrons. Try to follow a pattern when drawing diagrams of compounds.

The following steps are useful in determining the dot diagrams of compounds.

1. Determine the total number of valence electrons of the atoms in the compound.

   Consider the compound $CH_3Cl$:
   1 carbon with 4 valence electrons   =   4
   3 hydrogens with 1 electron each   =   3
   1 chlorine with 7 valence electrons   =   7
   Total valence electrons   =  14

   The final diagram must contain 14 electrons.

2. Arrange the atoms to show bonds between them. The central atom often has the smallest electronegativity value, and generally appears once in the formula. Remember that hydrogen cannot be the central atom since it can only form one single covalent bond. If more than one atom of an element is present, they generally surround the central atom. Use a dash to show a covalent bond between the atoms. Remember that each dash represents two electrons in a covalent bond.

$$
\begin{array}{c}
Cl \\
| \\
H - C - H \\
| \\
H
\end{array}
$$

These 4 bonds account for 8 of the 14 electrons needed. The carbon atom has a complete octet of electrons. Distribute the remaining 6 electrons around the chlorine. Check to see that each atom has an octet of electrons except for hydrogen which needs only two. In this example the six remaining electrons should be distributed around the chlorine to provide it with an octet of electrons.

$$
\begin{array}{c}
:\ddot{C}l: \\
| \\
H-C-H \\
| \\
H
\end{array}
$$

If each of the atoms does not have an octet of electrons, you will probably also have some "left over" or unassigned electrons. These can be placed as double bonds or triple bonds between atoms that do not have complete octets.

Consider the compound $C_2H_2$:
  2 carbon atoms with

| | |
|---|---|
| 4 electrons | = 8 electrons |
| 2 hydrogen atoms with | |
| 1 electron | = 2 electrons |
| Total | = 10 electrons |

Join the carbons and hydrogens with bonds:

$$H-C-C-H$$

The three bonds account for 6 of the 10 electrons. Distributing the four remaining electrons around the carbons will not produce octets of electrons, but forming a triple bond between the two carbons will.

$$H-C\equiv C-H$$

# Review Questions

**6.** Atom X has an electron configuration of 2-8-2. Which electron dot diagram correctly represents this atom?

(1) $:\ddot{X}:$    (2) $\cdot\ddot{X}:$    (3) $X:$    (4) $\cdot\dot{X}:$

**7.** A) Draw a Lewis dot diagram of water
B) Draw a Lewis dot diagram of carbon dioxide

**8.** Which electron dot diagram represents an atom of chlorine in the ground state?

(1) $C\,l:$  (2) $\cdot\ddot{C}\,l\cdot$  (3) $:\ddot{C}\,l\cdot$  (4) $:\ddot{C}\,l:$

**9.** A) Draw an electron dot diagram of ammonia.
B) Draw an electron dot diagram of the ammonium ion

## Metallic Bonds

Metallic atoms have few valence electrons and low ionization energies. The bonds holding metallic atoms together in the solid and liquid phases, however, are apparently strong, as metals have fairly high melting and boiling points. A metallic atom may be considered to have a central portion, or kernel, made up of its nucleus and its nonvalence electrons. The atom's valence electrons surround the kernel. The kernels of the metallic atoms making up a metallic solid are arranged in the fixed positions of a crystalline lattice. The valence electrons move freely throughout the crystal and do not belong to any given atom. The freely moving valence electrons give metals properties of good electrical and thermal conductivity. A **metallic bond** results from the force of attraction of the mobile valence electrons for an atom's positively charged kernel.

**Figure 6-4. Metallic bonding:** When hammered, the positively charged kernels are moved, but they are still attracted by the valence electrons.

As shown in Figure 6-4, metals can be hammered into shapes, which is a property known as **malleability.** Although hammering forces the kernels to move to new locations, they are still surrounded by the valence electrons. The freedom of the valence electrons often leads to the use of the term "sea of mobile electrons" to describe metallic bonding.

# Review Questions

10. Metallic bonding occurs between metal atoms that have

    (1) full valence orbitals, low ionization energies
    (2) full valence orbitals, high ionization energies
    (3) vacant valence orbitals, low ionization energies
    (4) vacant valence orbitals, high ionization energies

11. Which element has a crystalline lattice through which electrons flow freely?

    (1) bromine        (3) carbon
    (2) calcium        (4) sulfur

12. Which element has properties of good electrical conductivity and luster and exists as a liquid at STP?

    (1) Hg      (2) Br      (3) I      (4) C

## The Octet Rule

You may recall that the noble gases of Group 18 are extremely stable and undergo very few chemical reactions. Although there are a few stable compounds of argon and xenon combined with fluorine, these compounds are some of the rare exceptions to the noble gases' lack of reactivity. What is it about the structure of the noble gases that leads to their stability? The answer lies in their number of valence electrons. Except for helium (which only has two valence electrons) all of the noble gas atoms have eight valence electrons. The configuration of eight valence electrons is known as an **octet.** An octet represents the maximum number of valence electrons that an atom can have.

Ordinary chemical reactions result in changes to the valence electron configurations of the atoms involved. A complete octet of eight valence electrons results in an exceptionally stable electron configuration. This stable configuration is the reason why noble gases are so unreactive. Note that the noble gas helium requires only two electrons to fill its valence shell. The **octet rule** states that atoms generally react by gaining,

## Digging Deeper

The composition of all substances cannot be explained by the octet rule. For example, boron hydride ($BH_3$) and sulfur hexafluoride ($SF_6$) do not obey the octet rule because their stable electron configurations do not contain eight valence electrons. Chemists use concepts such as resonance and expanded valence shells to explain some of the compounds that do not conform to the octet rule.

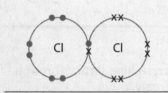

**Figure 6-5. A diatomic chlorine molecule:** Each chlorine atom has an octet of valence electrons.

**Figure 6-6. A diatomic hydrogen molecule:** Each hydrogen atom has two valence electrons in its completely filled valence level.

**Figure 6-7. A diatomic oxygen molecule with a double covalent bond:** Each oxygen atom shares two pairs of valence electrons.

losing, or sharing electrons in order to achieve a complete octet of eight valence electrons—the configuration of a noble gas.

## Covalent Bonds

When two atoms approach one another, their electrons repel each other, tending to push the atoms apart. Their positive nuclei also repel each other. An attractive force between the atoms comes from the attraction of the positively charged nucleus of one atom for the negatively charged electrons of the other atom. Chemical bonds occur when the attractive forces between atoms are greater than the repulsive forces.

A **covalent bond** is formed when two nuclei share electrons in order to achieve a stable arrangement of electrons. Covalent bonds are often formed between two nonmetal atoms of the same element. The diatomic chlorine molecule ($Cl_2$) is an example of a covalent bond. Atoms of different elements may also combine to form covalent bonds. Sulfur and oxygen combine covalently to form sulfur dioxide ($SO_2$).

**Nonpolar Covalent Bonds** When one chlorine atom forms a bond with another chlorine atom, they share a pair of electrons between them and form diatomic $Cl_2$. See Figure 6-5. In this way, the shared electrons of the bond are counted as part of each atom's stable octet. This bond is a **nonpolar covalent bond** because the attraction of the two chlorine nuclei for the shared electrons is equal, causing the pair of electrons to be shared equally. Nonpolar covalent bonds are formed between atoms having equal or close electronegativity values. Similar nonpolar bonds exist between each of the other Group 17 atoms in their diatomic molecules, namely $F_2$, $Br_2$, and $I_2$.

In a similar way, two hydrogen atoms share a pair of electrons to form diatomic $H_2$. See Figure 6-6. In this case there is not an octet of electrons because hydrogen only needs two electrons to fill its valence level.

**Multiple Covalent Bonds** Atoms may share more than one pair of electrons, resulting in the formation of a **multiple covalent bond.** Oxygen atoms combine with other oxygen atoms to form $O_2$ and achieve a stable octet configuration. In achieving this arrangement, the oxygen nuclei must share two pairs of electrons. The sharing of two pairs of valence electrons results in the type of multiple covalent bond called a **double covalent bond.** See Figure 6-7.

Diatomic nitrogen ($N_2$) forms when two nitrogen atoms share three pairs of valence electrons. The sharing of three pairs of valence electrons results in a **triple covalent bond.** See Figure 6-8.

**Polar Covalent Bonds** The different atoms involved in a bond are likely to have unequal <u>electronegativity</u> values. As you may recall, electronegativity is a measure of an atom's tendency to attract bonded electrons. When the electronegativity values of the two atoms in a covalent bond are different, the sharing of electrons in the bond is unequal. The unequal sharing of electrons in a covalent bond results in a **polar covalent bond.** The element with the higher electronegativity value attracts the shared electrons more strongly, causing that portion of the molecule to acquire a partially negative charge. Likewise, the other end of the polar covalent bond acquires a partially positive charge. Hydrogen chloride (HCl) and hydrogen iodide (HI) are examples of polar covalent compounds. Look at the electron distribution for different types of bonds, as shown in Figure 6-11.

**Figure 6-8. A diatomic nitrogen molecule with a triple covalent bond:** Each nitrogen atom shares three pairs of valence electrons.

## SAMPLE PROBLEM

Which of the following bonds is the most polar in nature? (a) $O_2$ (b) HCl (c) $NH_3$ (d) HBr

**SOLUTION:** Consult the *Reference Tables for Physical Setting/Chemistry* to determine the electronegativity values of each element. For each bond, determine the difference of the two electronegativity values. The bond with the smallest difference in electronegativity is the least polar, whereas the bond with the largest difference in electronegativity is the most polar.

(a) Because both oxygen atoms have the same electronegativity value (3.4), the difference is 0. This is a nonpolar covalent bond.

(b) Chlorine has an electronegativity of 3.2, and hydrogen has an electronegativity of 2.1. The electronegativity difference is 1.1, and the bond is polar covalent.

(c) Nitrogen has an electronegativity of 3.0, and hydrogen has an electronegativity of 2.1. The electronegativity difference is 0.9, and the bond is polar covalent.

(d) Bromine has an electronegativity of 3.0, and hydrogen has an electronegativity of 2.1. The electronegativity difference is 0.9, and the bond is polar covalent.

The largest electronegativity difference occurs in the bonds of HCl, hence it is the most polar in nature. The bond in diatomic oxygen is the least polar; diatomic oxygen has a nonpolar covalent bond.

# Review Questions

13. The correct electron dot diagram for hydrogen chloride is

    (1)  H:Cl

    (2)  :H:Cl

    (3)  H:Cl:

    (4)  :H:Cl:

14. A covalent bond forms when

    (1) two nuclei share electrons in order to achieve a complete octet of electrons
    (2) atoms form ions and then electrostatic forces of attraction bond the ions together
    (3) repulsive forces between atoms are greater than the attractive forces
    (4) a metal atom combines with a nonmetal atom

15. Which of the following bonds is the most polar in nature?

    (1) $Cl_2$
    (2) HCl
    (3) HBr
    (4) HI

16. Polar covalent bonds are caused by

    (1) unbalanced ionic charges
    (2) unequal electronegativity values
    (3) the transfer of electrons from one atom to another
    (4) equally shared valence electrons

17. The bond in a diatomic nitrogen molecule ($N_2$) is best described as

    (1) polar
    (2) polar double covalent
    (3) nonpolar triple covalent
    (4) polar ionic

## Molecular Substances

A <u>molecule</u> is the smallest discrete particle of an element or compound formed by covalently bonded atoms. Each atom in a molecule usually has the electron configuration of a noble gas. Molecular substances may exist as solids, liquids, or gases, depending on the strength of the forces of attraction between the molecules.

Molecules generally have properties associated with covalent bonding. Molecules are generally soft, are poor conductors of heat and electricity, and have relatively low melting and boiling points.

Water ($H_2O$), carbon dioxide ($CO_2$), and ammonia ($NH_3$) are examples of molecular compounds. The diatomic gases, such as oxygen ($O_2$) and nitrogen ($N_2$), are also molecular substances. Some common molecular substances are represented in Figure 6-9.

**Polar Molecules** Although a molecule may contain polar bonds, it does not necessarily follow that the molecule itself is polar. Molecules such as hydrogen chloride and water have polar bonds and are also polar molecules. Carbon dioxide and carbon tetrachloride, however, contain polar bonds but are not polar molecules. To understand why these molecules are polar or nonpolar, you must examine their molecular shapes.

Study the shapes of the molecules in Figure 6-10. The water, hydrogen chloride, and ammonia molecules are asymmetrical, whereas the carbon dioxide and carbon tetrachloride molecules are symmetrical. The symmetrical shape of the carbon dioxide and carbon tetrachloride molecules causes the pull of the various polar bonds to be offset by other bonds—the net result is a nonpolar molecule.

**Memory Jogger**

**Symmetrical molecules** have identical parts on each side of an axis; **asymmetrical molecules** lack identical parts on each side of an axis.

| Name | Molecular Formula | Structural Formula | Ball-and-Stick Model | Space-Filling Model |
|---|---|---|---|---|
| Hydrogen | $H_2$ | H—H | | |
| Water | $H_2O$ | O—H, H | | |
| Ammonia | $NH_3$ | H—N—H, H | | |

**Figure 6-9. Models of some common molecular substances**

| Symmetrical Molecules | | Asymmetrical Molecules | | |
|---|---|---|---|---|
| O = C = O | Cl—C—Cl with Cl above and below | H—O—H | H — Cl | N with H, H, H |
| Carbon dioxide | Carbon tetrachloride | Water | Hydrogen chloride | Ammonia |

**Figure 6-10. Five compounds with polar bonds:** The symmetrical molecules are nonpolar; the asymmetrical molecules are polar.

**Figure 6-11. Three bond types that are dependent on electron distribution**

The charge distribution within a bond affects the nature of the bond. Figure 6-11 shows the changes in bond types with different electron distributions. The nonpolar covalent bond has an even electron distribution. As the electron distribution becomes unequal, a polar covalent bond is formed. When the electron is actually transferred, an ionic bond is formed. You will learn about ionic bonds in the next section.

# Review Questions

**18.** Which electron dot diagram represents a polar molecule?

(1) H : H

(2) H : C̈l :

(3) H : C̈ : H with H above and below

(4) : F̈ : F̈ :

**19.** Which electron dot diagram represents a polar molecule?

(1) Ö : : C : : Ö

(2) H with H : C̈ : H and H

(3) H : Ö : with H below

(4) : C̈l : with : C̈l : C̈ : C̈l : and : C̈l : below

**20.** Which electron dot diagram represents $H_2$?

(1) H • H

(2) H ⦙ H

(3) dots surrounding H • H

(4) dots surrounding H ⦙ H

**21.** The diagram below represents a hydrogen fluoride molecule.

H : F̈ :

This molecule is best described as

(1) polar with polar covalent bonds
(2) polar with nonpolar covalent bonds
(3) nonpolar with polar covalent bonds
(4) nonpolar with nonpolar covalent bonds

**22.** Which diagram best represents a polar molecule?

(1) $Cl_2$

(2) $H_2$

(3) HCl

(4) NaCl

**23.** Which is the correct electron dot formula for a chlorine molecule?

(1) Cl • Cl

(2) • C̈l : C̈l •

(3) : C̈l • C̈l :

(4) : C̈l : C̈l :

**24.** Which molecule contains a polar covalent bond?

(1) $\overset{xx}{\underset{xx}{\overset{\cdot\cdot}{x}}} \text{I} \overset{\cdot\cdot}{\underset{\cdot\cdot}{x}} \text{I} \overset{\cdot\cdot}{\underset{\cdot\cdot}{}}$

(3) H $\overset{\cdot\cdot}{\underset{\cdot x}{x}}$ N $\overset{\cdot\cdot}{x}$ H
    H

(2) H $\overset{}{x}$ H

(4) : N $\overset{x}{\underset{x}{x}}$ N $\overset{x}{\underset{x}{}}$

**25.** Which electron dot diagram represents the atom in Period 4 with the highest first ionization energy?

(1) $\overset{\cdot\cdot}{X}$

(3) $\overset{\cdot\cdot}{X} \cdot$

(2) $\overset{\cdot\cdot}{X} \cdot$

(4) $\overset{\cdot\cdot}{\underset{\cdot\cdot}{:}} X \overset{\cdot\cdot}{\underset{\cdot\cdot}{:}}$

---

# Ionic Bonding

Recall that when atoms gain or lose electrons they become charged particles called ions. An ionic bond is formed when ions bond together because of the electrostatic attraction of oppositely charged ions. Figure 6-12 shows the formation of an ionic bond by the transfer of an electron.

$$\text{Na}^x + \cdot \overset{\cdot\cdot}{\underset{\cdot\cdot}{\text{Cl}}} : \longrightarrow \left[\text{Na}\right]^+ + \left[\overset{\cdot\cdot}{\underset{\cdot\cdot}{\text{Cl}}} :\right]^-$$

**Figure 6-12. The formation of an ionic bond by the transfer of an electron**

**Ion Formation in Metals** As atoms form ions, they tend to do so in a manner that results in the formation of ions with noble gas electron configurations. Consider the metals of Group 1 with their single valence electron. When a Group 1 metallic atom reacts, it loses its electron and forms an ion with a 1+ charge. By losing its valence electron, the atom acquires the octet arrangement of a noble gas. The resulting ion is quite stable. The loss of the valence electron from the atom's outer energy level results in the ions having a smaller radius than the atom from which it was formed.

**Ion Formation in Nonmetals** Now consider a nonmetal atom from Group 17 with its seven valence electrons. This nonmetal atom reacts by gaining a single electron to form an ion with a 1− charge. By gaining an electron, the atom has acquired the noble gas electron configuration (eight valence electrons). The resulting ion is quite stable. The addition of the valence electron to the atom's outer energy level results in the ions having a larger radius than the atom from which it was formed. See Table 6-1 that summarizes the reactions of metals and nonmetals.

**Ion Formation and the Octet Rule** Look at Figure 6-13. Each of the atoms has a different number of electrons. When each atom reacts, it does so by losing or gaining electrons. Notice that as ions, each has an octet of valence electrons—the same number of electrons as the noble gas neon.

When metallic atoms lose electrons to form positive ions, they acquire the electron configuration of the noble gas preceding them on the

| Table 6–1. Reactions of Metals and Nonmetals | |
|---|---|
| **When metals react they:** | **When nonmetals react they:** |
| 1. Lose electrons | 1. Gain electrons |
| 2. Become positively charged | 2. Become negatively charged |
| 3. Have smaller radii | 3. Have larger radii |
| 4. Acquire the electron configuration of a noble gas | 4. Acquire the electron configuration of a noble gas |

**Nonmetals gain electrons**

Oxygen atom
**O**

Fluorine atom
**F**

$+2e^-$

$+1e^-$

Oxygen ion
**O$^{2-}$**

Fluorine ion
**F$^-$**

Neon atom
**Ne**

**Metals lose electrons**

Sodium atom
**Na**

Magnesium atom
**Mg**

$-1e^-$

$-2e^-$

Sodium ion
**Na$^+$**

Magnesium ion
**Mg$^{2+}$**

**Figure 6-13. Atoms tend to gain or lose electrons and acquire the electron configuration of the nearest noble gas:** All of the ions and neon are isoelectronic, that is, they have the same electron configuration.

periodic table. When nonmetals gain electrons, they form negative ions and acquire the electron configuration of the noble gas that follows them on the table.

**Electronegativity** As you just learned, as the electronegativity difference between two atoms in a bond increases, the bond becomes more polar in nature. Figure 6-14 summarizes the relationship between electronegativity and bond type. As shown, as the electronegativity difference increases, the bond becomes more ionic in character. At some point the bond can no longer be considered as a sharing of electrons, but rather as a bond in which one or more electrons have actually been transferred from one atom to another. The transfer of electrons from one atom to another results in an ionic bond.

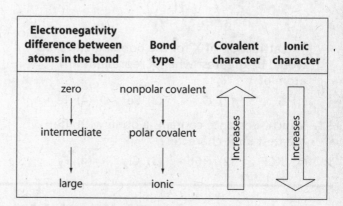

| Electronegativity difference between atoms in the bond | Bond type | Covalent character | Ionic character |
|---|---|---|---|
| zero | nonpolar covalent | | |
| intermediate | polar covalent | Increases | Increases |
| large | ionic | | |

**Figure 6-14. Electronegativity and bond type**

If the electronegativity difference between the bonding atoms is 1.7 or greater, the bond is generally considered to be ionic. Ionic bonds are generally formed between metals and nonmetallic atoms. Refer to Table S in the *Reference Tables for Physical Setting/Chemistry* for (R) electronegativity values.

**Polyatomic Ions** Any compound containing a polyatomic ion must also contain an ionic bond. Consider the ionic compound ammonium carbonate $(NH_4)_2CO_3$. The ammonium ion is attracted to the carbonate ion by an ionic bond. Within the ammonium and carbonate ions, there is a second type of bond. The nitrogen atom and hydrogen atoms of the ammonium ion and the carbon atom and oxygen atoms of the carbonate ion are held together by covalent bonds. That is, the bonds holding the atoms within the ion are themselves covalent. All compounds with polyatomic ions contain both ionic and covalent bonds.

# Review Questions

26. When a calcium atom loses its valence electrons, the ion formed has an electron configuration that is the same as an atom of

(1) Cl      (2) Ar      (3) K      (4) Sc

27. The bond between which pair of elements is the least ionic in character?

(1) H-F      (2) H-Cl      (3) H-I      (4) H-O

28. Which compound has the greatest degree of ionic character?

(1) NaF      (2) $MgF_2$      (3) $AlF_3$      (4) $SiF_4$

29. Which compound contains a bond with the least ionic character?

(1) CO      (2) CaO      (3) $K_2O$      (4) $Li_2O$

30. Look at the electron dot formula shown below.

$$H : \overset{\displaystyle ..}{\underset{\displaystyle H}{X}} :$$

The attraction of X for the bonding electrons would be greatest when X represents an atom of

(1) S      (2) O      (3) Se      (4) Te

31. Which substance contains a bond with the greatest ionic character?

(1) KCl      (2) HCl      (3) $Cl_2$      (4) $F_2$

32. Which compound contains both ionic and covalent bonds?

(1) HBr      (2) $CBr_4$      (3) NaBr      (4) NaOH

33. Which element forms an ionic bond with fluorine?

(1) fluorine      (3) potassium
(2) carbon      (4) oxygen

34. Which compound is described correctly?

(1) $BaCl_2$ is covalent and molecular.
(2) $H_2O_2$ is covalent and empirical.
(3) $H_2O$ is ionic and molecular.
(4) NaCl is ionic and empirical.

35. The elements Li and F combine to form an ionic compound. The electron configurations within this compound are the same as the electron configurations of atoms of Group

(1) 1      (2) 14      (3) 17      (4) 18

36. An atom of which element has the same electron configuration as $O^{2-}$?

(1) Li      (2) Na      (3) Ar      (4) Ne

37. Which ion has the electron configuration of a noble gas?

(1) $Cu^{2+}$      (2) $Fe^{2+}$      (3) $Ca^{2+}$      (4) $Hg^{2+}$

## Distinguishing Bond Types

Metallic, covalent, and ionic bonds have different properties that can be used to distinguish among them. Metals generally have high melting points. Mercury, which is a liquid at standard conditions, is an exception, as are the metals of Group 1. Ionic compounds also have high melting points, while covalently bonded molecules have relatively low melting points.

Of course, melting point alone will not accurately differentiate between bond types. Other properties must also be considered. Metallic bonds are the only type that result in good thermal and electrical conductivity. Neither ionic solids nor molecular solids are good conductors. Ionic substances become conductors when they are melted (fused) or dissolved in aqueous solutions.

Molecular substances are held together by covalent bonds. Thus, there are no charged particles to conduct an electric current. Molecular substances are poor conductors, whether they are in the solid state, in the liquid state, or in aqueous solution.

The three bond types also differ in hardness. Ionic and metallic solids are generally hard, while a majority of covalently bonded solids are soft. Table 6-2 summarizes some of the properties of the various bond types.

### Table 6-2. Properties of Metallic, Ionic, and Covalent Bonds

| Bond Type | Melting and Boiling Points | Hardness | Conductivity | | |
| --- | --- | --- | --- | --- | --- |
| | | | Solid | Liquid | Aqueous |
| Metallic | High | Hard | Yes | Yes | Yes |
| Covalent | Low | Soft | No | No | No |
| Ionic | High | Hard | No | Yes | Yes |

**Digging** Deeper

Why do ionic substances conduct electricity when melted or when in aqueous solution, but not when in the solid state? In solids, electrical current is carried by electrons. In liquids, however, electrical current is carried by charged particles (ions). The ions in an ionic solid are not able to move from their fixed positions and conduct electrical current. When the ionic solid is melted or dissolved in water, the ions are free to move and conduct electrical current.

# Review Questions

**38.** The electrical conductivity of KI(*aq*) is greater than the electrical conductivity of $H_2O(\ell)$ because the KI(*aq*) contains mobile

(1) molecules of $H_2O$
(2) ions from $H_2O$
(3) molecules of KI
(4) ions from KI

**39.** Which factor distinguishes a metallic bond from an ionic or a covalent bond?

(1) the mobility of electrons
(2) the mobility of protons
(3) the equal sharing of electrons
(4) the unequal sharing of electrons

**40.** Which substance has a high melting point and conducts electricity in the liquid phase?

(1) Ne     (2) Hg     (3) NaCl     (4) CO

**41.** Which compound in the solid state has a high melting point and conducts electricity when it is liquefied?

(1) carbon dioxide
(2) silicon dioxide
(3) hydrogen chloride
(4) potassium chloride

**42.** Which substance is a conductor of electricity in the liquid phase but not in the solid phase?

(1) $Br_2$     (2) HBr     (3) Na     (4) NaCl

**43.** The water solution of which of the following substances is the best conductor of electricity?

(1) KCl
(2) $C_6H_{12}O_6$
(3) $CO_2$
(4) CO

**44.** Which substance is a conductor of electricity?

(1) NaCl(*s*)
(2) NaCl(*ℓ*)
(3) $C_6H_{12}O_6(s)$
(4) $C_6H_{12}O_6(\ell)$

## Intermolecular Forces

Just as atoms are held together by chemical bonds, molecules also have attractive forces acting on them in the solid and liquid states. It is fairly easy to understand how polar molecules are attracted to each other. Because polar molecules have positive and negative ends, polar molecules are also called <u>dipoles</u>. The positive area of one dipole molecule is attracted to the negative portion of an adjacent dipole molecule. These attractive forces are known as dipole-dipole forces.

**Hydrogen Bonds**  A **hydrogen bond** is an intermolecular bond between a hydrogen atom in one molecule and a nitrogen, oxygen or fluorine atom in another molecule. See Figure 6-15. Perhaps the most important example of

**Digging** Deeper

Perhaps you remember from your biology class that thymine and adenine are bonded to each other as are cytosine and quanine in the DNA molecule. The bonds that hold these parts to each other are hydrogen bonds. Hydrogen bonds are also important in holding many enzymes on to their targets.

hydrogen bonding is found in water. Water is a polar molecule, so you might expect it to be held to other water molecules by dipole-dipole attractions. However, if only dipole-dipole forces acted to hold water molecules together, all of the water on Earth would have boiled away. The water has not boiled away because there are relatively strong hydrogen bonding forces acting on water molecules. Hydrogen bonding forces are much stronger than dipole-dipole attractions. Hydrogen bonding is responsible for the relatively high boiling point of water. Water has an abnormally high boiling point for a substance with such a small molecular mass.

Hydrogen bonding only occurs between hydrogen and the three atoms noted earlier. It is worth noting that nitrogen, oxygen, and fluorine are highly electronegative and have small radii. Ammonia ($NH_3$) and hydrogen fluoride (HF) are two other examples of substances with strong hydrogen bonds.

**Figure 6-15. Covalent and hydrogen bonding in water**

# Review Questions

**45.** Which molecule is a dipole?

(1)  H—S
         |
         H

(2)      H
         |
     H—C—H
         |
         H

(3)  O=C=O

(4)  N≡N

**46.** Hydrogen bonding is strongest between molecules of

(1) $H_2S$    (2) $H_2O$    (3) $H_2Se$    (4) $H_2Te$

**47.** In which liquid is hydrogen bonding the most significant force of attraction?

(1) HF    (2) HCl    (3) HBr    (4) HI

**48.** Which atom has the least attraction for the electrons in a bond between that atom and an atom of hydrogen?

(1) carbon          (2) nitrogen
(3) oxygen          (4) fluorine

**49.** The unusually high boiling point of water is due to the

(1) network bonds between the molecules
(2) hydrogen bonds between the molecules
(3) linear structure of the molecules
(4) nonpolar character of the molecules

**50.** The strongest hydrogen bonds are formed between molecules of

(1) $H_2Te$    (2) $H_2Se$    (3) $H_2S$    (4) $H_2O$

## Directions

Review the Test-Taking Strategies section of this book. Then answer the following questions. Read each question carefully and answer with a correct choice or response.

## Part A

**1** Which kind of energy is stored within a chemical bond?
(1) free energy
(2) activation energy
(3) kinetic energy
(4) potential energy

**2** Which particles may be gained, lost, or shared by an atom when it forms a chemical bond?
(1) protons
(2) electrons
(3) neutrons
(4) nucleons

**3** The forces between atoms that create chemical bonds are the result of the interactions between
(1) nuclei
(2) electrons
(3) protons and electrons
(4) protons and nuclei

**4** At STP, potassium is classified as
(1) a metallic solid
(2) a molecular solid
(3) a network solid
(4) an ionic solid

**5** Which element consists of positive ions immersed in a "sea" of mobile electrons?
(1) sulfur
(2) nitrogen
(3) calcium
(4) chlorine

**6** The degree of polarity of a bond is indicated by
(1) ionization energy difference
(2) the shape of the molecule
(3) electronegativity difference
(4) the charge on the kernel

**7** In a nonpolar covalent bond, electrons are
(1) located in a mobile "sea" shared by many ions
(2) transferred from one atom to another
(3) shared equally by two atoms
(4) shared unequally by two atoms

**8** Which type of bond is formed when an atom of potassium transfers an electron to a bromine atom?
(1) metallic
(2) ionic
(3) nonpolar covalent
(4) polar covalent

**9** Which type of bonding is characteristic of a substance that has a high melting point and is a good electrical conductor only when in the liquid phase?
(1) nonpolar covalent
(2) polar covalent
(3) ionic
(4) metallic

**10** Which terms describe a substance that has a low melting point and poor electrical conductivity?
(1) covalent and metallic
(2) covalent and molecular
(3) ionic and molecular
(4) ionic and metallic

**11** The unusually high boiling point of water is due to the presence of
(1) hydrogen bonds
(2) ionic bonds
(3) network bonds
(4) molecule-ion attractions

**12** When two atoms form a chemical bond by sharing electrons, the resulting molecule will be
(1) polar only
(2) nonpolar only
(3) either polar or nonpolar
(4) neither nonpolar nor polar

**13** Which type of substance is soft, has a low melting point, and is a poor conductor of electricity?
(1) covalent solid
(2) ionic solid
(3) metallic solid
(4) network solid

**14** Oxygen, nitrogen, and fluorine bond with hydrogen to form molecules. These molecules are attracted to each other by
(1) ionic bonds
(2) hydrogen bonds
(3) polar covalent bonds
(4) nonpolar covalent bonds

**15** Which kind of compound generally results when nonmetal atoms chemically combine with metal atoms?
(1) network
(2) molecular
(3) ionic
(4) metallic

# Part B

16 Which statement is true concerning the reaction
$N(g) + N(g) \rightarrow N_2(g) +$ energy?
(1) A bond is broken and energy is absorbed.
(2) A bond is broken and energy is released.
(3) A bond is formed and energy is absorbed.
(4) A bond is formed and energy is released.

17 The bond between which pair of elements is the
least ionic in character?
(1) H—F        (3) H—S
(2) H—Br       (4) H—O

18 Which compound has the greatest degree of ionic
character?
(1) NaCl       (3) $AlCl_3$
(2) $MgCl_2$   (4) $SiCl_4$

19 Look at the electron dot diagram below.

$$H \overset{\cdot \cdot}{\underset{\cdot \cdot}{:}} F \overset{\cdot \cdot}{\underset{\cdot \cdot}{:}}$$

The electrons in the bond between hydrogen and
fluorine are more strongly attracted to the atom of
(1) hydrogen, which has the higher
electronegativity
(2) hydrogen, which has the lower
electronegativity
(3) fluorine, which has the higher
electronegativity
(4) fluorine, which has the lower
electronegativity

20 Which type of bond is formed between the two
chlorine atoms in a chlorine molecule?
(1) polar covalent
(2) nonpolar covalent
(3) metallic
(4) ionic

21 Which diagram best represents the structure of a
water molecule?

22 Which electron dot formula represents a
substance that contains a nonpolar covalent
bond?

23 Which electron dot diagram represents a molecule
that has a polar covalent bond?

24 When a sodium atom reacts with a chlorine atom
to form a compound, the electron configuration of
the ions forming the compound are the same as
those in which noble gases?
(1) krypton and neon    (3) neon and helium
(2) krypton and argon   (4) neon and argon

25 Which atom will form an ionic bond with a Br
atom?
(1) N          (3) O
(2) Li         (4) C

26 A white crystalline salt conducts electricity when
it is melted and when it is dissolved in water.
Which type of bond does this salt contain?
(1) ionic              (3) nonpolar covalent
(2) metallic           (4) polar covalent

27 In which molecule is hydrogen bonding the
strongest?
(1) HF         (3) HBr
(2) HCl        (4) HI

28 Which statement correctly describes the bonds in
the electron dot diagram shown below?

(1) One of the bonds is ionic.
(2) One of the bonds is metallic.
(3) All of the bonds are covalent.
(4) None of the bonds are covalent.

**29** Which electron dot diagram best represents a compound that contains both ionic and covalent bonds?

(1) H :S:
      H

(3) K⁺ [ :Br: ]⁻

(2) Ca²⁺ [ :O:
         :O:S:O:
         :O: ]²⁻

(4) :Br:Br:

**30** What is the correct Lewis electron-dot diagram for the compound magnesium fluoride?

# Part C

**31** Explain, in terms of electronegativity, why the H—F bond is expected to be more polar than the H—I bond [1]

**Base your answers to questions 32 through 34 on your knowledge of chemical bonding and on the Lewis electron-dot diagrams of $H_2S$, $CO_2$, and $F_2$ below.**

H :S:       :O::C::O:       :F:F:
   H

**32** Which atom, when bonded as shown, has the same electron configuration as an atom of argon? [1]

**33** Explain, in terms of *structure* and/or *distribution of charge*, why $CO_2$ is a nonpolar molecule. [1]

**34** Explain, in terms of *electronegativity*, why a C=O bond in $CO_2$ is more polar than the F—F bond in $F_2$. [1]

**35** Draw an electron dot structure of a fluorine molecule ($F_2$) and an iodide ion (1⁻). [2]

**36** The hydrides of Group 16 are all dipoles. The graph below shows the boiling points of $H_2S$, $H_2Se$, and $H_2Te$.

**Boiling Points of the Group 16 Hydrides**

On the basis of the trend shown by the connected points, extrapolate the data to predict the boiling point of water. What is the approximate value of the extrapolated boiling point? The actual boiling point of water is plotted on the graph at 100°C. Why is there such a difference between the extrapolated boiling point and the actual boiling point? [3]

**37** Draw a diagram that shows hydrogen bonding between ammonia molecules. Use dotted lines to show hydrogen bonds. [1]

**38** Carbon atoms form four bonds with other elements or other carbon atoms. These bonds can be either single or multiple bonds. In ethane ($C_2H_6$), ethene ($C_2H_4$), and ethyne ($C_2H_2$), each carbon atom is bonded to the other carbon atom as well as one or more hydrogen atoms. From your knowledge of the number of bonds each atom can form, draw Lewis electron dot diagrams for each of these three compounds. [3]

39. The following table shows the percent ionic character of a bond based on the electronegativity of the elements involved.

| Electronegativity difference | Percent ionic character |
|---|---|
| 0.00 | 0 |
| 0.65 | 10 |
| 0.94 | 20 |
| 1.19 | 30 |
| 1.43 | 40 |
| 1.67 | 50 |
| 1.91 | 60 |
| 2.19 | 70 |
| 2.54 | 80 |
| 3.03 | 90 |

Using Table S in the *Reference Tables for Physical Setting/Chemistry*, list two elements that would react to produce a bond that has a 40% ionic character. (Remember that a chemical bond will not form between two metals. The pair of elements must be either a metal and a nonmetal or two nonmetals.) What would be the estimated ionic character for a bond formed between nickel and oxygen? [2]

**Use the following information to answer questions 40 through 44.**

Element X is a solid metal that reacts with chlorine to produce a water-soluble binary compound.

40 What is the most likely type of bond formed between the metal and chlorine? [1]

41 The metal combines with chlorine to form a compound with the formula MCl2. What Group of the Periodic Table is M a member of? [1]

42 After reacting, with which noble gas are the metal and chlorine isoelectronic? [1]

43 Explain, in terms of particles, why an aqueous solution of the binary compound conducts an electric current. [1]

44 What is the oxidation number of the metal in this binary compound? [1]

45 Explain, in terms of electronegativity, why a P—Cl bond in PCl5 is more polar than a P—S bond in P2S5. [1]

46 What type of bond is formed between P and Cl? [1]

**Use the following information to answer questions 47 through 49. Metal X is recovered from a rock sample and found to combine with iodine in a 1:1 ratio.**

47 What is the oxidation number of element X?

48 What is the most likely type of bond formed between element X and iodine? [1]

49 Explain, in terms of electrons, why element X is a good conductor of electricity. [1]

50 When an element reacts, it forms an ion that is smaller than the radius of an atom of the element. Explain why. [1]

# Properties of Solutions

## What You Know About Solutions

**What can you tell about the saturation of a solution using a crystal of the solute?**

Can you do an experiment to determine if a solution is saturated?

Sure. Take a crystal of the solute and drop it into the solution, then observe what happens:

If it dissolves, the solution is unsaturated.

If it falls to the bottom, the solution is saturated.

If more crystals form, the solution is supersaturated.

Learn more about solutions and their properties while studying this topic.

117

# Properties of Solutions

## Vocabulary

| | | |
|---|---|---|
| boiling point | saturated | supersaturated |
| molarity | solute | unsaturated |
| parts per million (ppm) | solution | vapor |
| percent by volume | solvent | vapor pressure |
| percent mass | | |

## Topic Overview

Most of the materials that you use every day are not pure substances. It is more likely that they are mixtures. This topic will explore an important type of mixture, the solution. The nature and properties of solutions are important concepts used in chemistry. One reason they are so important is that most chemical reactions take place in solutions. In this topic you will study the nature and properties of solutions and ways to express the concentration of solutions.

## Solutions

A **solution** is a homogeneous mixture of substances in the same physical state. Solutions contain atoms, ions, or molecules of one substance spread uniformly throughout a second substance. When salt (NaCl) is stirred into water, the individual ions of the salt separate and uniformly spread throughout the water, forming a solution.

### Types of Solutions

A solid may be dissolved in another solid. Brass is a mixture of zinc and copper. When metals are mixed to form a solution, the result is called an <u>alloy</u>. Air is an example of a mixture of gases forming a solution.

Although solutions exist in all three states, the discussion in this topic will be limited to liquid solutions. Perhaps the most common type of solution is one in which a solid or a liquid is dissolved in a liquid.

The terms *solute* and *solvent* are commonly used to identify the parts of a solution. In general terms, the **solute** is the substance that is being dissolved, and it is the substance present in the smaller amount. When solid sodium nitrate dissolves in water, the sodium nitrate is the solute. The substance that dissolves the solute is the **solvent**, and it is present in the greater amount. Water is, perhaps, the most common solvent. Water solutions are called <u>aqueous</u> solutions, and the notation (aq) is used in equations to show that the substance is dissolved in water.

$$NaCl(s) \rightarrow Na^+(aq) + Cl^-(aq)$$

### Memory Jogger

Mixtures do not have definite composition. For example, air is a mixture. The percentage of water vapor present in the air varies from day to day. Photosynthesis increases the concentration of oxygen in the air and reduces carbon dioxide. Respiration has the opposite effect, decreasing oxygen and increasing carbon dioxide.

Once the salt and water are stirred and the mixture becomes homogeneous, the dissolved particles will not settle. Liquid solutions are clear, and light will pass through a solution without being dispersed, as shown in Figure 7-1.

Solutions may or may not have color. For example, solutions of copper salts have a characteristic blue color, while a solution of sodium nitrate is colorless.

The following list summarizes characteristics of liquid solutions.

- Solutions are homogeneous mixtures.
- Solutions are clear and do not disperse light.
- Solutions can have color.
- Solutions will not settle on standing.
- Solutions will pass through a filter.

## Solubility Factors

You've noticed that some things easily dissolve in water or other solvents. When you make a cup of coffee, certain materials in the coffee grounds dissolve but other materials don't. Sugar will readily dissolve in the cup of coffee but the spoon you use to stir the solution does not dissolve. How much of a solute will dissolve in a certain amount of solvent at a certain temperature is known as solubility. Materials with a high solubility are said to be soluble; materials with a low solubility are said to be insoluble. What factors determine the solubility of a solute in a solvent?

**Nature of Solute and Solvent** When sodium chloride dissolves in water it does so because its positively and negatively charged ions are attracted to the oppositely charged ends of the polar water molecule. The dissolving process is shown in Figure 7-2. The positively charged sodium ions are attracted to the negative pole of the water molecules. The attractive forces between the water molecules and sodium ions are greater than the attractive forces between the sodium and chloride ions. In like manner, the negatively charged chloride ions are attracted to the positive end of the water dipole and are dissolved. Ionic and polar substances dissolve in polar solvents.

Nonpolar substances, such as fats, do not dissolve in water because there aren't strong attractive forces between the fat molecules and the water molecules. Fat molecules will dissolve in nonpolar solvents. The forces that hold the nonpolar molecules to each other are quite weak, and the molecules simply mix together. The term "like

Beam of light     Solution     Not a solution

**Figure 7-1. Light passing through a solution:** The particles in a solution are too small to disperse light. When light passes through a liquid with larger particles, such as gelatin in water, you can see the beam because larger particles disperse light.

$Cl^-$ ion          $Na^+$ ion

Water molecules

**Figure 7-2. The dissolving process:** Ionic and polar solutes dissolve in polar solvents because unlike charges attract each other.

| Table 7-1. Solubility Summary | | |
|---|---|---|
| Solute Type | Nonpolar Solvent | Polar Solvent |
| nonpolar | soluble | insoluble |
| polar | insoluble | soluble |
| ionic | insoluble | soluble |

dissolves like" is often used to describe what solutes will dissolve in what solvents. Table 7-1 summarizes this concept.

An interesting and important case of "like dissolves like" is found in the action of soaps. Greases, which are nonpolar, won't easily wash off our hands in water, which is polar. Soaps are long carbon chains that have one end that is polar, allowing the soap to dissolve in water. The other end of the soap is nonpolar, and grease will dissolve in it.

**Temperature**   As temperature increases, most solids become more soluble in water. A few exceptions exist. Gases react in the opposite manner. As temperature rises, the solubility of all gases in liquids decreases.

**Pressure**   Pressure has little or no effect on the solubility of solid or liquid solutes. Pressure does affect the solubility of gases in liquids. As pressure increases, the solubility of gases in liquids increases. When a can of soda is opened, the pressure decreases. The carbon dioxide is no longer as soluble at the lowered pressure, and it escapes as bubbles.

# Review Questions

1. In a true solution, the dissolved particles
   (1) are visible to the eye
   (2) will settle out on standing
   (3) are always solids
   (4) cannot be removed by filtration

2. When a teaspoon of sugar is added to water and stirred, the sugar
   (1) melts
   (2) dissolves
   (3) condenses
   (4) evaporates

3. In an aqueous solution of potassium chloride, the solute is
   (1) $Cl^-$ only
   (2) $K^+$ only
   (3) $K^+Cl^-$
   (4) $H_2O$

4. Which sample of matter is a mixture?
   (1) $H_2O(s)$
   (2) $H_2O(\ell)$
   (3) $NaCl(\ell)$
   (4) $NaCl(aq)$

5. Most ionic substances are soluble in water because water molecules are
   (1) nonpolar
   (2) inorganic
   (3) ionic
   (4) polar

6. An aqueous solution of copper sulfate is poured into a filter paper cone. What passes through the filter paper?
   (1) only the solvent
   (2) only the solute
   (3) both solvent and solute
   (4) neither the solute nor solvent

7. Nonpolar solvents will most easily dissolve solids that are
   (1) ionic
   (2) covalent
   (3) metallic
   (4) colored

8. As the temperature rises, the solubility of all gases in water
   (1) decreases
   (2) increases
   (3) remains the same

9. A decrease in pressure has the greatest effect on a solution that contains
   (1) a gas in a liquid
   (2) a liquid in a liquid
   (3) a solid in a solid
   (4) a solid in a liquid

10. Which diagram best illustrates the ion-molecule attractions that occur when the ions of NaCl(s) are added to water?

    (1)

    (2)

    (3)

    (4)

**11.** What happens when NaCl(s) is dissolved in water?

(1) $Cl^-$ ions are attracted to the oxygen atoms of the water.

(2) $Cl^-$ ions are attracted to the hydrogen atoms of the water.

(3) $Na^+$ ions are attracted to the hydrogen atoms of the water.

(4) No attractions are involved; the crystal just falls apart.

**12.** Under which conditions are gases most soluble in water?

(1) high temperature and high pressure
(2) high temperature and low pressure
(3) low temperature and high pressure
(4) low temperature and low pressure

## Looking at Solubility

Solubility information may be presented in different ways. Solubility Curves in the *Reference Tables for Physical Setting/Chemistry* presents quantitative information showing the relationship of grams of solute that may be dissolved at various temperatures. Solubility Guidelines provides some general guidelines about the solubility of ionic substances. You will need to be able to interpret information from both tables.

**Solubility Graphs** The Solubility Curves table shows the number of grams of a substance that can be dissolved in 100. g of water at temperatures between 0°C and 100°C. Each line represents the maximum amount of that substance that can be dissolved at a given temperature. All of the lines that show an increase in solubility as temperatures increase represent solids being dissolved in water. Although these lines on the graph show an increase in solubility as temperature increases, a few solids, such as cesium sulfate, become less soluble as temperature increases.

Three lines show decreasing solubility with increasing temperature. These three lines represent the gases $NH_3$, HCl, and $SO_2$. The solubility of all gases decreases with increasing temperature.

Figure 7-3 shows four positions relative to a line of maximum solubility. Position A is below the maximum line of solubility. At this position, the temperature is 35°C, and 25 g of solute X dissolve. Because at this point the solution holds less solute than the maximum it can hold, the solution is said to be **unsaturated.** If there is not a temperature change, an additional 30 g can be added to bring X to position B.

Position B is on the line of maximum solubility. A solution that contains a maximum amount of solute that will dissolve at a specific temperature is **saturated.** At this position, the solution contains 55 g of X. The addition of more solid solute will not result in more being dissolved. Any additional solid that is added will simply settle to the bottom of the container.

If the temperature is reduced to 20°C, only 35 g of X can dissolve. When the temperature of the solution at B is reduced, the most likely event is that the excess 20 g of X will precipitate, and the solution will remain

**Figure 7-3. A solubility curve**

There are two terms that are somewhat useful in describing concentrations of solutions. <u>Dilute</u> solutions contain relatively small amounts of dissolved solute in a large amount of solvent. For example, 5 g of a substance dissolved in 100. g of $H_2O$ would be a dilute solution. <u>Concentrated</u> solutions contain relatively large amounts of solute. These terms should not be confused with saturated and unsaturated. Five grams of potassium chlorate dissolved in 100. g of water at 0°C would be dilute, but the solution would be saturated; 80. g of $NaNO_3$ dissolved in the same amount of water would be concentrated, but unsaturated.

**Memory Jogger**

Recall that double-replacement reactions have the general formula:

AB + CD → AD + CB

saturated at point C. On rather rare occasions, as the temperature decreases, crystals do not form and the substance may be at position D.

At position D, there is more solid dissolved than normal. A solution that holds more solute than is present in a saturated solution at that temperature is **supersaturated.** These solutions are quite unstable. The addition of a single solid crystal of the substance will cause additional solid to form, and the solution will return to a saturated condition. If no temperature change occurred, the solution would become saturated at point C, with 20 g of the substance precipitating. The only way to make a supersaturated solution is to cool a saturated solution in which there are no crystals or impurities, such as dust, present.

**Solubility Tables** The Solubility Guidelines of *Reference Tables for Physical* ®
*Setting/Chemistry* contains some guidelines for the solubility of common ionic compounds. The table shows that all compounds of the ammonium and the nitrate ion are soluble. All of the halide ions, such as $Cl^-$, form compounds that are soluble, but three exceptions are listed. Silver chloride is not soluble, nor are $Pb^{2+}$ nor $Hg_2^{2+}$ chlorides, and they are precipitates if they form in a double-replacement reaction. This table is useful in predicting whether or not a precipitate will form when two ionic solutions are mixed. A reaction will take place if one or both of the products is listed as insoluble.

**Recognizing Unsaturated, Saturated, and Supersaturated Solutions** Because solutions are clear, it is difficult to simply look at a solution and determine whether it is unsaturated, saturated, or supersaturated.

One method of recognizing the type of solution narrows the choices. If a solution contains some undissolved solute, it must be a saturated solution.

The addition of a solute crystal can also be used to determine its condition. If it dissolves, the original solution was unsaturated. If it simply falls to the bottom, the solution is saturated. If it causes additional crystals to form, the original solution was supersaturated.

## SAMPLE PROBLEM

Silver nitrate and sodium chromate solutions are mixed together. Will a precipitate form? If so, what is the name of the precipitate?

**SOLUTION:** Identify the known and unknown values.

*Known*
Formulas of reactants
Solubility table

*Unknown*
Solubility of products
Identity of precipitate

1. Write the word equation for a double-replacement reaction between silver nitrate and sodium carbonate.

   silver nitrate + sodium chromate →
   silver chromate + sodium nitrate

2. Check the solubilities of the products.

   Chromates are listed as insoluble, with the exception of Group 1 ions or the ammonium ion. Nitrates are soluble.

   A precipitate of silver chromate will form.

# Review Questions

Use the tables in *Reference Tables for Physical Setting/Chemistry* as needed in answering the following questions.

13. Which compound's solubility decreases most rapidly as the temperature changes from 10°C to 70°C?

    (1) $NH_4Cl$    (2) $NH_3$    (3) HCl    (4) KCl

14. Solubility for salt X is shown in the table below.

| Temperature (°C) | Solubility $\left(\dfrac{g \ salt \ X}{100 \ g \ H_2O}\right)$ |
|---|---|
| 10 | 5 |
| 20 | 10 |
| 30 | 15 |
| 40 | 20 |
| 50 | 30 |
| 60 | 35 |

    Which graph most closely represents the data shown in the table?

16. Which salt has the greatest change in solubility between 30°C and 50°C?

    (1) $KNO_3$  (2) KCl  (3) $NaNO_3$  (4) NaCl

17. Which of the following substances is least soluble in 100. g of water at 50°C?

    (1) NaCl    (2) KCl    (3) $NH_4Cl$  (4) HCl

18. A student obtained the following data in a chemistry laboratory.

| Trial | Temperature (°C) | Solubility (g $KNO_3$/100 g $H_2O$) |
|---|---|---|
| 1 | 25 | 40 |
| 2 | 32 | 50 |
| 3 | 43 | 70 |
| 4 | 48 | 60 |

    Based on the reference tables, which of the four trials listed seems to be in error?

    (1) 1        (2) 2        (3) 3        (4) 4

19. How many grams of the compound potassium chloride (KCl) must be dissolved in 200. g of water to make a saturated solution at 60°C?

    (1) 30 g    (2) 45 g    (3) 56 g    (4) 90 g

20. Which of the following is insoluble?

    (1) calcium chloride
    (2) ammonium phosphate
    (3) barium sulfate
    (4) potassium chromate

21. Which of the following is not soluble?

    (1) sodium chromate    (3) lithium hydroxide
    (2) lead(II) iodide    (4) ammonium sulfate

22. If solutions of sodium chromate and potassium carbonate are mixed and poured into a filter, what will pass through the filter?

    (1) sodium, chromate, potassium, and carbonate ions
    (2) sodium and carbonate ions only
    (3) potassium and chromate ions only
    (4) water only

15. A solution contains 14 g of KCl in 100. g of water at 40°C. What is the minimum amount of KCl that must be added to make this a saturated solution?

    (1) 14 g    (2) 19 g    (3) 25 g    (4) 44 g

23. Which amount of a compound dissolved in 100. g of water at the stated temperature represents a solution that is saturated?

    (1) 20 g $KClO_3$ at 80°C
    (2) 40 g $KNO_3$ at 25°C
    (3) 40 g KCl at 60°C
    (4) 60 g $NaNO_3$ at 40°C

## Concentration of Solutions

Because solutions are homogeneous mixtures, their compositions can vary. Sometimes, it is adequate to refer to a solution as dilute or concentrated. However, *dilute* and *concentrated* are relative terms and are not precise regarding the amount of solute involved. In most cases it is the specific amount, or concentration, of the solute that is important. In this section you will learn several methods of expressing the specific concentration of solute in a solution.

## Molarity

One of the most important methods of stating the concentration of a solution is in terms of the number of moles of solute in a given volume of solution. The **molarity** (M) of a solution is the number of moles of solute in 1 L of solution. The relationship is listed in Important Formulas and Equations of *Reference Tables for Physical Setting/Chemistry*.

$$\text{molarity} = \frac{\text{moles of solute}}{\text{liters of solution}}$$

### SAMPLE PROBLEM

What is the molarity of a solution that contains 4.0 mol of NaOH in 0.50 L of solution?

**SOLUTION:** Identify the known and unknown values.

*Known*
amount NaOH = 4.0 mol
volume of solution = 0.50 L

*Unknown*
molarity = ? M

Substitute known values into the equation for molarity, and solve for molarity.

$$M = \frac{\text{moles of solute}}{\text{liters of solution}}$$

$$M = \frac{4.0 \text{ moles NaOH}}{0.50 \text{ liter}}$$

$$M = 8.0$$

In the previous sample problem, the molarity of the solution is 8.0 M. A liter of this solution would contain 8.0 mol of the solute, NaOH. However, in many problems, the mass of solute is given instead of the number of moles. To solve this type of problem, convert grams of solute to moles of solute and solve as above.

## SAMPLE PROBLEM

What is the molarity of a solution containing 82.0 g of $Ca(NO_3)_2$ in 2.0 liters of solution?

**SOLUTION:** Identify the known and unknown values.

_Known_
mass of $Ca(NO_3)_2$ = 82.0 g
volume of solution = 2.0 L

_Unknown_
molarity = ? M

**1.** Calculate the formula mass of $Ca(NO_3)_2$.

For Ca: 1 atom × 40. amu/atom  =  40 amu
For N:  2 atoms × 14 amu/atom  =  28 amu
For O:  6 atoms × 16 amu/atom  =  96 amu
             Formula mass $Ca(NO_3)_2$  = 164 amu

**2.** Change the formula mass to gram formula mass.

gram formula mass = formula mass in grams
gram formula mass $Ca(NO_3)_2$ = 164 g/mol

**3.** Convert grams of $Ca(NO_3)_2$ to moles.

$$\text{moles } Ca(NO_3)_2 = \frac{\text{grams } Ca(NO_3)_2}{\text{gram formula mass } Ca(NO_3)_2}$$

$$\text{moles } Ca(NO_3)_2 = \frac{82.0g}{164 \text{ g/mol}} = 0.500 \text{ mol}$$

**4.** Calculate molarity.

$$M = \frac{\text{moles of solute}}{\text{liters of solution}}$$

$$M = \frac{0.500 \text{ mol NaOH}}{2.0 \text{ L solution}}$$

$$M = 0.250$$

## Percent by Mass

It is common to find labels that list the concentration of the ingredients by percent mass. Fertilizers often list the active ingredients as a percentage of the entire mass of the fertilizer. **Percent mass** is simply the mass of an ingredient divided by the total mass, expressed as a percent (parts per hundred). Percent mass problems are essentially the same as the percent composition problems found in Topic 3. To calculate the percent mass, use the following relationship.

$$\text{percent mass} = \frac{\text{mass of part}}{\text{mass of whole}} \times 100\%$$

## Percent by Volume

When two liquids are mixed to form a solution, it is common to express the concentration of the solute as a percent by volume. A label on a bottle of rubbing alcohol shows a common example. Usually the label will show that the solution is 70% isopropyl alcohol by volume. The rest of the solution is water.

**Percent by volume** is the ratio of the volume of an ingredient divided by the total volume and expressed as a percent.

$$\text{percent by volume} = \frac{\text{volume of solute}}{\text{volume of solution}} = 100\%$$

**Memory Jogger**

In math class you have learned how to rearrange an equation to solve for an unknown variable. Analyze these formulas to remind yourself how to do it.

$$a = bc$$
$$b = a/c$$
$$c = a/b$$

Recognize that the molarity equation can also be rearranged to solve for any variable included in the equation.

$$\text{molarity} = \frac{\text{moles solute}}{\text{liters of solution}}$$

$$\text{moles solute} = (\text{molarity})(\text{liters of solution})$$

$$\text{liters of solution} = \frac{\text{moles solute}}{\text{molarity}}$$

## SAMPLE PROBLEM

What is the percent mass of sodium hydroxide if 2.50 g of NaOH are added to 50.00 g of $H_2O$?

**SOLUTION:** Identify the known and unknown values.

*Known*
mass of NaOH = 2.50 g
mass of $H_2O$ = 50.00 g

*Unknown*
Percent mass
NaOH ?%

Substitute known values into the percent mass equation, and solve for percent mass.

$$\% \text{ mass} = \frac{\text{mass of part}}{\text{mass of whole}} \times 100 \%$$

$$\% \text{ mass NaOH} = \frac{2.50 \text{ g NaOH}}{(2.50 + 50.00) \text{ g solution}} \times 100\%$$

$$\% \text{ mass NaOH} = 4.76\%$$

## SAMPLE PROBLEM

What is the percent by volume of alcohol if 50.0 mL of ethanol is diluted with water to form a total volume of 300. mL?

**SOLUTION:** Identify the known and unknown values.

*Known*
volume of ethanol = 50.0 mL
total volume = 300. mL

*Unknown*
percent by volume
ethanol = ? %

Substitute known values into the percent by volume equation, and solve for percent by volume.

$$\% \text{ by volume} = \frac{\text{volume of solute}}{\text{volume of solution}} \times 100\%$$

$$\% \text{ by volume ethanol} = \frac{50.0 \text{ mL ethanol}}{300. \text{ mL solution}} \times 100\%$$

$$\% \text{ by volume ethanol } 16.7\%$$

## Parts per Million

Parts per million is similar to percent composition because it compares masses. **Parts per million (ppm)** is a ratio between the mass of a solute and the total mass of the solution. This method of reporting concentrations is useful for extremely dilute solutions when molarity and percent mass would be difficult to interpret. For example, chlorine is used as a disinfectant in swimming pools. Only about 2 g of chlorine per 1,000,000 g of swimming pool water is necessary to keep the pool sanitized. Finding molarity and percent mass would result in numbers too small to be useful. Parts per million is often used to report a measured amount of air or water pollutants.

Percent composition uses the amount present per hundred parts because it is a percent. The only difference in finding ppm is that you multiply by 1,000,000 ppm instead of 100 percent.

$$\text{ppm} = \frac{\text{grams of solute}}{\text{grams of solution}} \times 1,000,000 \text{ ppm}$$

## SAMPLE PROBLEM

Approximately 0.0043 g of oxygen can be dissolved in 100. mL of water at 20°C.
Express this in terms of parts per million.

**SOLUTION:** Identify the known and unknown values.

*Known*
mass of $O_2$ = 0.0043 g
volume of $H_2O$ = 100. mL

*Unknown*
ppm $O_2$ = ?

Substitute known values into the ppm equation, and solve for ppm $O_2$.

$$ppm = \frac{\text{grams of solute}}{\text{grams of solution}} \times 1{,}000{,}000 \text{ ppm}$$

$$ppm\ O_2 = \frac{0.0043\ \cancel{g}}{100.0043\ \cancel{g}} \times 1{,}000{,}000 \text{ ppm}$$

$$ppm\ O_2 = 43 \text{ ppm}$$

## Preparation of a Solution of Known Concentration

It is important to be able to calculate the amount of solute to be added to a known volume of solvent to make a solution of specified concentration. The following sample problem shows you how to determine the amount of solute needed to prepare a solution of known molarity.

You now know how much solute and solvent you need to actually prepare the solution in the sample problem, but the procedure used in preparation

## SAMPLE PROBLEM

What mass of sodium carbonate is required to prepare 2.00 L of a 0.250 M sodium carbonate solution?

**SOLUTION:** Identify the known and unknown values.

*Known*
concentration of
  solution = 0.250 M
volume of solution = 2.00 L

*Unknown*
mass of $Na_2CO_3$ = ? g

Determine the number of moles of solute needed by using molarity and volume.

moles = MV = molarity × liters of solution

$$\text{moles }Na_2CO_3 = \frac{0.250 \text{ mol}}{1\ \cancel{L}} \times 2.00\ \cancel{L} = 0.500 \text{ mol}$$

The following steps are used to convert moles $Na_2CO_3$ to grams $Na_2CO_3$:

**1.** Determine the formula mass of $Na_2CO_3$.

For Na: 2 atoms × 23.0 amu/atom = 46.0 amu
For C:  1 atom × 12.0 amu/atom  = 12.0 amu
For O:  3 atoms × 16.0 amu/atom = <u>48.0</u> amu
        formula mass $Na_2CO_3$ = 106.0 amu

**2.** Change the formula mass to gram formula mass.

gram formula mass = formula mass in grams
gram formula mass $Na_2CO_3$ = 106.0 g/mol

**3.** Convert moles of $Na_2CO_3$ into grams of $Na_2CO_3$.

mass = moles × gram formula mass
mass $Na_2CO_3$ = 0.500 $\cancel{mol}$ × 106.0 g/$\cancel{mol}$
mass $Na_2CO_3$ = 53.0 g

is also essential. The steps listed below apply to the preparation of any solution of known concentration:

1. Add the desired amount of solute to a volumetric flask.
2. Add some distilled water and mix until the solute is dissolved and the solution is homogeneous.
3. Fill the volumetric flask to the mark on the neck of the flask, stopper, and again mix to ensure that the solution is homogeneous.

The reason the water is added in two steps is that it is easier to dissolve the solute if the flask is not full and there is room for the water to be adequately stirred or shaken.

# Review Questions

**24.** What is the molarity of a KF(aq) solution containing 116 g of KF in 1.00 L of solution?

(1) 1.00 M  (2) 2.00 M  (3) 3.00 M  (4) 4.00 M

**25.** What is the molarity of an $H_2SO_4$ solution if 0.25 L of the solution contains 0.75 mol of $H_2SO_4$?

(1) 0.33 M  (2) 0.75 M  (3) 3.0 M  (4) 6.0 M

**26.** What is the total number of moles of the solute $H_2SO_4$ needed to prepare 5.0 L of a 2.0 M solution of $H_2SO_4$?

(1) 2.5 mol      (3) 10. mol
(2) 5.0 mol      (4) 20. mol

**27.** What volume of a 2.0 M solution is needed to provide 0.50 mol of NaOH?

(1) 0.25 L  (2) 0.50 L  (3) 1.0 L  (4) 2.0 L

**28.** What is the molarity of a solution that contains 40. g of NaOH in 0.50 L of solution?

(1) 1.0 M  (2) 2.0 M  (3) 0.50 M  (4) 0.25 M

**29.** If 100. mL of a 1.0 M solution is evaporated to a volume of 25 mL, what will be the concentration of the resulting solution?

(1) 0.25 M  (2) 0.50 M  (3) 2.0 M  (4) 4.0 M

**30.** What is the percent by mass of a solution in which 60. g of NaOH are dissolved in sufficient water to make 100 g of solution?

(1) 16%    (2) 40%    (3) 60%    (4) 160%

**31.** What is the percent by mass of a solution if 60. g of acetic acid are added to 90. g of water?

(1) 20%    (2) 30%    (3) 40%    (4) 67%

**32.** Carbon dioxide gas has a solubility of 0.0972 g/100 g $H_2O$ at 40°C. Expressed in parts per million, this concentration is closest to

(1) 0.972 ppm        (3) 97.2 ppm
(2) 9.72 ppm         (4) 972 ppm

**33.** A substance has a solubility of 350 ppm. How many grams of the substance are present in 1.0 L of a saturated solution?

(1) 0.0350 g        (3) 3.50 g
(2) 0.350 g         (4) 35.0 g

Use the reference tables and your knowledge of chemistry to answer each of the following questions. Be sure to show all work if calculations are needed.

**34.** What is the percent mass of a saturated solution of $KClO_3$ at 20°C?

**35.** A saturated solution of ammonium chloride in 100. g $H_2O$ at 85°C is cooled to 20°C and filtered. What was the mass of the solution at 85°C? What is the mass of the liquid that passes through the filter?

**36.** Barium sulfate is listed as insoluble on solubility tables. It does, however, dissolve to a small extent. Its solubility at 50°C is 0.00034 g in 100. g of water. Express this solubility in parts per million.

**37.** The table below gives the solubility of $Ca(OH)_2(s)$ in 100. g of $H_2O$ at various temperatures. What is unusual about the behavior of the solubility of this salt?

| Temperature (°C) | Solubility (g $Ca(OH)_2$/100. g $H_2O$) |
|---|---|
| 0 | 0.189 |
| 20 | 0.173 |
| 40 | 0.141 |
| 60 | 0.121 |
| 80 | 0.094 |

## Colligative Properties

The freezing and boiling points of water change when nonvolatile solutes are added. When any salt is added to water, the freezing point of the water decreases. This helps explain why salt is applied to roads and sidewalks when they are covered with snow and ice. The added salt lowers the freezing point and helps to melt the snow or ice. The amount of the lowering of the freezing point is not dependent on the nature of the added particle but only on the total number of dissolved particles. One mole of any particles will have the same effect on the freezing point. One mole of particles lowers the freezing point of 1000 g of water by 1.86°C.

### Molecular Versus Ionic

When one mole of sugar, a molecular substance, is dissolved in water, one mole of particles is produced in solution.

$$C_{12}H_{22}O_{11}(s) \rightarrow C_{12}H_{22}O_{11}(aq)$$
$$\text{1 mol} \qquad\qquad \text{1 mol}$$

When one mole of an ionic substance is dissolved in water, the results are different. The ionic substance separates into individual ions.

$$NaCl(s) \rightarrow Na^+ (aq) \quad + Cl^- (aq)$$
$$\text{1 mol NaCl} \rightarrow \text{1 mol Na}^+ + \text{1 mol Cl}^-$$

Thus, one mole of sodium chloride produces two moles of particles and will depress the freezing point of water twice as much as the mole of sugar. The greater the number of ions, the greater the effect on the freezing point. $CaCl_2$ contains three ions, and one mole of this salt will depress the freezing point three times as much as a mole of sugar.

The situation is similar with the boiling point. One mole of particles will elevate the boiling point of 1000. g of water by 0.52°C. One mole of dissolved sugar will elevate the boiling point of 1000. g of water by 0.52°C. One mole of dissolved sodium chloride contains two moles of ions, and will raise the boiling point of 1000.g of water by 1.04°C.

## Review Questions

**38.** Why is salt (NaCl) put on icy roads and sidewalks in the winter?

   (1) It is ionic and lowers the freezing point of water.

   (2) It is ionic and raises the freezing point of water.

   (3) It is covalent and lowers the freezing point of water.

   (4) It is covalent and raises the freezing point of water.

**39.** What occurs as a salt dissolves in water?

   (1) The number of ions in the solution decreases, and the freezing point decreases.

   (2) The number of ions in the solution decreases, and the freezing point increases.

   (3) The number of ions in the solution increases, and the freezing point decreases.

   (4) The number of ions in the solution increases, and the freezing point increases.

**40.** Assume equal aqueous concentrations of each of the following substances. Which has the lowest freezing point?

(1) $C_2H_{12}O_6$
(2) $CH_3OH$
(3) $C_{12}H_{22}O_{11}$
(4) NaOH

**41.** What occurs when sugar is added to water?

(1) The freezing point of the water will decrease, and the boiling point will decrease.
(2) The freezing point of the water will decrease, and the boiling point will increase.
(3) The freezing point of the water will increase, and the boiling point will decrease.
(4) The freezing point of the water will increase, and the boiling point will increase.

**42.** Which solution has the highest boiling point?

(1) 1.0 M $KNO_3$
(2) 2.0 M $KNO_3$
(3) 1.0 M $Ca(NO_3)_2$
(4) 2.0 M $Ca(NO_3)_2$

**43.** Which property of a distilled water solution will not be affected by adding 50 mL of $CH_3OH$ to 100. mL of the water solution at 25°C?

(1) conductivity
(2) mass
(3) freezing point
(4) boiling point

---

**Memory Jogger**

Hydrogen bonds are formed when a hydrogen atom in one molecule is attracted to an oxygen, nitrogen, or fluorine atom in another molecule. Because hydrogen bonding is stronger than dipole-dipole attraction, substances with hydrogen bonding have abnormally high boiling points.

## Vapor Pressure

The molecules in a liquid are held together by rather weak forces. Polar molecules called dipoles are held in the liquid phase by dipole-dipole forces. In molecules containing hydrogen and one atom of oxygen, nitrogen, or fluorine, the force of attraction holding them in the liquid phase are hydrogen bonds.

In any sample of a liquid, some of the particles at the surface have sufficient energy to escape from their neighboring molecules and enter the gas phase. When a substance that is normally a solid or a liquid at room temperature enters the gas phase it is called a **vapor.** Thus, you will often hear about water vapor or gasoline vapor, as water and gasoline are normally liquids at room temperature.

As the temperature of a liquid increases, the particles have more energy, and more particles escape from the surface. These vapor particles are gaseous particles and exert pressure in the gaseous phase. The pressure that a vapor exerts is called **vapor pressure.** Table H of *Reference Tables for Physical Setting/Chemistry* is a graph showing the vapor pressure of four substances measured in pressure units of kilopascals (kPa).

Of the substances shown on the graph, propanone exerts the most pressure, about 93 kPa at a temperature of 50°C. It can be inferred that propanone has the weakest intermolecular forces holding it in the liquid phase, while ethanoic acid has the greatest, exerting only about 8 kPa of pressure.

## Boiling Point

As the temperature of a liquid rises, vapor pressure increases. Finally the vapor pressure becomes equal to atmospheric pressure. At this point the gas may vaporize, not only on the surface but at any point in the container. A bubble of vapor below the surface has enough pressure that it does not collapse from the atmospheric pressure pushing against it. When a bubble can occur at any point in the liquid, the process is called boiling. The normal **boiling point** of a liquid is the temperature at which the vapor pressure of the liquid is 101.3 kPa, standard atmospheric pressure. Equivalent pressures are 1 atm, 760 mm Hg, and 760 torr. The heat required to change 1 mol of a substance from a liquid at its boiling point to 1 mol of a vapor is termed the <u>heat of vaporization.</u>

The normal boiling point of water is 100.°C. At this temperature, the vapor pressure of water is 101.3 kPa. The line representing 101.3 kPa on Table H shows the normal boiling point of ethanol to be 78°C. When the pressure is less than 101.3 kPa, the boiling point will be less than the normal value. Water will boil at about 70°C when the pressure is about 30 kPa. If the pressure is greater than normal, liquids will boil at temperatures above their normal boiling points. When atmospheric pressure is about 145 kPa, water boils at 110.°C.

# Review Questions

**Use the tables in *Reference Tables for Physical Setting/Chemistry* as needed in answering the following questions.**

**44.** What is the vapor pressure of water at 105°C?

(1) 100 kPa
(2) 101.3 kPa
(3) 110 kPa
(4) 120 kPa

**45.** As the pressure on a liquid is changed from 100. kPa to 120. kPa, the temperature at which the liquid will boil

(1) decreases
(2) increases
(3) remains the same

**46.** In a closed system at 40°C, a liquid has a vapor pressure of 50 kPa. The liquid's normal boiling point could be

(1) 10°C      (3) 40°C
(2) 30°C      (4) 60°C

**47.** If the pressure on the surface of water in the liquid state is 30 kPa, the water will boil at

(1) 0°C       (3) 70°C
(2) 30°C      (4) 100°C

**48.** A sample of ethanoic acid at 100°C has a vapor pressure of

(1) 53 kPa
(2) 100 kPa
(3) 101.3 kPa
(4) 125 kPa

**49.** Which substance has the greatest intermolecular forces of attraction between molecules?

(1) propanone
(2) ethanol
(3) water
(4) ethanoic acid

**50.** The vapor pressure of ethanol at its normal boiling point would be

(1) 80 kPa
(2) 101.3 kPa
(3) 273 kPa
(4) 373 kPa

**Directions**

Review the Test-Taking Strategies section of this book. Then answer the following questions. Read each question carefully and answer with a correct choice or response.

## Part A

1 When a teaspoon of sugar is added to water in a beaker, the sugar dissolves. The resulting mixture is
(1) a compound
(2) a homogeneous solution
(3) a heterogeneous solution
(4) an emulsion

2 A small quantity of a salt is stirred into a liter of water until it dissolves. In the resulting mixture, the water is
(1) the solvent
(2) the solute
(3) dispersed material
(4) a precipitate

3 A solution
(1) will separate on standing
(2) may have color
(3) can be cloudy
(4) can be heterogeneous

4 Nonpolar solvents will most easily dissolve solids that are
(1) ionic
(2) covalent
(3) metallic
(4) heterogeneous

5 What happens when a crystal of a salt is dropped into an unsaturated solution of the same salt?
(1) Excess solute crystals form.
(2) The crystal dissolves.
(3) The crystal drops to the bottom, unchanged.
(4) The solution becomes colorless.

6 The depression of the freezing point is dependent on
(1) the nature of the solute
(2) the formula mass of the solute
(3) the concentration of dissolved particles
(4) hydrogen bonding

7 The process of recovering a salt from a solution by evaporating the solvent is known as
(1) crystallization
(2) filtration
(3) reduction
(4) decomposition

8 What happens when a crystal of solute is dropped into a supersaturated solution of the salt?
(1) The crystal dissolves.
(2) Excess solute crystals form.
(3) The crystal drops to the bottom, unchanged.
(4) The solution begins to boil.

9 Under which conditions are gases most soluble in water?
(1) high temperature and high pressure
(2) high temperature and low pressure
(3) low temperature and high pressure
(4) low temperature and low pressure

10 As the temperature of a liquid decreases, the amount of a gas that can be dissolved
(1) decreases
(2) increases
(3) remains the same

11 As the temperature of liquid water decreases, its vapor pressure
(1) decreases
(2) increases
(3) remains the same
(4) disappears

12 The heat energy required to change one mole of a liquid into a vapor at the boiling point is called the
(1) heat of vaporization
(2) heat of formation
(3) heat of solution
(4) heat of fusion

## Part B

**13** Which substance increases in solubility as the temperature decreases?
(1) $KClO_3$  (2) $NH_3$  (3) $KNO_3$  (4) NaCl

**14** The diagrams below represent an ionic crystal being dissolved in water.

Ionic crystal

Water molecule

According to the diagrams, the dissolving process takes place by
(1) hydrogen bond formation
(2) metallic bonding
(3) dipole-dipole attractions
(4) molecule-ion attractions

**15** If solutions of barium nitrate and sodium sulfate are mixed and then poured into a filter, the solid remaining on the filter will be
(1) barium nitrate   (3) barium sulfate
(2) sodium nitrate   (4) sodium sulfate

**16** A student tested the solubility of a salt at different temperatures and then used the *Reference Tables for Physical Setting/Chemistry* to identify the salt. The student's data appears below.

| Temperature (°C) | Solubility Data (g of salt per 10 g of water) |
|---|---|
| 30 | 1.2 |
| 50 | 2.2 |
| 62 | 3.0 |
| 76 | 4.0 |

What is the identity of the salt?
(1) potassium nitrate   (3) potassium chlorate
(2) sodium chloride   (4) ammonium chloride

**17** A student drops a crystal of NaCl into a beaker of NaCl(aq) and the crystal dissolves. The original solution must have been
(1) supersaturated
(2) saturated
(3) unsaturated
(4) heterogeneous

**18** If 100. g of water at 80°C contains 45 g of KCl and 45 g of $NaNO_3$, the solution is
(1) saturated with respect to both KCl and $NaNO_3$
(2) saturated with respect to KCl and unsaturated with respect to $NaNO_3$
(3) unsaturated with respect to both KCl and $NaNO_3$
(4) supersaturated with respect to both KCl and $NaNO_3$

**19** What happens when KI(s) is dissolved in water?
(1) $I^-$ ions are attracted to the oxygen atoms of the water.
(2) $K^+$ ions are attracted to the oxygen atoms of the water.
(3) $K^+$ ions are attracted to the hydrogen atoms of the water.
(4) No attractions are involved; the crystal just falls apart.

**20** Which two compounds contain only polar molecules?
(1) $CCl_4$ and $CH_4$   (3) HCl and $NH_3$
(2) HCl and $Cl_2$   (4) CO and $CO_2$

**21** A saturated solution of potassium chloride at 10°C is heated to 30°C. As the solution is heated in a closed container, the total mass of the solution
(1) decreases   (3) remains the same
(2) increases

**22** Water boils at 90°C when the pressure exerted on the liquid equals
(1) 82 kPa   (3) 101.3 kPa
(2) 90 kPa   (4) 120 kPa

**23** Consider the following data for NaCl:

| Temperature (°C) | 0 | 20 | 50 | 100 |
|---|---|---|---|---|
| Solubility (g/100 g $H_2O$) | 35.7 | 36.0 | 37.0 | 39.2 |

When the salt is added to water, the temperature of the solution decreases. Which of the following statements is correct?
(1) The process is endothermic, and solubility and temperature are directly related.
(2) The process is endothermic, and solubility and temperature are indirectly related.
(3) The process is exothermic, and solubility and temperature are directly related.
(4) The process is exothermic, and solubility and temperature are indirectly related.

24 Which sample of ethanol will have the highest vapor pressure?
 (1) 10. mL at 62°C    (3) 30. mL at 42°C
 (2) 20.0 mL at 52°C    (4) 40 mL at 32°C

25 The vapor pressure of water is 50 kPa. The temperature of this sample of water is
 (1) 37°C    (2) 62°C    (3) 82°C    (4) 92°C

26 What is the percent mass of NaOH if 12.5 g is dissolved in 100. g of water?

27 What volume of 3.0 M HCl contains 0.20 mol of HCl?

28 A student is instructed to make 0.250 Liter of a 0.200 M aqueous solution of $Ca(NO_3)_2$. In order to prepare the described solution in the laboratory, two quantities must be measured accurately. One of these quantities is the volume of the solution. What is the other quantity that must be measured to prepare this solution? [1]

29 What is the molarity of a solution that contains 24 g of $NaNO_3$ in 200 mL of solution?

30 How many grams of $KNO_3$ are present in 250 mL of 2.0 M potassium nitrate solution?

# Part C

31 Describe two methods by which you could remove gases that are dissolved in water. [2]

32 Consider the following data for $Na_2SO_4$.

| Temperature (°C) | 0 | 20 | 50 | 100 |
|---|---|---|---|---|
| Solubility (g/100 g $H_2O$) | 4.76 | 62 | 50. | 41 |

 What is the relationship between the temperature and the amount of dissolved material? Given that sodium sulfate is a solid, what is unusual about the data given above? [2]

33 Four flasks are prepared, each containing 100 mLs of aqueous solutions of equal concentration. Flask A contains KCl(aq), flask B contains $CH_3OH(aq)$, flask C contains $Ba(OH)_2(aq)$ and flask D contains $CH_3COOH(aq)$. Which solution has the lowest freezing point? Explain your answer. [2]

34 Describe how to prepare 500. mL of 4.0 M NaOH(aq). Show any calculations. [2]

**Use the following figure to answer questions 35 and 36.**

35 The figure represents the line showing the solubility of substance X. A solution of substance X is represented by point D. What are two ways that this solution can be made saturated? [2]

36 Point B represents a supersaturated solution. Consider the equation:

$$X(aq) \rightarrow X(s) + heat$$

When a crystal is placed into the supersaturated solution, additional crystals form and fall to the bottom of the beaker, and the solution returns to a saturated condition. Which of the two positions shown on the line of saturation would best represent the solution when the crystals first settled to the bottom? Explain the reason for your answer. [2]

37 State the relationship between the solubility of sulfur dioxide gas and temperature. [1]

38 What is the boiling point of propanone at an atmospheric pressure of 70 kPa? (11–58) [1]

39 What are two ways to make a saturated solution of $NH_3$ in 100.g $H_2O$ at 60°C become unsaturated? [2]

40 Describe the effect on the solubility of $KNO_3(s)$ in water when the pressure is increased. [1]

# Kinetics and Equilibrium

## What Scientists Know About Chemical Reactions

**?** **What do car accidents and chemical reactions have in common?** **?**

Well, they both must involve collisions. Just like all car collisions do not cause damage, not all chemical collisions cause a reaction. Consider that most cars have bumpers that can absorb energy at low speeds and avoid damage. But at higher speeds—CRUNCH! Colliding molecules also need a minimum amount of energy, called the activation energy, to cause changes and start chemical reactions.

# 8 Kinetics and Equilibrium

## Vocabulary

| | | |
|---|---|---|
| activated complex | entropy | potential energy diagram |
| activation energy | equilibrium | stress |
| catalyst | Le Châtelier's principle | |

## Topic Overview

In this topic you will be introduced to two important ideas in chemistry—the collision theory and equilibrium. The collision theory explores why reactions occur, and the factors that affect those reactions. Equilibrium introduces an important surprise. Not only do reactant particles produce products, but often, these products can react to regenerate the reactants. Many reactions can proceed in two directions. These processes are not only vital in industry, but even more in our own bodies. We have many equilibrium systems that help maintain our health on an even keel.

## Kinetics

Kinetics is the branch of chemistry that is concerned with the rates of chemical reactions. Several different factors affect how quickly chemical reactions occur. One of the basic concepts of kinetics is that in order for a reaction to occur, reactant particles must collide. This is called the collision theory. Collisions between particles can produce a reaction if both the spatial orientation and energy of the colliding particles are conducive to a reaction.

### Factors Affecting Rates of Reaction

The rate of a chemical reaction is dependent on factors such as the nature of the reactants, concentration, surface area, the presence of a catalyst, and temperature. All these factors affect rate of reaction by changing the number of effective collisions that take place between particles. Pressure can also be a factor that affects the rate of reactions involving gases.

**Nature of the Reactants** Reactions involve the breaking of existing bonds and the formation of new ones. In general, covalently bonded substances are slower to react than ionic substances due to the greater number of bonds that must be broken before a reaction can occur. Breaking more bonds requires that the particles must have more energy when they collide.

**Concentration** Most chemical reactions will proceed at a faster rate if the concentration of one or more reactants is increased. An obvious example is the rate of combustion of paper in air, which is 20% oxygen, compared with the much faster rate in pure oxygen. The kinetic molecular theory would predict that because there are more collisions between the paper and oxygen in pure oxygen than in air, the rate in pure oxygen would be faster. Indeed, this is the case.

**Surface Area** When more surface area of a substance is exposed, there are more chances for reactant particles to collide, thus increasing the reaction rate. A finely divided powder will react more rapidly than a single lump of the same mass.

**Pressure** While pressure has little or no effect on the rate of reactions between solids or liquids, it has a pronounced effect on gases. An increase in pressure has the effect of increasing the concentration of gaseous particles. Therefore, it increases the rate of a reaction that involves gases.

**The Presence of a Catalyst** **Catalysts** are substances that increase the rate of a reaction by providing a different and easier pathway for a reaction. Catalysts take part in a reaction, but they are unchanged when the reaction is complete.

**Temperature** By definition, temperature implies that the greater the temperature of a substance, the faster the molecules move. The kinetic molecular theory states that collisions must occur in order for a reaction to take place. When these two concepts are put together you can see that if the particles are moving faster, there will be more collisions, thus increasing the likelihood that a reaction will occur. At a higher temperature, not only will there be more collisions, but the reacting particles will have more energy, making it more likely that the collisions will be effective.

| Table 8-1. Factors that Affect Rate of Reaction | |
|---|---|
| **Factor** | **Increases Rate** |
| Nature of reactants | ionic more than covalent |
| Concentration | increased concentration |
| Pressure | increased pressure for gases |
| Temperature | increased temperature |
| Surface area | increased surface area |
| Catalyst | presence of a catalyst |

# Review Questions

1. As the number of effective collisions between reacting particles increases, the rate of the reaction
   (1) decreases     (3) remains the same
   (2) increases

2. Which of the following pairs of reactants will react most quickly?
   (1) sodium chloride and silver nitrate
   (2) water and hydrogen chloride
   (3) hydrogen and propene
   (4) oxygen and methane

3. In the reaction $2Mg(s) + O_2(g) \rightarrow 2MgO(s)$, as the surface area of $Mg(s)$ increases, the rate of the reaction
   (1) decreases     (3) remains the same
   (2) increases

4. Consider the following equation.
   $$A(g) + B(g) \rightarrow C(g)$$
   As the concentration of $A(g)$ increases, the frequency of collisions of $A(g)$ with $B(g)$
   (1) decreases     (3) remains the same
   (2) increases

5. The reaction $A(g) + B(g) \rightarrow C(g)$ is occurring in the apparatus shown below.

   The rate of the reaction can be decreased by increasing the
   (1) pressure on the reactants
   (2) temperature of the reactants
   (3) concentration of reactant $A(g)$
   (4) volume of the reaction chamber

6. Consider the following equation.
   $$Mg(s) + 2H_2O(\ell) \rightarrow Mg(OH)_2(s) + H_2(g)$$
   For the reaction to occur at the fastest rate, 1 g of $Mg(s)$ should be added in the form of
   (1) large chunks     (3) a ribbon
   (2) small chunks     (4) a powder

**7.** Raising the temperature speeds up the rate of chemical reaction by increasing

(1) the effectiveness of the collisions only
(2) the frequency of the collisions only
(3) both the effectiveness and frequency of the collisions
(4) neither the effectiveness nor frequency of the collisions

**8.** Consider the following equation.

$$Fe(s) + CuSO_4(aq) \rightarrow Cu(s) + FeSO_4(aq)$$

The Fe reacts more rapidly when it is powdered because the increased surface due to powdering permits

(1) increased reactant contact
(2) decreased reactant contact
(3) pressure to affect reaction rate
(4) warmer solution to be used

**9.** If the pressure on gaseous reactants is increased, the rate of reaction is increased because there is an increase in the

(1) temperature
(2) volume
(3) concentration
(4) heat of reaction

**10.** Consider the following equation.

$$Zn(s) + 2HCl(aq) \rightarrow ZnCl_2(aq) + H_2(g)$$

The reaction occurs more slowly when a single piece of zinc is used than when the same mass of powdered zinc is used. Why does this happen?

(1) The powdered zinc is more concentrated.
(2) The powdered zinc has a greater surface area.
(3) The powdered zinc requires less activation energy.
(4) The powdered zinc generates more heat energy.

**Figure 8-1. Collisions of molecules:** If HI molecules collide in any arrangement other than the one shown in part E, the collision is not effective and no products form.

## Potential Energy Diagram

As was mentioned when discussing the nature of the reactants, chemical bonds contain energy. Specifically, they contain potential chemical energy. A diagram, called a **potential energy diagram,** illustrates the potential energy change that occurs during a chemical reaction. The vertical axis of this diagram represents the change in potential energy. The horizontal axis is called the <u>reaction coordinate</u>, which represents the progress of the reaction.

In order for a reaction to occur, the reactants must have sufficient energy to collide effectively. As the reactant particles approach each other, kinetic energy is converted into potential energy.

Not only must the particles collide in order for a reaction to occur, they must be properly positioned. Look at Figure 8-1. If the particles collide in the proper orientation, an activated complex is formed. This **activated complex** is a temporary, intermediate product that may either break apart and reform the reactants or rearrange the atoms and form new products.

Figure 8-2 shows a potential energy diagram for the following reaction.

$$A + B \rightarrow C + D + heat$$

Line 1 extends from the origin of the y-axis to the reactants and represents the amount of potential

Figure 8-2. **Potential energy diagram:** This figure shows the potential energy of the reactants, the activated complex, and the products of the reaction.

Figure 8-3. **Activation energies and heat of reaction**

energy of the reactants. Line 2 extends from the origin of the *y*-axis to the activated complex and represents the potential energy of the complex. Line 3 represents the potential energy of the products. Any line that begins at the origin of the *y*-axis of such a graph is a measure of potential energy.

Figure 8-3 shows the same potential energy diagram, but the lines represent the differences between the potential energies of different substances. Line 4 represents the difference in potential energy between the reactants and the activated complex. The amount of energy needed to form the activated complex from the reactants is called the **activation energy.** Because the diagram is read from left to right, it is also called the activation energy of the forward reaction.

Line 5 represents the difference between the potential energy of the reactants and the potential energy of the products. The difference between the potential energy of the reactants and products is called the <u>heat of reaction</u> and is represented by $\Delta H$.

Line 6 represents the difference between the potential energies of the products and the activated complex. How can this be useful? Some reactions can proceed, not only in the forward direction, but also in the reverse, or right to left on the diagram. In this case, the line represents the activation energy of the reverse reaction.

Figure 8-4 is similar to the previous diagrams, but a new line has been added. This new line represents the effect of a catalyst on the reaction.

Figure 8-4. **Effect of a catalyst on activation energy:** Note that the heat of reaction is unchanged with the addition of a catalyst, but the activation energy is decreased.

**Figure 8-5. Potential energy diagram of an endothermic reaction:** Note that there is a gain in potential energy from reactants to products.

**Figure 8-6. Potential energy diagram of an exothermic reaction:** Note that there is a loss of potential energy from reactants to products.

Note that the only difference between a reaction with a catalyst and a reaction without a catalyst is the activation energy. Most catalysts speed up a reaction by providing a new pathway with a lower activation energy. The activation energy of the reverse reaction is also lowered. Note that $\Delta H$ remains unchanged.

As the reaction proceeds toward the product side, two outcomes are possible.

1. As the activated complex changes to become the product, it will lose energy. If the product has more potential energy than the reactants, the reaction will be <u>endothermic</u>. Because more energy was absorbed to form the activated complex than was released to form the product, there was a net gain of energy. Because there has been a gain in energy, the heat of reaction has a positive value ($\Delta H = +$), as shown in Figure 8-5.

2. If the product is lower on the vertical axis than the reactants, all of the energy that was absorbed to form the activated complex is recovered, plus the difference between the potential energy of the reactants and products. This represents a loss of potential energy compared to the reactants, indicating a release of energy and an <u>exothermic</u> reaction. In this case the heat of reaction has a negative value ($\Delta H = -$), as shown in Figure 8-6.

# Review Questions

**Base your answers to Questions 11 and 12 on the diagram below, which represents the reaction:**

$$A + B \rightarrow C + energy$$

**11.** Which statement correctly describes this reaction?

(1) It is endothermic and energy is absorbed.
(2) It is endothermic and energy is released.
(3) It is exothermic and energy is absorbed.
(4) It is exothermic and energy is released.

**12.** Which numbered interval will change with the addition of a catalyst to the system?

(1) 1
(2) 2
(3) 3
(4) 4

**13.** A potential energy diagram of a chemical system is shown below.

Reaction coordinate

What is the difference between the potential energy of the reactants and the potential energy of the products?

(1) 20. kcal
(2) 40. kcal
(3) 60. kcal
(4) 80. kcal

**14.** Consider the reaction for which $\Delta H = +$ 33 kJ/mol.

$$N_2(g) + 2O_2(g) \rightleftharpoons 2NO_2(g)$$

The potential energy diagram of the reaction is shown below.

Which arrow represents the heat of reaction for the reverse reaction?

(1) 1
(2) 2
(3) 3
(4) 4

**15.** The potential energy diagram of a chemical reaction is shown below.

Reaction coordinate

Which letter in the diagram represents the heat of reaction?

(1) A      (2) B      (3) C      (4) D

**16.** A potential energy diagram is shown below.

Without catalyst

With catalyst

Reaction coordinate

Which reaction would have the lowest activation energy?

(1) the forward catalyzed reaction
(2) the forward uncatalyzed reaction
(3) the reverse catalyzed reaction
(4) the reverse uncatalyzed reaction

**17.** In the potential energy diagram below, which arrow represents the potential energy of the activated complex?

Reaction coordinate

(1) A      (2) B      (3) C      (4) D

Open container
$H_2O(\ell) \rightarrow H_2O(g)$

Closed container
$H_2O(\ell) \rightleftarrows H_2O(g)$

**Figure 8-7. Equilibrium in a closed container:** In the open container, the liquid evaporates at a constant rate until it is all evaporated. In the closed container, evaporation continues, but it is balanced by condensation.

# Equilibrium

Each of the potential energy diagrams shown depicts a reaction that is proceeding from left to right, that is, in the forward direction. The reactants first collide to form the activated complex, and then they form products. Can the reverse ever happen? Can the products collide to form the activated complex and become reactants? Not only can a reverse reaction occur, but both the forward and reverse reactions can occur at the same time. When both the forward and reverse reactions occur at the same rate, the condition is called **equilibrium.** An equation representing equilibrium uses a double arrow ($\rightleftarrows$) instead of a single arrow ($\rightarrow$) to show that reactions are proceeding in both directions.

Equilibrium is a state of balance between the rates of two opposite processes that are taking place at the same rate. Equilibrium can only occur in a system in which neither reactants nor products can leave the system.

Equilibrium is a dynamic process, that is, it implies motion in which the interactions of reactant particles are balanced by the interactions of product particles. Equilibrium is an important concept because many chemical reactions and physical processes are reversible, that is, they are able to proceed in both directions.

It must be emphasized that the quantities of reactants and products are not necessarily equal at equilibrium. Indeed, it would be unusual if they were equal. It is the rates of the two reactions, forward and reverse, that are equal. As shown in Figure 8-7, in a closed container half-filled with water, there is equilibrium between the evaporating liquid water and the condensing water vapor. Obviously there is far more liquid water than water vapor. At equilibrium, it is the rate of evaporation and condensation that are equal.

## Physical Equilibrium

Although many examples of equilibrium involve chemical reactions, equilibrium also occurs during physical processes such as change of state (phase) or dissolving.

**Phase Equilibrium** Phase equilibrium can exist between the solid and liquid phases of a substance. We define this condition as the melting point of the solid phase or the freezing point of the liquid phase. At 0°C in a closed container, both water and ice exist at the same time. Some of the ice is melting, and some of the water is freezing. An equation can be written to show that both the forward and reverse processes are taking place. The double-pointed arrow shows that both reactions are taking place at the same rate.

$$H_2O(s) \rightleftarrows H_2O(\ell)$$

There may not be the same amounts of solid and liquid present, but the rate of melting will be equal to the rate of freezing.

A similar relationship can exist in a closed container for liquid-gas equilibrium, where the rate of evaporation is equal to the rate of condensation.

$$H_2O(\ell) \rightleftarrows H_2O(g)$$

**Solution Equilibrium** Solids in liquids exist in equilibrium in a saturated solution. When solid sugar is first placed into water, the sugar dissolves, but no sugar is recrystallizing. When all of the sugar dissolves that can be dissolved at that temperature, the solution is saturated. If additional solid sugar is placed into the saturated solution, the process of dissolving will continue, but it is exactly balanced by the process of recrystallization. When the rate of dissolving and recrystallizing are equal, equilibrium exists, and the solution is saturated.

$$C_{12}H_{22}O_{11}(s) \rightleftharpoons C_{12}H_{22}O_{11}(aq)$$

Equilibrium may also be attained in a closed system between a gas dissolved in a liquid and the undissolved gas. In a closed bottle or can of soda there is equilibrium between the gaseous and dissolved state of carbon dioxide.

$$CO_2(g) \rightleftharpoons CO_2(aq)$$

In both of these cases, the equilibrium can be disturbed by a change in temperature. If the temperature is raised, a solid generally becomes more soluble in a liquid. For a short time the rate of dissolving exceeds the rate of recrystallization. As more solid is placed into solution, the rate of recrystallization increases until a new equilibrium is reached.

The opposite is true when the temperature of a solution of a gas in a liquid is raised. As the temperature increases, the rate of the gas escaping from the liquid increases, while the rate at which gas particles dissolve decreases. This decreases the solubility of the gas in the liquid. As the temperature rises, the solubility of all gases decreases in a liquid.

## Chemical Equilibrium

When reactants are first mixed and no products are present, only the forward reaction can occur. Examine what happens in the chemical reaction between water vapor and methane.

$$CH_4(g) + H_2O(g) \rightarrow 3H_2(g) + CO(g)$$

As time progresses, the concentrations of $CH_4(g)$ and $H_2O(g)$ decrease, causing the forward reaction to slow, while the concentrations of $H_2(g)$ and $CO(g)$ increase, causing the rate of the reverse reaction to increase.

**Figure 8-8. Chemical equilibrium:** Equilibrium occurs when opposite reactions occur at the same rate.

This slowing of the forward reaction and speeding up of the reverse reaction continues until the rates of the two reactions become the same. At this point, chemical equilibrium exists. Figure 8-8 summarizes this process.

As with physical equilibrium, it is important to remember that no reactant or product can leave the system. If a precipitate is formed or a gas is formed in a system that is not closed, equilibrium will not be reached. The effect of any change in equilibrium is explained by Le Châtelier's principle.

## Le Châtelier's Principle

Any change in temperature, concentration or pressure on an equilibrium system is called a **stress**. **Le Châtelier's principle** explains how a system at equilibrium responds to relieve any stress on the system. Examined below are several types of stress and how equilibrium shifts to relieve them.

**Concentration Changes** Again consider the reaction represented by the following equation.

$$CH_4(g) + H_2O(g) \rightleftharpoons 3H_2(g) + CO(g)$$

If the stress is the addition of more methane ($CH_4$), the rate of the forward reaction will increase and more products will form. If the concentration of one substance is increased, the reaction that reduces the amount of the added substance is favored. In this example, the system is said to shift to the right as more product is formed. As more product forms, the rate of the reverse reaction also increases until once again the rates of the forward and reverse reactions are equal.

If the concentration of methane is reduced, the rate of the forward reaction decreases. When the concentration of a substance decreases, the reaction that produces that substance is favored. Initially the reverse reaction will take place faster than the forward reaction, and the system is said to be shifting to the left, or toward the reactant side.

Tables 8-2 and 8-3 show how a change in concentration affects equilibrium. A plus sign (+) means the concentration increases, and a minus sign (−) means that the concentration decreases. An increase causes the system to shift away from the stress, causing the stress to be lessened. In this example, the addition of $NH_3$ causes the system to shift to the right.

| Table 8-2. Effect of Increasing the Concentration of $NH_3$ | | | | | |
|---|---|---|---|---|---|
| $4NH_3(g)$ + $5O_2(g)$ | | $\rightleftharpoons$ | $4NO(g)$ + | $6H_2O(g)$ + | heat |
| Stress | Effect | System shift | Effect | Effect | Effect |
| $+NH_3$ | $-O_2$ | $\rightarrow$ | $+NO$ | $+H_2O$ | + heat |
| Increase | Decrease | Away from stress | Increase | Increase | Increase |

| Table 8-3. Effect of Decreasing the Concentration of $NH_3$ | | | | | |
|---|---|---|---|---|---|
| $4NH_3(g)$ + $5O_2(g)$ | | $\rightleftharpoons$ | $4NO(g)$ + | $6H_2O(g)$ + | heat |
| Stress | Effect | System shift | Effect | Effect | Effect |
| $-NH_3$ | $+O_2$ | $\leftarrow$ | $-NO$ | $-H_2O$ | $-$heat |
| Decrease | Increase | Toward the stress | Decrease | Decrease | Decrease |

A decrease of $NH_3$ causes the system to move toward the stress, or a shift to the left, replacing some of the lost substance.

Notice that all factors on the same side of the arrow as the stress do the opposite of the stress. For example, as the $NH_3$ increases, $O_2$ decreases. All factors on the opposite side of the arrow from the stress increase or decrease in the same way as the stress.

**Temperature Changes** Consider the production of ammonia:

$$N_2(g) + 3H_2(g) \rightleftharpoons 2NH_3(g) + \text{heat}$$

Le Châtelier's principle states that a system will undergo changes to reduce a stress. For this reaction, heat can be considered as a product. If the temperature is raised, the rates of both the forward and reverse reactions are increased, but not equally. The reverse reaction is endothermic and will absorb some of the applied heat. The endothermic reverse reaction is favored over the exothermic forward reaction. In other words, more reactants will form when temperature is increased in this reaction. A decrease in temperature will favor the exothermic reaction and, for this reaction, more products will form.

| Table 8-4: Effect of Increasing the Heat | | | | | |
|---|---|---|---|---|---|
| $4NH_3(g)$ + | $5O_2(g)$ | $\rightleftharpoons$ | $4NO(g)$ + | $6H_2O(g)$ + | heat |
| Effect | Effect | System shift | Effect | Effect | Stress |
| $+NH_3$ | $+O_2$ | $\leftarrow$ | $-NO$ | $-H_2O$ | + heat |
| Increase | Increase | Away from stress | Decrease | Decrease | Increase |

| Table 8-5: Effect of Decreasing the Heat | | | | | |
|---|---|---|---|---|---|
| $4NH_3(g)$ + | $5O_2(g)$ | $\rightleftharpoons$ | $4NO(g)$ + | $6H_2O(g)$ + | heat |
| Effect | Effect | System shift | Effect | Effect | Stress |
| $-NH_3$ | $-O_2$ | $\rightarrow$ | $+NO$ | $+H_2O$ | − heat |
| Decrease | Decrease | Toward the stress | Increase | Increase | Decrease |

In the following representation of how a temperature change affects equilibrium, note that the results are seen in a change of concentration of reactants and products, even though the stress is actually a change of energy. Because heat is a product of the reaction, a change in temperature is essentially a change in the concentration of that product.

**Pressure Changes** Remember that pressure changes do not have an effect on the rate of reaction when only solids and liquids are involved. They do, however, have an effect on gases. An increase in pressure increases the concentration of the gases.

Consider the following system.

$$CO_2(g) \rightleftharpoons CO_2(aq)$$

When the pressure increases, the concentration of the gaseous $CO_2$ increases. Le Châtelier's principle predicts that the system will move away from the added stress—the system will shift to the right, causing more dissolved $CO_2$. Conversely, when the pressure on this system is reduced, the system shifts to the left, forming more gaseous $CO_2$. Recall what happens when a soda bottle is opened. The pressure is reduced, and the dissolved gas becomes bubbles of gaseous $CO_2$.

In the $CO_2(g) \rightleftharpoons CO_2(aq)$ reaction, only one side of the equation contains a gaseous molecule. How will a system react when there are gaseous molecules on both sides? An increase in pressure will increase the concentration of gaseous molecules on both reactant and product sides of the equation, but the effects will be unequal. An increase in pressure will favor the reaction toward the side with fewer gas molecules. In the system:

$$N_2(g) + 3H_2(g) \rightleftharpoons 2NH_3(g)$$

there are four gaseous molecules on the reactant side and only two on the product side. An increase in pressure will favor the reaction toward the product side, increasing the amount of $NH_3$ formed.

A decrease in pressure has the opposite effect. A decrease in pressure favors the reaction toward the side with the greater number of gas molecules. Thus, when the pressure is reduced the reaction shifts to the left, forming more $N_2(g)$ and $H_2(g)$ and decreasing the amount of $NH_3(g)$.

One more case remains. What happens if there are the same number of gaseous molecules on both sides? In the equation, $H_2(g) + Cl_2(g) \rightleftharpoons 2HCl(g)$, the reactant and product sides each have two gaseous molecules. Where there are the same number of gaseous reactants and product molecules, pressure changes have no effect on the system.

The following points summarize how pressure changes affect the rate of reaction when gases are involved.

- An increase in pressure will favor the reaction toward the side with the fewer number of gas molecules.
- A decrease in pressure will favor the reaction toward the side with the greater number of gas molecules.
- A change in pressure will not affect a system if there are no gas molecules or the same number of gas molecules on both sides.
- A catalyst has no net effect on an equilibrium system.

**Effect of a Catalyst** The addition of a catalyst changes the rates of both the forward and reverse reactions equally. A catalyst may cause equilibrium to be established more quickly but does not change any of the equilibrium concentrations.

# Review Questions

18. Which factors must be equal when a reversible chemical process reaches equilibrium?
    (1) mass of the reactants and mass of the products
    (2) rate of the forward reaction and rate of the reverse reaction
    (3) concentration of the reactants and concentration of the products
    (4) activation energy of the forward reaction and activation energy of the reverse reaction

19. A solute is added to water and a portion of the solute remains undissolved. When equilibrium between the dissolved and undissolved solute is reached, the solution must be
    (1) dilute
    (2) saturated
    (3) unsaturated
    (4) supersaturated

20. Which description applies to a system in a sealed flask that is half full of water?

    (1) Only evaporation occurs, but it eventually stops.
    (2) Only condensation occurs, but it eventually stops.
    (3) Neither evaporation nor condensation occurs.
    (4) Both evaporation and condensation occur.

21. Solution equilibrium always exists in a solution that is

    (1) unsaturated      (3) dilute
    (2) saturated        (4) concentrated

22. Given the reaction at equilibrium:

$$A(g) + B(g) \rightleftharpoons C(g) + D(g)$$

    The addition of a catalyst will

    (1) shift the equilibrium to the right
    (2) shift the equilibrium to the left
    (3) increase the rate of forward and reverse reactions equally
    (4) have no effect on the forward or reverse reactions

23. If a catalyst is added to a system at equilibrium and the temperature and pressure remain constant, there will be no effect on the

    (1) rate of the forward reaction
    (2) rate of the reverse reaction
    (3) activation energy of the reaction
    (4) heat of reaction

24. Consider the equation for the following reaction at equilibrium.

$$X + Y \rightleftharpoons 2Z + heat$$

    The concentration of the product could be increased by

    (1) adding a catalyst
    (2) adding more heat to the system
    (3) increasing the concentration of Y
    (4) decreasing the concentration of X

25. In a reversible reaction, chemical equilibrium is attained when the

    (1) rate of the forward reaction is greater than the rate of the reverse reaction
    (2) rate of the reverse reaction is greater than the rate of the forward reaction
    (3) concentration of the reactants reaches zero
    (4) concentration of the products remains constant

26. Consider the following equation.

$$N_2(g) + 3H_2(g) \rightleftharpoons 2NH_3(g) + heat$$

    What stress would cause the equilibrium to shift to the left?

    (1) increasing the temperature
    (2) increasing the pressure
    (3) adding $N_2(g)$ to the system
    (4) adding $H_2(g)$ to the system

27. Consider the equation for the following reaction at equilibrium.

$$CaSO_4(s) \rightleftharpoons Ca^{2+}(aq) + SO_4^{2-}(aq)$$

    When $Na_2SO_4$ is added to the system, how will the equilibrium shift?

    (1) The amount of $CaSO_4$ will decrease, and the concentration of $Ca^{2+}(aq)$ will decrease.
    (2) The amount of $CaSO_4$ will decrease, and the concentration of $Ca^{2+}(aq)$ will increase.
    (3) The amount of $CaSO_4$ will increase, and the concentration of $Ca^{2+}(aq)$ will decrease.
    (4) The amount of $CaSO_4$ will increase, and the concentration of $Ca^{2+}(aq)$ will increase.

28. Consider the following equation.

$$Zn(s) + HCl(aq) \rightarrow ZnCl_2(aq) + H_2(g)$$

    As the concentration of the $HCl(aq)$ decreases at constant temperature, the rate of the forward reaction

    (1) decreases
    (2) increases
    (3) remains the same

29. Consider the following equation.

$$H_2(g) + F_2(g) \rightleftharpoons 2HF(g) + heat$$

    Which change will not shift the point of equilibrium?

    (1) changing the pressure
    (2) changing the temperature
    (3) changing the concentration of $H_2(g)$
    (4) changing the concentration of $HF(g)$

30. Consider the following equation.

$$H_2(g) + Cl_2(g) \rightleftharpoons 2HCl(g)$$

    As the pressure increases at constant temperature, the mass of $H_2(g)$

    (1) decreases
    (2) increases
    (3) remains the same

31. Consider a reaction at STP and at equilibrium.

$$H_2(g) + Cl_2(g) \rightleftharpoons 2HCl(g)$$

Which change will result in an increase in the concentration of $Cl_2(g)$?

(1) decreasing the pressure on the system
(2) decreasing the concentration of HCl
(3) increasing the concentration of $H_2(g)$
(4) increasing the concentration of HCl

32. Consider the following equation.

$$N_2(g) + O_2(g) \rightleftharpoons 2NO(g)$$

As the concentration of $N_2(g)$ increases, the concentration of $O_2(g)$ will

(1) decrease
(2) increase
(3) remain the same

33. Consider the following equation.

$$2SO_2(g) + O_2(g) \rightleftharpoons 2SO_3(g) + heat$$

Which change will shift the equilibrium to the right?

(1) decreasing the concentration of $SO_2$
(2) decreasing the pressure
(3) increasing the concentration of $O_2$
(4) increasing the temperature

34. The addition of a catalyst to a system at equilibrium will increase the rate of

(1) the forward reaction only
(2) the reverse reaction only
(3) both the forward and reverse reactions
(4) neither the forward nor the reverse reaction

35. A system is said to be in a state of dynamic equilibrium when the

(1) concentration of products is greater than the concentration of reactants
(2) concentration of products is less than the concentration of reactants
(3) rate at which products are formed is greater than the rate at which reactants are formed
(4) rate at which products are formed is the same as the rate at which reactants are formed

## Entropy And Enthalpy

What are the factors that cause chemical and physical changes to occur? There are two fundamental tendencies in nature that help determine whether or not these changes will occur.

### Enthalpy

There is a tendency in nature to change to a state of lower energy (enthalpy). Exothermic reactions move toward a lower energy state because some of the energy contained in the reactants is released. The products have less potential energy than do the reactants.

A study of potential energy diagrams for reversible chemical reactions shows that the activation energy for the exothermic direction is less than that for the endothermic direction. Therefore, at any given temperature, the particles in a system are more likely to collide with enough energy to react in the exothermic direction than in the endothermic direction. On the basis of energy change alone, we expect reactions to go in the exothermic direction. This drive toward lower energy is also called a drive toward lower enthalpy.

### Entropy

There is a tendency in nature to change to a state of greater randomness or disorder, which refers to the lack of regularity in a system. **Entropy** is a measure of the disorder or randomness of a system. The greater the

Figure 8-9. Entropy: Entropy is a measure of disorder or randomness.

Low entropy → Entropy increases → Slightly higher entropy → Entropy increases → Still higher entropy

High entropy

Low entropy

disorder, the higher the entropy. Figure 8-9 illustrates the concept of increasing entropy as an originally ordered state becomes "messy" or more random.

It is usually necessary for particles to collide in a special way in order to form a more highly organized or regular arrangement. On the other hand, there are many ways in which they can collide to produce more disorder. Therefore, it is to be expected that systems will often go from conditions of greater order (lower entropy) to conditions of greater disorder (higher entropy). On the basis of entropy change alone, we expect reactions to go in the direction of greater entropy.

Examples of entropy change are physical changes from the solid, crystalline phase (great order, low entropy), to the liquid phase (more randomness, higher entropy), to the gaseous phase (maximum randomness, highest entropy). For chemical changes, compounds represent a state of greater order and lower entropy than the free elements of which they are composed.

To identify whether reactants or products have the greater amount of entropy consider:

1.  The solid phase has less entropy than the liquid phase, which has less entropy than the gaseous phase.
2.  Generally, the side of the equation with the greater number of molecules has the greater amount of entropy.

# Review Questions

**36.** Which change in a sample of water is accompanied by the greatest increase in entropy?

(1) $H_2O(\ell)$ at 100°C is changed to $H_2O(g)$ at 200°C
(2) $H_2O(g)$ at 100°C is changed to $H_2O(g)$ at 200°C
(3) $H_2O(s)$ at −100°C is changed to $H_2O(s)$ at 0°C
(4) $H_2O(s)$ at 0°C is changed to $H_2O(\ell)$ at 0°C

**37.** What occurs when a sample of $CO_2(s)$ changes to $CO_2(g)$?

(1) The gas has greater entropy and less order.
(2) The gas has greater entropy and more order.
(3) The gas has less entropy and less order.
(4) The gas has less entropy and more order.

**38.** The diagram below shows a system of gases with the valve closed.

Valve

As the valve is opened, the entropy of the gaseous system

(1) decreases
(2) increases
(3) remains the same

**39.** Which series of physical changes represents an entropy increase during each change?

(1) gas → liquid → solid
(2) liquid → gas → solid
(3) solid → gas → solid
(4) solid → liquid → gas

**40.** Which tendencies favor a spontaneous reaction?

(1) lower energy and decreasing entropy
(2)) lower energy and increasing entropy
(3) higher energy and decreasing entropy
(4) higher energy and increasing entropy

**41.** Consider the following equation.

$$H_2O(\ell) + heat \rightleftharpoons H_2O(g)$$

Which will occur if the temperature of the system is increased?

(1) The average kinetic energy of the system will decrease.
(2) The entropy of the system will increase.
(3) The number of moles of $H_2O(g)$ will decrease.
(4) The number of moles of $H_2O(\ell)$ will increase.

**42.** As NaCl(s) dissolves according to the equation $NaCl(s) \rightarrow Na^+(aq) + Cl_2(aq)$, the entropy of the system

(1) decreases
(2) increases
(3) remains the same

**43.** Which change results in an increase in entropy?

(1) $H_2O(g) \rightarrow H_2O(\ell)$
(2) $H_2O(s) \rightarrow H_2O(\ell)$
(3) $H_2O(\ell) \rightarrow H_2O(s)$
(4) $H_2O(g) \rightarrow H_2O(s)$

**44.** A reaction must be spontaneous if its occurrence is

(1) endothermic with an increase in entropy
(2) endothermic with a decrease in entropy
(3) exothermic with an increase in entropy
(4) exothermic with a decrease in entropy

## The Equilibrium Expression

The mathematical expression that shows the relationship of reactants and products in a system at equilibrium is called the <u>equilibrium expression.</u> It is a fraction with the concentrations of reactants and products expressed in moles per liter. Each concentration is then raised to the power of its coefficient in a balanced equation. This expression equals a value called the equilibrium constant ($K_{eq}$), which remains the same for a particular reaction at a specified temperature.

To write an equilibrium expression, follow these steps.

1. Write a balanced equation for the system.
2. Place the products as factors in the numerator of a fraction and the reactants as factors in the denominator.
3. Place a square bracket around each formula. The square bracket means *molar concentration*.
4. Write the coefficient of each substance as the power of its concentration. The resulting expression is the equilibrium expression, which should be set equal to the $K_{eq}$ for that reaction.

## SAMPLE PROBLEM

Write the equilibrium expression for the equilibrium system of nitrogen, hydrogen, and ammonia.

**SOLUTION:** Identify the known and unknown values.

*Known*
reactants = $N_2$, $H_2$
product = $NH_3$

*Unknown*
equilibrium expression = $K_{eq}$

**1.** Write a balanced equation for the reaction.

$$N_2(g) + 3H_2(g) \rightleftharpoons 2NH_3(g) + heat$$

**2.** Place the products as factors in the numerator of a fraction and the reactants as factors in the denominator.

$$\frac{NH_3}{H_2 \times N_2}$$

**3.** Place a square bracket around each formula to show the concentration of each.

$$\frac{[NH_3]}{[H_2][N_2]}$$

**4.** Write the coefficient of each substance as the power of its concentration. This is the equilibrium expression, labeled $K_{eq}$.

$$K_{eq} = \frac{[NH_3]^2}{[H_2]^3[N_2]}$$

The equilibrium constant is a specific numerical value for a given system at a specified temperature. Changes in concentrations will not cause a change in the value of $K_{eq}$, nor will the addition of a catalyst. Only a change in temperature will affect the value of $K_{eq}$.

When the value of $K_{eq}$ is large, the numerator is larger than the denominator, indicating that the products are present in larger concentration than the reactants. Chemists would simply say that the products are favored. If the value is small, the opposite is true, and the reactants are favored.

**Directions**

Review the Test-Taking Strategies section of this book. Then answer the following questions. Read each question carefully and answer with a correct choice or response.

## Part A

1  In order for a chemical reaction to occur, there must always be
 (1) an effective collision between reacting particles
 (2) a bond that breaks in a reactant particle
 (3) reacting particles with a high charge
 (4) reacting particles with high kinetic energy

2  As the number of effective collisions between reacting particles increases, the rate of reaction
 (1) decreases
 (2) increases
 (3) remains the same

3  Activation energy is required to initiate
 (1) exothermic reactions only
 (2) endothermic reactions only
 (3) both endothermic and exothermic reactions
 (4) neither endothermic nor exothermic reactions

4  In a chemical reaction, as the concentrations of the reacting particles increase, the rate of reactions generally
 (1) decreases
 (2) increases
 (3) remains the same
 (4) reaches equilibrium

5  Which conditions will increase the rate of a chemical reaction?
 (1) decreased temperature and decreased concentration of reactants
 (2) decreased temperature and increased concentration of reactants
 (3) increased temperature and decreased concentration of reactants
 (4) increased temperature and increased concentration of reactants

6  What will change when a catalyst is added to a chemical reaction?
 (1) activation energy
 (2) heat of reaction
 (3) potential energy of the reactants
 (4) potential energy of the products

7  The energy needed to start a chemical reaction is called
 (1) potential energy
 (2) kinetic energy
 (3) activation energy
 (4) ionization energy

**Use the potential energy diagram of a chemical reaction shown below to answer questions 8 and 9.**

8  Which arrow represents the part of the reaction most likely to be changed by the addition of a catalyst?
 (1) A    (3) C
 (2) B    (4) D

9  Which letter represents the activation energy for the reverse reaction?
 (1) A    (3) C
 (2) B    (4) D

**10** Adding a catalyst to a chemical reaction will
(1) lower the activation energy needed
(2) lower the potential energy of the reactants
(3) increase the activation energy
(4) increase the potential energy of the reactants

**11** Given the potential energy diagram below, which lettered interval represents the potential energy of the activated complex?

(1) A          (3) C
(2) B          (4) D

**12** The graph below is a potential energy diagram of a compound that is formed from its elements. Which interval represents the heat of reaction?

(1) A          (3) C
(2) B          (4) D

**13** For any chemical reaction at equilibrium, the rate of the forward reaction is
(1) less than the rate of the reverse
(2) greater than the rate of the reverse
(3) equal to the rate of the reverse
(4) unrelated to the rate of the reverse

**14** As the temperature of a system increases, the entropy of the system
(1) decreases
(2) increases
(3) remains the same

**15** Which potential energy diagram represents the reaction A + B → C + energy?

**16** Given the potential energy diagram below, what does interval B represent?

(1) potential energy of the reactants
(2) potential energy of the products
(3) activation energy
(4) activated complex

17 Solution equilibrium most likely exists in which type of solution?
(1) supersaturated
(2) unsaturated
(3) saturated
(4) dilute

# Part B

18 A student adds two 50-milligram pieces of Ca(s) to water. A reaction takes place according to the following equation.

$$Ca(s) + 2H_2O(\ell) \rightarrow Ca(OH)_2(aq) + H_2(g)$$

Which change could the student have made that would most likely have increased the rate of the reaction?
(1) used 10 10-mg pieces of Ca(s)
(2) used one 100-mg piece of Ca(s)
(3) decreased the amount of water
(4) decreased the temperature of the water

19 Under which conditions will the forward rate of a chemical reaction most often decrease?
(1) The concentration of the reactants decreases, and the temperature decreases.
(2) The concentration of the reactants decreases, and the temperature increases.
(3) The concentration of the reactants increases, and the temperature decreases.
(4) The concentration of the reactants increases, and the temperature increases.

20 The diagram below shows a bottle containing $NH_3(g)$ dissolved in water. How can the equilibrium $NH_3(g) \rightleftharpoons NH_3(aq)$ be reached?

(1) Add more water.
(2) Add more $NH_3$.
(3) Cool the contents.
(4) Stopper the bottle.

21 A 1-cm³ cube of sodium reacts more rapidly in water at 25°C than does a 1-cm³ cube of calcium at 25°C. This difference in rate of reaction is most closely associated with the different
(1) surface area of the metal cubes
(2) nature of the metals
(3) density of the metals
(4) concentration of the metals

22 At room temperature, which reaction would be expected to have the fastest reaction rate?
(1) $Pb^{2+}(aq) + S^{2-}(aq) \rightarrow PbS(s)$
(2) $2H_2(g) + O_2(g) \rightarrow 2H_2O(\ell)$
(3) $N_2(g) + 2O_2(g) \rightarrow 2NO_2(g)$
(4) $2KClO_3(s) \rightarrow 2KCl(s) + 3O_2(g)$

23 Consider the following equation.

$$A(s) + B(aq) \rightarrow C(aq) + D(s)$$

Which change would most likely increase the rate of this reaction?
(1) a decrease in pressure
(2) an increase in pressure
(3) a decrease in temperature
(4) an increase in temperature

24 The potential energy diagram shown below represents the reaction $A + B \rightarrow AB$.

Which statement correctly describes this reaction?
(1) It is endothermic and energy is absorbed.
(2) It is endothermic and energy is released.
(3) It is exothermic and energy is absorbed.
(4) It is exothermic and energy is released.

25 Consider the following equation.

$$AgBr(s) \rightleftharpoons Ag^+(aq) + Br^-(aq)$$

Which change occurs when KBr(s) is dissolved in the reaction mixture?
(1) The amount of AgBr(s) decreases.
(2) The amount of AgBr(s) remains the same.
(3) The concentration of $Ag^+(aq)$ decreases.
(4) The concentration of $Ag^+(aq)$ remains the same.

26 Consider the following equation.

$$C(s) + O_2(g) \rightleftharpoons CO_2(g) + \text{heat}$$

Which stress on the system will increase the concentration of $CO_2(g)$?
(1) increasing the temperature of the reaction
(2) increasing the concentration of $O_2(g)$
(3) decreasing the pressure on the reaction
(4) decreasing the amount of $C(s)$

27 Consider the following equation.

$$2SO_2(g) + O_2(g) \rightleftharpoons 2SO_3(g) + \text{heat}$$

The concentration of $SO_3(g)$ will be increased by
(1) decreasing the concentration of $SO_2(g)$
(2) decreasing the concentration of $O_2(g)$
(3) increasing the pressure
(4) increasing the temperature

28 Consider the following equilibrium at constant pressure.

$$2HBr(g) + 73 \text{ kJ} \rightleftharpoons H_2(g) + Br_2(g)$$

When the temperature is increased, the equilibrium is shifted to the
(1) right, and the concentration of $HBr(g)$ will decrease
(2) right, and the concentration of $HBr(g)$ will increase
(3) left, and the concentration of $HBr(g)$ will decrease
(4) left, and the concentration of $HBr(g)$ will increase

29 Consider the following change of phase.

$$CO_2(g) \rightarrow CO_2(s)$$

As $CO_2(g)$ changes to $CO_2(s)$, the entropy of the system
(1) decreases
(2) increases
(3) remains the same

30 Which reaction system tends to become less random as reactants form products?
(1) $C(s) + O_2(g) \rightarrow CO_2(g)$
(2) $S(s) + O_2(g) \rightarrow SO_2(g)$
(3) $I_2(s) + Cl_2(g) \rightarrow 2ICl(g)$
(4) $2Mg(s) + O_2(g) \rightarrow 2MgO(s)$

31 In which reaction will the point of equilibrium shift to the left when the pressure on the system is increased?
(1) $C(s) + O_2(g) \rightleftharpoons CO_2(g)$
(2) $CaCO_3(s) \rightleftharpoons CaO(s) + CO_2(g)$
(3) $2Mg(s) + O_2(g) \rightleftharpoons 2MgO(s)$
(4) $2H_2(g) + O_2(g) \rightleftharpoons 2H_2O(g)$

32 Consider the following equation.

$$A(g) + B(g) \rightleftharpoons C(g) + D(g)$$

Which relationship is an indication that this reaction has reached equilibrium?
(1) The concentration of A equals the concentration of B.
(2) The concentration of C equals the concentration of D.
(3) The concentrations of A, B, C, and D are constant.
(4) The concentrations of A, B, C, and D are equal.

33 Consider the following equation.

$$N_2(g) + O_2(g) \rightleftharpoons 2NO(g)$$

If the temperature remains constant and the pressure increases, the number of moles of $NO(g)$ will
(1) decrease
(2) increase
(3) remain the same

34 Which two fundamental tendencies favor a chemical reaction occurring spontaneously?
(1) toward higher energy and less randomness
(2) toward higher energy and greater randomness
(3) toward lower energy and less randomness
(4) toward lower energy and greater randomness

## Part C

The equation for the saturated solution equilibrium of potassium nitrate ($KNO_3$) is shown below.

$$KNO_3(s) + energy \rightleftharpoons K^+(aq) + NO_3^-(aq)$$

35 Diagram the products, using the key provided. Indicate the exact arrangement of the particles you diagram. [2]

36 In the equation shown above, compare the rate of dissolving $KNO_3$ with the rate of recrystallization of $KNO_3$ for the saturated solution. [1]

**Base your answers to questions 37 and 38 on the following information: When cola, a type of soda pop, is manufactured, $CO_2(g)$ is dissolved in it.**

37 A capped bottle of cola contains $CO_2(g)$ under high pressure. When the cap is removed, how does pressure affect the solubility of the dissolved $CO_2(g)$? [1]

38 A glass of cold cola is left to stand at room temperature for 5 minutes. How does temperature affect the solubility of the $CO_2(g)$? [1]

39 Explain how a catalyst may increase the rate of a chemical reaction. [1]

40 On the set of axes provided, sketch the potential energy diagram for an endothermic reaction that shows the activation energy and the potential energy of the reactants and the potential energy of the products. [1]

41 Human blood contains dissolved carbonic acid in equilibrium with carbon dioxide and water according to the equilibrium system:

$$H_2CO_3(aq) \rightleftharpoons CO_2(aq) + H_2O(l)$$

Explain, using Le Chatelier's principle, why decreasing the concentration of $CO_2$ decreases the concentration of $H_2CO_3$. [1]

**Base your answers to questions 42 and 43 on the equilibrium system:**
$$2SO_2(g) + O_2(g) \rightleftharpoons 2SO_3(g) + \text{energy}$$

42 Explain, in terms of Le Chatelier's principle, why the concentration of $SO_2(g)$ increases when the temperature is increased. [1]

43 Explain, in terms of collisions between molecules, why increasing the concentration of $O_2(g)$ produces a decrease in the concentration of $SO_2(g)$. [1]

44 Explain, in terms of collision theory, why an increase in temperature increases the rate of a chemical reaction.

45 A potential energy diagram is shown below. For each of the measures of energy described in parts a–e below, draw an arrow on the diagram. Label each arrow with the correct letter. Then answer question f.
   a. activation energy for the forward reaction [1]
   b. potential energy of the reactants [1]
   c. potential energy of the products [1]
   d. activation energy for the reverse reaction [1]
   e. heat of reaction [1]
   f. Is the reaction endothermic or exothermic? [2] Explain your answer.

46 Consider the following equation.

$$N_2(g) + 3H_2(g) \rightleftharpoons 2NH_3(g) + \text{heat}$$

Propose changes in concentration, pressure and temperature that would increase the production of $NH_3$. [3]

# Oxidation–Reduction

## How Scientists Study Oxidation–Reduction

**?** **Will we all drive electric cars in the future?** **?**

It's a re-volt-olution!! After 100 years of using the internal combustion engine to run our cars and trucks, a new era is emerging—the age of the electric car.

Today, we see hybrid cars that make use of both combustion engines and batteries to power vehicles. A large car company is introducing an all-electric car. A smaller car company is already delivering an electric car. The future will see more and more cars using electric motors powered by batteries.

In this topic you will learn the essentials of changing chemical energy into electrical energy.

# 9 Oxidation–Reduction

## Vocabulary

| | | |
|---|---|---|
| anode | electrolytic cell | redox |
| cathode | half-reaction | reduction |
| electrochemical cell | oxidation | salt bridge |
| electrode | oxidation number (state) | voltaic cell |
| electrolysis | | |

## Topic Overview

Oxidation and reduction are important chemical reactions. They work both for our benefit, in forms such as batteries, and against us, in ways such as the corrosion of important metals. Originally, the term *oxidation* meant the combination of a substance with oxygen. *Reduction* was the opposite, the loss of oxygen. Today, both terms have a wider interpretation. They are also recognized as interdependent—one cannot occur without the other.

## Oxidation and Reduction

When magnesium is burned in oxygen, the octet rule allows us to understand the transfer of electrons. Each magnesium atom loses two electrons as each oxygen atom gains two electrons. Both atoms acquire a stable octet, as shown in Figure 9-1.

$$Mg: + \cdot \ddot{O}: \longrightarrow Mg^{2+} + \left[ :\ddot{O}: \right]^{2-}$$

$$Mg + \tfrac{1}{2}O_2 \longrightarrow MgO$$

**Figure 9-1. Chemical reaction between magnesium and oxygen:** In the reaction between magnesium and oxygen, a magnesium atom transfers two electrons to an oxygen atom.

The same electron transfer occurs as magnesium reacts with chlorine, as shown in Figure 9-2. Again the magnesium atom loses two electrons, while the two chlorine atoms each accept an electron, acquiring a stable octet.

In both of the equations, while the magnesium atom was losing electrons, other atoms were gaining them. **Oxidation** is defined as the loss of electrons by an atom or ion. **Reduction** is the gain of electrons by an atom or ion.

**Redox** Whenever one atom loses an electron, there must be another atom available to gain the electron. Neither reduction nor oxidation can ever occur alone. Whenever one occurs, the other must occur at the same time. Because these reactions must accompany each other, the two terms are often combined, and reactions in which both reduction and oxidation occur are called **redox** reactions.

$$Mg: + \begin{matrix} \cdot \ddot{C}l: \\ \cdot \ddot{C}l: \end{matrix} \longrightarrow Mg^{2+} + 2\left[ :\ddot{C}l: \right]^{-}$$

$$Mg + Cl_2 \longrightarrow MgCl_2$$

**Figure 9-2. Chemical reaction between magnesium and chlorine:** In the reaction between magnesium and chlorine, a magnesium atom transfers one electron to each of two chlorine atoms.

## Oxidation Numbers

It is not always possible to simply read an equation and determine whether atoms have exchanged electrons. However, chemists have devised a system that makes it easy to keep track of the number of electrons lost or gained by an atom in a reaction. Positive, negative, or neutral values known as **oxidation numbers (states)** can be assigned to atoms. Changes in oxidation states identify how many electrons are either gained or lost by an atom or ion. The use of these oxidation numbers also provides a more complete way to define oxidation and reduction.

- Oxidation is defined as the loss of electrons and a gain in oxidation number.
- Reduction is defined as the gain of electrons and a loss in oxidation number.

Oxidation numbers are used to identify the path of electrons in redox reactions. A simple device may help in remembering the definitions.

> **LEO** says **GER**
> **LEO** = **L**oss of **E**lectrons is **O**xidation
> **GER** = **G**ain of **E**lectrons is **R**eduction

Oxidation numbers are written differently than ionic charges. The charge on the magnesium ion is 2+, while the oxidation number is written as +2. The periodic table in the *Reference Tables for Physical Setting/Chemistry* Ⓡ supplies some common oxidation numbers for elements in compounds.

It is important to learn the rules for assigning oxidation states to atoms in an equation. These numbers are used to identify what has been oxidized and what has been reduced. Here are some rules for assigning oxidation numbers.

1. Every uncombined element has an oxidation number of zero. In the chemical equation $2Na + Cl_2 \rightarrow 2NaCl$, both the uncombined Na and $Cl_2$ have oxidation numbers of 0.

2. Monatomic ions have an oxidation number equal to the ionic charge. In the equation $2Na + Cl_2 \rightarrow 2NaCl$, the sodium in the product NaCl has a charge of 1+ and an oxidation number of +1. The chlorine in NaCl has a charge of 1− and an oxidation number of −1.

3. The metals of Group 1 always have an oxidation number of +1 in compounds, and the metals of Group 2 always have an oxidation number of +2 in compounds.

4. Fluorine is always −1 in compounds. The other halogens are also −1 when they are the most electronegative element in the compound.

5. Hydrogen is +1 in compounds unless it is combined with a metal, in which case it is −1. Hydrogen is +1 in HCl but −1 in LiH.

6. Oxygen is usually −2 in compounds. When it is combined with fluorine, which is more electronegative, it is +2. Oxygen is −2 in $H_2O$, and +2 in $OF_2$. In the peroxide ion ($O_2^{2-}$), oxygen is −1.

   These six rules can be used to assign oxidation numbers to many atoms in equations. They can be used with the following two additional rules to calculate oxidation numbers for other elements in compounds or polyatomic ions.

7. The sum of the oxidation numbers in all compounds must be zero.

8. The sum of the oxidation numbers in polyatomic ions must be equal to the charge on the ion.

## SAMPLE PROBLEM

What are the oxidation numbers of the atoms in $HNO_3$?

**SOLUTION:** Identify the known and unknown values.

*Known*
formula $HNO_3$

*Unknown*
oxidation number of H = ?
oxidation number of N = ?
oxidation number of O = ?

Use as many of the first six rules as possible.

Hydrogen has an oxidation number of +1 (Rule 5). Each oxygen atom has an oxidation number of −2 (Rule 6), making the total for three oxygen atoms −6.

The sum of all oxidation numbers is zero.

oxidation number of N + (+1) + (−6) = 0
$$\text{oxidation number of N} = +5$$

The oxidation number for H is +1; for N, +5; and for O, −2.

## SAMPLE PROBLEM

What is the oxidation number of chromium in the dichromate ion ($Cr_2O_7^{2-}$)?

**SOLUTION:** Identify the known and unknown values.

*Known*
formula $Cr_2O_7^{2-}$

*Unknown*
oxidation number of Cr = ?

Use as many of the first six rules as possible. O has an oxidation number of −2, producing a total of −14 for the seven O atoms.

The sum of the atoms in a polyatomic ion must equal the charge on the ion.

$$2(\text{oxidation number of Cr}) + (-14) = -2$$

$$\text{oxidation number of Cr} = \frac{+12}{2}$$

$$\text{oxidation number of Cr} = +6$$

# Review Questions

1. What is the sum of the oxidation numbers in the compound $CO_2$?

   (1) 0    (2) −2    (3) −4    (4) +4

2. The oxidation number of nitrogen in $N_2$ is

   (1) +1    (2) 0    (3) +3    (4) −3

3. What is the oxidation number of Pt in $K_2PtCl_6$?

   (1) −2    (2) +2    (3) −4    (4) +4

4. In which substance does phosphorus have a +3 oxidation state?

   (1) $P_4O_{10}$    (3) $Ca_3(PO_4)_2$
   (2) $PCl_5$    (4) $KH_2PO_3$

5. What is the oxidation number of sulfur in $H_2SO_4$?

   (1) 0    (2) −2    (3) +6    (4) +4

**6.** In which substance does sulfur have a negative oxidation number?

(1) $Na_2S$  (2) $CaSO_4$  (3) $S$  (4) $SO_2$

**7.** In which compound is the oxidation number of oxygen $-1$?

(1) $CO$  (2) $CO_2$  (3) $H_2O$  (4) $H_2O_2$

**8.** Oxygen has an oxidation number of $-2$ in

(1) $O_2$  (2) $NO_2$  (3) $Na_2O_2$  (4) $OF_2$

**9.** Oxygen will have a positive oxidation number when combined with

(1) fluorine  (3) bromine
(2) chlorine  (4) iodine

**10.** In which compound does hydrogen have an oxidation number of $-1$?

(1) $NH_3$  (3) $HCl$
(2) $KH$  (4) $H_2O$

# Examining Redox Reactions

Sometimes it's important to know whether a reaction is redox or not. Once it has been determined that a reaction is redox, it is important to know what is oxidized, what is reduced, and what brings about oxidation and reduction.

## Recognizing Redox Reactions

Not all reactions are redox reactions. To determine whether or not a reaction is redox, assign oxidation numbers to each atom, both on the reactant and product side. If there is a change in oxidation number for a particular type of atom, the reaction is redox.

Sometimes it is easy to spot a redox reaction. If an uncombined element appears on one side of an equation and is in a compound on the other side, the reaction must be a redox reaction. If you recognize a reaction as a double replacement reaction, it is not redox.

For example:

Redox: $Zn + HCl \rightarrow ZnCl_2 + H_2$

Not Redox: $NaCl + AgNO_3 \Rightarrow AgCl + NaNO_3$

## Identifying Oxidation and Reduction

Once oxidation numbers are assigned, the atom that has shown an increase can be identified as the one that has undergone oxidation. The atom that has a decrease in oxidation number has undergone reduction.

Consider the following reaction.

$$MnO_2 + 4HCl \rightarrow MnCl_2 + Cl_2 + 2H_2O$$

In the equation, chlorine has an oxidation number of $-1$ as a reactant in HCl. On the product side, some chlorine ions are still $-1$, but others have an oxidation state of $0$ in $Cl_2$. Because the chloride ion ($Cl^-$) changes from a lower oxidation number to a higher one, it has been oxidized. Manganese changes from $+4$ as a reactant to $+2$ as a product. Because it changed from a higher oxidation number to a lower one, $Mn^{4+}$ has undergone reduction.

## Oxidizing Agents and Reducing Agents

In the previous reaction, $Mn^{+4}$ underwent reduction, having received electrons from the $Cl^-$. The $Cl^-$ caused the reduction of the $Mn^{+4}$ and is called the reducing agent. By accepting electrons from $Cl^-$, the $Mn^{+4}$

caused the $Cl^-$ to be oxidized. The $Mn^{+4}$ is the <u>oxidizing agent.</u>
In summary,

- the substance oxidized is the reducing agent.
- the substance reduced is the oxidizing agent.

# Review Questions

11. Which equation represents an oxidation-reduction reaction?

(1) $HCl + KOH \rightarrow KCl + H_2O$
(2) $4HCl + MnO_2 \rightarrow MnCl_2 + 2H_2O + Cl_2$
(3) $2HCl + CaCO_3 \rightarrow CaCl_2 + H_2O + CO_2$
(4) $2HCl + FeS \rightarrow FeCl_2 + H_2S$

12. Which equation represents an oxidation-reduction reaction?

(1) $Zn + 2HCl \rightarrow ZnCl_2 + H2$
(2) $Zn(OH)_2 + 2HCl \rightarrow ZnCl_2 + 2H_2O$
(3) $H_2O + NH_3 \rightarrow NH^{4+} + OH^-$
(4) $H_2O + H_2O \rightarrow H_3O^+ + OH^-$

13. Which equation represents an oxidation-reduction reaction?

(1) $HCl + KOH \rightarrow KCl + H_2O$
(2) $4HCl + MnO_2 \rightarrow MnCl_2 + 2H_2O + Cl_2$
(3) $2HCl + CaCO_3 \rightarrow CaCl_2 + H_2O + CO_2$
(4) $2HCl + FeS \rightarrow FeCl_2 + H_2S$

14. Oxidation-reduction reactions occur because of the competition between particles for

(1) neutrons        (3) protons
(2) electrons       (4) positrons

15. Which statement correctly describes a redox reaction?

(1) Oxidation and reduction occur simultaneously.
(2) Oxidation occurs before reduction.
(3) Oxidation occurs after reduction.
(4) Oxidation occurs, but reduction does not.

16. A redox reaction is a reaction in which

(1) only reduction occurs
(2) only oxidation occurs
(3) reduction and oxidation occur at the same time
(4) reduction occurs first and then oxidation occurs

17. All redox reaction involve

(1) the gain of electrons only
(2) the loss of electrons only
(3) both the gain and the loss of electrons
(4) neither the gain nor the loss of electrons

18. Consider the following equation.

$$Zn(s) + Cu^{2+}(aq) \rightarrow Zn^{2+}(aq) + Cu(s)$$

Which particles must be transferred from one reactant to the other reactant?

(1) ions
(2) neutrons
(3) protons
(4) electrons

19. What occurs during the reaction below?

$$4HCl + MnO_2 \rightarrow MnCl_2 + 2H_2O + Cl_2$$

(1) The manganese is reduced and its oxidation number changes from +4 to +2.
(2) The manganese is oxidized and its oxidation number changes from +4 to +2.
(3) The manganese is reduced and its oxidation number changes from +2 to +4.
(4) The manganese is oxidized and its oxidation number changes from +2 to +4.

20. What occurs when an atom is oxidized in a chemical reaction?

(1) a loss of electrons and a decrease in oxidation number
(2) a loss of electrons and an increase in oxidation number
(3) a gain of electrons and a decrease in oxidation number
(4) a gain of electrons and an increase in oxidation number

21. When a substance is oxidized, it

(1) loses protons
(2) gains protons
(3) acts as an oxidizing agent
(4) acts as a reducing agent

22. Consider the following redox reaction.

$$Co(s) + PbCl_2(aq) \rightarrow CoCl_2(aq) + Pb(s)$$

Which statement correctly describes the oxidation and reduction that occur?

(1) $Co(s)$ is oxidized and $Cl^-(aq)$ is reduced.
(2) $Co(s)$ is oxidized and $Pb^{2+}(aq)$ is reduced.
(3) $Co(s)$ is reduced and $Cl^-(aq)$ is oxidized.
(4) $Co(s)$ is oxidized and $Pb^{2+}(aq)$ is oxidized.

**23.** Consider the following equation.

$$MnO_2(s) + 4H^+(aq) + 2Fe^{2+}(aq) \rightarrow Mn^{2+}(aq) + 2Fe^{3+}(aq) + 2H_2O(\ell)$$

Which species is oxidized?

(1) $H^+(aq)$
(2) $H_2O(\ell)$
(3) $Fe^{2+}(aq)$
(4) $MnO_2(s)$

**24.** Consider the following equation.

$$Zn(s) + 2HCl(aq) \rightarrow ZnCl_2(aq) + H_2(g)$$

Which substance is oxidized?

(1) $Zn(s)$
(2) $HCl(aq)$
(3) $Cl^-(aq)$
(4) $H^+(aq)$

**25.** Consider the following redox reaction.

$$Ni + Sn^{4+} \rightarrow Ni^{2+} + Sn^{2+}$$

Which species has been reduced?

(1) $Ni$
(2) $Sn^{4+}$
(3) $Ni^{2+}$
(4) $Sn^{2+}$

**26.** Consider the following equation.

$$2Fe^{3+} + Sn^{2+} \rightarrow 2Fe^{2+} + Sn^{4+}$$

Which species is the oxidizing agent?

(1) $Fe^{3+}$
(2) $Sn^{2+}$
(3) $Fe^{2+}$
(4) $Sn^{4+}$

**27.** Consider the following equation.

$$Pb^0(s) + Cu^{2+}(aq) \rightarrow Pb^{2+}(aq) + Cu^0(s)$$

What is the reducing agent?

(1) $Pb^{2+}(aq)$
(2) $Cu^{2+}(aq)$
(3) $Pb^0(s)$
(4) $Cu^0(s)$

**28.** Consider the following equation.

$$Mg(s) + CuSO_4(aq) \rightarrow MgSO_4(aq) + Cu(s)$$

Which species acts as the oxidizing agent?

(1) $Cu(s)$
(2) $Cu^{2+}(aq)$
(3) $Mg(s)$
(4) $Mg^{2+}(aq)$

**29.** In the reaction $2H_2S + 3O_2 \rightarrow 2SO_2 + 2H_2O$, the oxidizing agent is

(1) oxygen
(2) water
(3) sulfur dioxide
(4) hydrogen sulfide

**30.** In the reaction $Cu + 2Ag^+ \rightarrow Cu^{2+} + 2Ag$, the oxidizing agent is

(1) $Cu$
(2) $Cu^{2+}$
(3) $Ag^+$
(4) $Ag$

**31.** In a redox reaction, the reducing agent will

(1) lose electrons and be reduced
(2) lose electrons and be oxidized
(3) gain electrons and be reduced
(4) gain electrons and be oxidized

# Half-Reactions

Chemical equations show the formulas of reactants and products, but they do not show the exchange of electrons. A **half-reaction** shows either the oxidation or reduction portion of a redox reaction, including the electrons gained or lost.

A reduction half-reaction shows an atom or ion gaining one or more electrons while its oxidation number decreases.

$$Fe^{3+}(aq) + 3e^- \rightarrow Fe(s)$$

An oxidation half-reaction shows an atom or an ion losing one or more electrons while its oxidation number increases.

$$Fe(s) \rightarrow Fe^{3+}(aq) + 3e^-$$

Like other chemical equations, half-reactions follow the law of conservation of matter; that is, there must be the same number of atoms on both sides of the arrow. Generally, in a half reaction there will only be one type of atom or ion shown on both reactant and product side of the equation.

In addition to conservation of mass, there must also be a conservation of charge. In molecular equations, because no charges are shown, the net charge is zero on both reactant and product side. In half-reactions, the net charge must be the same on both sides of the equation, but it does not necessarily equal zero.

$$Fe^{3+}(aq) + 3e^- \rightarrow Fe(s) \qquad \text{Net charge/side} = 0$$
$$Fe(s) \rightarrow Fe^{3+}(aq) + 3e^- \qquad \text{Net charge/side} = 0$$
$$Sn^{4+}(aq) + 2e^- \rightarrow Sn^{2+}(aq) \qquad \text{Net charge/side} = 2+$$
$$Sn^{2+}(aq) \rightarrow Sn^{4+}(aq) + 2e^- \qquad \text{Net charge/side} = 2+$$

To write a half-reaction from an equation, first assign an oxidation number to each element.

$$\overset{0}{Cu} + \overset{+1 \ +5 \ -2}{AgNO_3} \rightarrow \overset{+2 +5 \ -2}{Cu(NO_3)_2} + \overset{0}{Ag}$$

Then write a partial half-reaction to show the change in oxidation state.

$$\text{Oxidation: } Cu \rightarrow Cu^{2+}$$
$$\text{Reduction: } Ag^+ \rightarrow Ag$$

Then show the number of electrons needed to explain how the oxidation number changed, and to achieve a conservation of charge. Check to see that the net charge is the same on both sides of these equations.

$$\text{Oxidation: } Cu \rightarrow Cu^{2+} + 2e^- \qquad \text{Net charge/side} = 0$$
$$\text{Reduction: } Ag^+ + e^- \rightarrow Ag \qquad \text{Net charge/side} = 0$$

In all redox reactions, there must be a balance between the number of electrons lost and gained. In the previous example,

$$\text{Oxidation: } Cu \rightarrow Cu^{2+} + 2e^-$$
$$\text{Reduction: } Ag^+ + e^- \rightarrow Ag$$

balance can be achieved by multiplying the reduction equation by two. Thus, there are two electrons lost and two electrons gained. $2Ag^+ + 2e^- \rightarrow 2Ag$. Since the number of electrons lost and gained are equal, we can cancel them and add the two half-reactions:

$$Cu \rightarrow Cu^{2+} + 2e^-$$
$$2\,Ag^+ + 2e^- \rightarrow 2Ag$$
$$2Ag^+ + Cu \rightarrow Cu^{2+} + 2Ag$$

Redox equations can be balanced by first balancing the number of electrons lost and gained. After balancing the redox portion of the equation, the remainder can be balanced by inspection.

# Review Questions

**32.** Which half-reaction correctly represents reduction?

(1) $Fe^{2+} + 2e^- \rightarrow Fe$    (3) $Fe + 2e^- \rightarrow Fe^{2+}$
(2) $Fe^{2+} + e^- \rightarrow Fe^{3+}$    (4) $Fe + e^- \rightarrow Fe^{3+}$

**33.** Consider the following oxidation reduction equation.

$$Hg^{2+} + 2I^- \rightarrow Hg + I_2$$

Which equation correctly represents the half-reaction for the oxidation that occurs?

(1) $Hg^{2+} \rightarrow Hg + 2e^-$    (3) $2I^- \rightarrow I_2 + 2e^-$
(2) $Hg^{2+} + 2e^- \rightarrow Hg$    (4) $2I^- + 2e^- \rightarrow I_2$

**34.** Which statement describes what occurs in the following redox reaction?

$$Cu(s) + 2Ag^+(aq) \rightarrow Cu^{2+}(aq) + 2Ag(s)$$

(1) Only mass is conserved.
(2) Only charge is conserved.
(3) Both mass and charge are conserved.
(4) Neither mass nor charge is conserved.

**35.** Which equation is correctly balanced?

    (1) $Fe^{3+} + 2Ni \rightarrow Fe^{2+} + 2Ni^{2+}$

    (2) $2Fe^{3+} + Ni \rightarrow 2Fe^{2+} + Ni^{2+}$

    (3) $Fe^{3+} + Ni \rightarrow Fe^{2+} + Ni^{2+}$

    (4) $2Fe^{2+} + 2Ni \rightarrow 2Fe^{2+} + 2Ni^{2+}$

**36.** Which equation is correctly balanced?

    (1) $Cr^{3+} + Mg \rightarrow Cr + Mg^{2+}$

    (2) $Al^{3+} + K \rightarrow Al + K^{+}$

    (3) $Sn^{4+} + H_2 \rightarrow Sn + 2H^{+}$

    (4) $Br_2 + Hg \rightarrow Hg^{2+} + 2Br^{-}$

---

# Electrochemical Cells

In redox reactions there is a chemical reaction and an exchange of electrons between the particles being oxidized and reduced. One practical use of such a reaction is in an electrochemical cell. An **electrochemical cell** involves a chemical reaction and a flow of electrons.

There are two common types of electrochemical cells. A **voltaic cell** is an electrochemical cell in which a spontaneous chemical reaction produces a flow of electrons. An **electrolytic cell** requires an electric current to force a nonspontaneous chemical reaction to occur.

Electrochemical cells have two surfaces called electrodes that can conduct electricity. An **electrode** is the site at which oxidation or reduction occurs. The electrode at which oxidation occurs is called the **anode**. The electrode at which reduction occurs is called the **cathode.**

## Spontaneous Reactions—Voltaic Cells

If a strip of zinc is placed into a solution of lead nitrate, the zinc will be oxidized and the copper ions will be reduced according to the following equation.

$$Zn(s) + Cu^{2+}(aq) \rightarrow Cu(s) + Zn^{2+}(aq)$$

The exchange of electrons takes place on the surface of the zinc, as shown by equations for the two half-reactions.

$$Zn(s) \rightarrow Zn^{2+}(aq) + 2e^{-}$$
$$Cu^{2+}(aq) + 2e^{-} \rightarrow Cu(s)$$

It is also possible to have these materials separated into two containers, so the electrons travel through a wire connecting them. In a voltaic cell, a **salt bridge** connects the two containers and provides a path for a flow of ions between the two beakers. This makes a complete circuit and allows the reaction to proceed. The diagram in Figure 9-3 shows a voltaic cell. In a voltaic cell, chemical energy is spontaneously converted to electrical energy.

In such a voltaic cell, when a strip of zinc metal is located in one beaker and copper ions are in solution in another beaker, the reaction can occur as if the solutions were in the same beaker. An electrical current is produced by separating the solutions into two beakers and forcing electrons to flow through the wire to complete the circuit.

When electrons are lost during oxidation at the anode, they travel through the wire to the cathode. At this electrode, the material being reduced gains

**Memory Jogger**

A metal will react with the ion of another metal found below it on the table. For example, zinc metal will react with lead nitrate, but not with aluminum nitrate.

$Zn + Pb(NO_3)_2 \rightarrow Pb + Zn(NO_3)_2$

$Zn + Al(NO_3)_3 \rightarrow$ no reaction

$Zn(s) \rightarrow Zn^{2+}(aq) + 2e^{-}$      $Cu^{2+}(aq) + 2e^{-} \rightarrow Cu(s)$

**Figure 9-3. A typical voltaic cell**

electrons. As with all redox reactions, the substance being oxidized loses electrons, and the substance being reduced gains them. The number of electrons lost must be equal to the number of electrons gained.

(R) The Activity series in *Reference Tables for Physical Setting/Chemistry* can be used to identify the anode and cathode in a voltaic cell. Identify the two metals shown in the cell, and locate them on the table. The metal that is higher on the chart will be oxidized, and is thus the anode. The lower metal is the site of reduction and will be the cathode. Notice that the cathode itself is not reduced; it is the place where the reduction occurs. Ions in solution are reduced. To help you identify the anode and cathode, remember **RED CAT** and **AN OX**.

**RED**uction occurs at the **CAT**hode.
**AN**ode is the site of **OX**idation.

## SAMPLE PROBLEM

Consider the following equation.

$$Zn^0(s) + Pb^{2+}(aq) \rightarrow Zn^{2+}(aq) + Pb^0(s)$$

Identify the anode and the cathode, and give the direction of electron flow.

**SOLUTION:** Identify the known and unknown values.

| *Known* | *Unknown* |
|---|---|
| reaction equation | anode = ? |
| Data in Table J | cathode = ? |
| | direction of electron flow |

Locate zinc and lead on Table J. Zinc is higher on the table. Thus, it is more reactive. Zinc will undergo oxidation and is the anode. The $Pb^{2+}$ ions are not the cathode, but they will be reduced at the cathode. If the cell has a strip of lead metal in the beaker with the $Pb^{2+}$ ions, the lead metal will be the cathode.

The zinc is oxidized and is losing electrons. The electrons will flow from the zinc to the lead, which is from anode to cathode. Electrons always flow from the anode to the cathode.

### Table 9-1. Reduction Potentials

| Ion/Metal | $E^0$ (Volts) |
|---|---|
| $Li^+/Li$ | −3.04 |
| $Rb^+/Rb$ | −2.98 |
| $K^+/K$ | −2.93 |
| $Cs^+/Cs$ | −2.92 |
| $Ba^{2+}/Ba$ | −2.91 |
| $Sr^{2+}/Sr$ | −2.89 |
| $Ca^{2+}/Ca$ | −2.87 |
| $Na^+/Na$ | −2.71 |
| $Mg^{2+}/Mg$ | −2.37 |
| $Al^{3+}/Al$ | −1.66 |
| $Mn^{2+}/Mn$ | −1.19 |
| $Zn^{2+}/Zn$ | −0.76 |
| $Cr^{3+}/Cr$ | −0.74 |
| $Co^{2+}/Co$ | −0.28 |
| $Ni^{2+}/Ni$ | −0.26 |
| $Pb^{2+}/Pb$ | −0.13 |
| $H^+/H_2$ | 0.00 |
| $Cu^{2+}/Cu$ | +0.34 |
| $Ag^+/Ag$ | +0.80 |
| $Au^{3+}/Au$ | +1.50 |

When a voltaic cell begins to react, the electrons flow from the anode to the cathode. A voltmeter placed in the circuit measures the electric potential between the metals in the electrodes in units of volts. Table 9-1 shows a series of reduction pairs as ions are reduced to the atomic state. The voltage for each pair is the voltage obtained when the given pair is compared to the standard hydrogen cell, which is assigned a value of 0.00 V.

The reductions at the top of the table are the least likely to occur. The more positive the $E^0$ value, the more likely the reduction. Thus, when $Zn^{2+}/Zn$ and $Cu^{2+}/Cu$ are in a voltaic cell, the reduction of $Cu^{2+}$ to Cu will occur, while the oxidation of Zn to $Zn^{2+}$ will supply the electrons. The voltage between the two can be calculated using the following relationship.

$$E^0_{cell} = E^0_{reduction} - E^0_{oxidation}$$
$$= E^0_{Cu^{2+}} - E^0_{Zn^{2+}}$$
$$= +0.34V - (-0.76V)$$
$$= +1.10V$$

## Nonspontaneous Reactions—Electrolytic Cells

In a voltaic cell, the electrons flow spontaneously from the anode to the cathode. In the example given, electrons from the oxidation of zinc travel through the wire to reduce lead ions. Can the reverse take place? Can the electrons travel from the lead to the zinc causing the lead metal to be oxidized and the zinc ions to be reduced? The answer is yes, but the reaction cannot occur spontaneously. There must be some electrical generator placed into the circuit to force the electrons to flow from the anode to the cathode. When electricity is used to force a chemical reaction to occur, the process is called **electrolysis.** In an automobile, both spontaneous and nonspontaneous redox reactions occur. When the car is started, a spontaneous chemical reaction occurs in the battery, providing electricity to start the car. Once the car has been started, the alternator, in a nonspontaneous reaction, recharges the battery.

Electrolysis can be used to obtain active elements such as sodium and chlorine by the electrolysis of fused (molten) salts.

$$2NaCl(\ell) \rightarrow 2Na(s) + Cl_2(g)$$

Electrolysis can also be used to electroplate metals onto a surface. The material to be plated with a metal is the cathode. The anode is made of the metal used for the plating. The electrolyte contains ions of the desired metal. Figure 9-4 shows the diagram of an apparatus used to plate silver. The anode is itself a piece of silver. As silver ions are produced by oxidation, they travel through the solution to the cathode. At the cathode, they are reduced back to silver atoms and adhere to the metal being plated.

Notice that the positive silver ions migrate away from the anode. Because like charges repel, the anode is positive in an electrolytic cell. The positive silver ions migrate through the solution toward the cathode, which must have a negative charge. The external power source forces the electrons in the wire to travel from the anode to the cathode.

Although there are distinct differences in voltaic and electrolytic cells, they also have several things in common.

- Both use redox reactions.
- The anode is the site of oxidation.
- The cathode is the site of reduction.
- The electrons flow through the wire from anode to cathode.

**Figure 9-4. An electroplating apparatus**

Differences between voltaic and electrolytic cells include the following.

- The redox reaction in a voltaic cell is spontaneous, but it is nonspontaneous in an electrolytic cell.
- In a voltaic cell the anode is negative and the cathode is positive. In an electrolytic cell, the anode is positive and the cathode is negative.

# Review Questions

**37.** The type of reaction in a voltaic cell is best described as

(1) spontaneous oxidation reaction only
(2) nonspontaneous oxidation reaction only
(3) spontaneous oxidation-reduction reaction
(4) nonspontaneous oxidation-reduction reaction

**38.** An electrochemical cell is made up of two half-cells connected by a salt bridge and an external conductor. What is the function of the salt bridge?

(1) to permit the migration of ions
(2) to prevent the migration of ions
(3) to permit the mixing of solutions
(4) to prevent the flow of electrons

**39.** Compared to the total mass and total charge at the beginning of a redox reaction, the total mass and total charge upon completion of the reaction is

(1) less
(2) greater
(3) the same
(4) dependent on what the reaction is

**40.** The diagram below shows an electrochemical cell.

When the switch is closed, which series of letters shows the path and direction of electron flow?

(1) ABC    (2) CBA    (3) DEF    (4) FED

**41.** Consider the following equation.

$$2H_2O + electricity \rightarrow 2H_2 + O_2$$

In which type of cell would this reaction most likely occur?

(1) a voltaic cell, because it releases energy
(2) an electrolytic cell, because it releases energy
(3) a voltaic cell, because it absorbs energy
(4) an electrolytic cell, because it absorbs energy

**42.** In an electrolytic cell, which ion would migrate through the solution to the positive electrode?

(1) a hydrogen ion
(2) a chloride ion
(3) an ammonium ion
(4) a hydronium ion

**43.** The overall reaction in a chemical cell is
$$Zn(s) + Cu^{2+}(aq) \rightarrow Zn^{2+}(aq) + Cu(s)$$
As the reaction takes place the

(1) mass of the Zn(s) electrode decreases
(2) mass of the Cu(s) electrode decreases
(3) $Cu^{2+}$ (aq) concentration stays the same
(4) $Zn^{2+}$ (aq) concentration stays the same

**44.** An electrolytic cell differs from an electrochemical cell in that the electrolytic cell

(1) involves redox
(2) is exothermic
(3) produces an electric current
(4) uses an applied electric current

**45.** In the electrolysis of fused (molten) silver chloride, the Ag+ ions are

(1) reduced at the negative electrode
(2) reduced at the e positive electrode
(3) oxidized at the negative electrode
(4) oxidized at the positive electrode

**46.** In an electrolytic cell, to which electrode will a positive ion migrate and undergo reduction?

(1) The anode, which is negatively charged
(2) The anode, which is positively charged
(3) The cathode, which is negatively charged
(4) The cathode, which is positively charged

## Directions

Review the Test-Taking Strategies section of this book. Then answer the following questions. Read each question carefully and answer with a correct choice or response.

## Part A

1  The oxidation number of an uncombined Group 2 metal is
   (1) +1      (2) +2      (3) −2      (4) 0

2  In all oxidation-reduction reactions there is conservation of
   (1) charge, but not mass
   (2) mass, but not charge
   (3) neither mass nor charge
   (4) both mass and charge

3  During a reduction reaction there is a
   (1) loss of electrons and a loss of oxidation number
   (2) loss of electrons and a gain of oxidation number
   (3) gain of electrons and a loss of oxidation number
   (4) gain of electrons and a gain of oxidation number

4  As an atom is oxidized, the number of protons in the nucleus
   (1) decreases
   (2) increases
   (3) remains the same
   (4) depends on the atom

5  In a redox reaction, the species reduced
   (1) gains electrons
   (2) gains oxidation number
   (3) loses electrons and is the oxidizing agent
   (4) loses electrons and is the reducing agent

6  A redox reaction always involves
   (1) a change in oxidation number
   (2) a change of phase
   (3) a transfer of protons
   (4) the formation of ions

7  The function of a salt bridge in a voltaic cell is to
   (1) allow the flow of electrons
   (2) allow the flow of protons
   (3) allow the flow of ions
   (4) provide a site for electron transfer

8  Which of the following occurs in an electrolytic cell?
   (1) A chemical reaction produces an electric current.
   (2) An electric current produces a chemical reaction.
   (3) An oxidation reaction takes place at the cathode.
   (4) A reduction reaction takes place at the anode.

9  Hydrogen has an oxidation number of
   (1) 0 only            (3) −1 only
   (2) +1 only           (4) 0, +1, or −1

10  Voltaic cells differ from electrolytic cells because in a voltaic cell
   (1) the cathode is positively charged
   (2) the anode is positively charged
   (3) electrons flow from anode to cathode
   (4) electrons flow from cathode to anode

11  In a half-reaction
   (1) mass only is conserved
   (2) charge only is conserved
   (3) both mass and charge are conserved
   (4) neither mass nor charge is conserved

12  Which reaction occurs at the anode in voltaic and electrolytic cells?
   (1) reduction only
   (2) oxidation only
   (3) both reduction and oxidation
   (4) neither reduction nor oxidation

## Part B

13  What is the oxidation number of carbon in $NaHCO_3$?
   (1) −2      (2) +2      (3) −4      (4) +4

14  Chlorine has an oxidation state of +3 in the compound
   (1) $HClO$   (2) $HClO_2$  (3) $HClO_3$  (4) $HClO_4$

15  What are the two oxidation states of nitrogen in the compound $NH_4NO_3$?
   (1) −3 and +5          (3) +3 and +5
   (2) −3 and −5          (4) +3 and −5

**16** Which equation represents a redox reaction?
(1) $NaCl + AgNO_3 \rightarrow AgCl + NaNO_3$
(2) $HCl + KOH \rightarrow H_2O + KCl$
(3) $2KClO_3 \rightarrow 2KCl + 3O_2$
(4) $H_2CO_3 \rightarrow H_2O + CO_2$

**17** Consider the equations A, B, C, and D.
(A) $AgNO_3 + NaCl \rightarrow AgCl + NaNO_3$
(B) $Cl_2 + H_2O \rightarrow HClO + HCl$
(C) $CuO + CO \rightarrow CO_2 + Cu$
(D) $NaOH + HCl \rightarrow NaCl + H_2O$

Which two reactions are redox equations?
(1) A and C          (3) C and D
(2) B and C          (4) A and D

**18** In the reaction $AgNO_3(aq) + NaCl(aq) \rightarrow$ $NaNO_3(aq) + AgCl(s)$, the reactants
(1) gain electrons only
(2) lose electrons only
(3) both gain and lose electrons
(4) neither gain nor lose electrons

**19** In the reaction $Cl_2 + H_2O \rightarrow HClO + HCl$, hydrogen is
(1) oxidized only
(2) reduced only
(3) both oxidized and reduced
(4) neither oxidized nor reduced

**20** In the reaction $2KCl(\ell) \rightarrow 2K(s) + Cl_2(g)$, the $K^+$ ions are
(1) reduced by losing electrons
(2) reduced by gaining electrons
(3) oxidized by losing electrons
(4) oxidized by gaining electrons

**21** Which equation correctly represents a reduction half-reaction?
(1) $Sn^0 + 2e^- \rightarrow Sn^{2+}$     (3) $Li^0 + e^- \rightarrow Li^+$
(2) $Na^0 + e^- \rightarrow Na^+$     (4) $Br_2{}^0 + 2e^- \rightarrow 2Br^-$

**22** In the reaction $Mg + Cl_2 \rightarrow MgCl_2$, the correct half-reaction for the oxidation that occurs is
(1) $Mg + 2e^- \rightarrow Mg^{2+}$
(2) $Cl_2 + 2e^- \rightarrow 2Cl^-$
(3) $Mg \rightarrow Mg^{2+} + 2e^-$
(4) $Cl_2 \rightarrow 2Cl^- + 2e^-$

**23** In an electrolytic cell, which ion would migrate through the solution to the positive electrode?
(1) a hydrogen ion          (3) an ammonium ion
(2) a chloride ion          (4) a hydronium ion

**24** The diagram below represents a voltaic cell.

What occurs when the switch is closed?
(1) Zn is reduced.
(2) Cu is oxidized.
(3) Electrons flow from Cu to Zn.
(4) Electrons flow from Zn to Cu.

**25** The diagram below shows a spoon that will be electroplated with nickel metal. What will occur when switch S is closed?

(1) The spoon will lose mass, and the Ni(s) will be reduced.
(2) The spoon will lose mass, and the Ni(s) will be oxidized.
(3) The spoon will gain mass, and the Ni(s) will be reduced.
(4) The spoon will gain mass, and the Ni(s) will be oxidized.

**26** The diagram below represents a chemical cell.

$$2Al(s) + 3Ni^{2+}(aq) \longrightarrow 2Al^{3+} + 3Ni(s)$$

When the switch is closed, electrons flow from
(1) $Al(s)$ to $Ni(s)$          (3) $Al^{3+}(aq)$ to $Ni^{2+}(aq)$
(2) $Ni(s)$ to $Al(s)$          (4) $Ni^{2+}(aq)$ to $Al^{3+}(aq)$

**27** The diagram below represents a voltaic cell.

$$Mg(s) + 2Ag^+(aq) \longrightarrow Mg^{2+}(aq) + 2Ag(s)$$

Which species is oxidized when the switch is closed?
(1) $Mg(s)$          (3) $Ag(s)$
(2) $Mg^{2+}(aq)$          (4) $Ag^+(aq)$

**28** The overall reaction in an electrochemical cell is $Zn(s) + Cu^{2+}(aq) \rightarrow Cu(s) + Zn^{2+}$. As the reaction in this cell takes place,
(1) oxidation occurs at the cathode
(2) the $Cu^{2+}$ is oxidized
(3) the concentration of $Zn^{2+}$ increases
(4) the concentration of $Cu^{2+}$ increases

**29** The diagram below represents an electrochemical cell.

$$Pb(s) + Cu^{2+}(aq) \longrightarrow Pb^{2+}(aq) + Cu(s)$$

Which change occurs when the switch is closed?
(1) Pb is oxidized, and electrons flow to the Cu electrode.
(2) Pb is reduced, and electrons flow to the Cu electrode.
(3) Cu is oxidized, and electrons flow to the Pb electrode.
(4) Cu is reduced, and electrons flow to the Pb electrode.

**30** Consider the following equation.
$$2Cr(s) + 3Cu^{2+}(aq) \rightarrow 2Cr^{3+}(aq) + 3Cu(s)$$

Which reaction occurs at the cathode in this voltaic cell?
(1) reduction of $Cu^{2+}(aq)$
(2) reduction of $Cu(s)$
(3) oxidation of $Cr^{3+}(aq)$
(4) oxidation of $Cr(s)$

## Part C

**Use the following balanced equation for questions 31 and 32.**

Given the reaction: $4\,Al(s) + 3O_2(g) \rightarrow 2Al_2O_3(s)$

**31** Write the balanced oxidation half-reaction for this oxidation-reduction reaction.

**32** What is the oxidation number of oxygen in $Al_2O_3$?

Base your answers to questions 33 through 37 on the diagram of the voltaic cell below.

**Voltaic Cell**

$$2\,Ag^+(aq) + Pb(s) \longrightarrow Pb^{2+}(aq) + 2\,Ag(s)$$

33 What is the direction of the electron flow through the wire? [1]

34 Write an equation for the half-reaction that occurs at the silver electrode. [1]

35 Explain the function of the salt bridge. [1]

36 When the switch is closed, in which half-cell does oxidation occur? [1]

37 Write the half-reaction that occurs in half-cell 1. [1]

Base your answers to questions 38 through 40 on the diagram of a voltaic cell below.

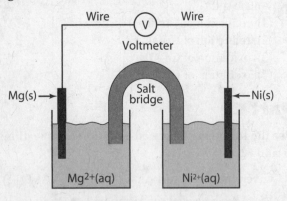

$$Mg(s) + Ni^{2+}(aq) \longrightarrow Mg^{2+}(aq) + Ni(s)$$

38 What is the total number of moles of electrons needed to completely reduce 6.0 moles of $Ni^{2+}(aq)$ ions? [1]

39 Identify one metal from Reference Table J that is more easily oxidized than $Mg(s)$. [1]

40 As the cell operates, the mass of the $Mg(s)$ decreases. Explain, in terms of particles, why this decrease occurs. [1]

Base your answers to questions 41 through 43 on the diagram and the balanced equation which represent the electrolysis of molten NaCl.

$$2NaCl \longrightarrow Cl_2 + 2Na$$

41 When the switch is closed, which electrode will attract the sodium ion? [1]

42 What is the purpose of the battery in this electrolytic cell? [1]

43 Write a balanced half-reaction for the reduction that occurs in this electrolytic cell. [1]

44 Because tap water is slightly acidic, water pipes made of iron corrode over time, as shown by the balanced equation below:

$$2Fe + 6H^+ \rightarrow 2Fe^{3+} + 3H_2$$

Explain, in terms of chemical reactivity, why copper pipes are less likely to corrode than iron pipes. [1]

Base your answers to questions 45 through 47 on the information below.

A flashlight can be powered by a rechargeable nickel-cadmium battery. In the battery, the anode is $Cd(s)$ and the cathode is $NiO_2(s)$. The unbalanced equation below represents the reaction that occurs as the battery produces electricity. When a nickel-cadmium battery is recharged, the reverse reaction takes place.

$$Cd(s) + NiO_2(s) + H_2O(l) \rightarrow Cd(OH)_2(s) + Ni(OH)_2(s)$$

45 Balance the equation for the reaction that produces electricity using the smallest whole-number coefficients. [1]

46 Determine the change in oxidation number for the element that makes up the anode in the reaction that produces electricity. [1]

47 Explain why Cd would be above Ni if placed on Table J. [1]

# Acids, Bases, and Salts

## How Scientists Study Acids, Bases, and Salts

**?** *What makes an acid strong or weak?* **?**

Why is HCl a strong acid and CH₃COOH a weak acid? Does it need more time at the gym to build molecules?

Quite the opposite. HCl has learned to relax and completely ionize its molecules into hydrogen and chloride ions. Acetic acid has many molecules and only a few ions. It's the number of hydrogen ions that determines if an acid is strong or weak.

# 10 Acids, Bases, and Salts

## Vocabulary

| | | |
|---|---|---|
| acidity | electrolyte | neutralization |
| alkalinity | hydrogen ion | pH scale |
| Arrhenius acid | hydronium ion | salt |
| Arrhenius base | indicator | titration |

## Topic Overview

Ⓡ Common Acids and Common Bases in the *Reference Tables for Physical Setting/Chemistry* list a few of the most common acids and bases. But what exactly are acids and bases? Acids and bases are classes of compounds that can be recognized by their easily observed properties. In this topic you will learn about these properties, the definitions that are used to explain these properties, and the important reactions that occur between acids and bases.

## Properties of Acids and Bases

Certain observable properties can be used to identify both acids and bases. Although these properties can indicate whether or not a substance is an acid or a base, they do not explain why acids and bases behave the way they do.

### Characteristic Properties of Acids

- *Dilute solutions of acids have a sour taste.* It would be foolish to taste a substance to see if it is an acid. However, there are acids in many of the foods that we eat. You have probably noticed the sour taste of lemons; the sour taste is due to the presence of citric acid. Vinegar contains acetic acid, and carbonated drinks have carbonic acid as one of the ingredients.

- *Aqueous solutions of acids conduct an electric current.* Substances that conduct an electric current are called **electrolytes**. The ability of a solution to conduct an electric current is dependent on the concentration (number) of ions in solution. That is, the greater the concentration of ions in solution, the greater the electrical conductivity. If a solution of an acid is a good conductor of electricity, it is called a strong acid. If such a solution is a poor conductor, it is termed a weak acid.

- *Acids react with bases to form water and a salt.* This type of reaction is called a **neutralization** reaction. Neutralization reactions are in fact a type of double replacement reaction. The **salt** that is formed as a product of a neutralization reaction is an ionic substance composed of a positively charged metallic or polyatomic ion and a negative ion other than the hydroxide ion.

- *Acids react with certain metals to produce hydrogen gas.* The metals listed in Table J of the *Reference Tables for Physical Setting/Chemistry* that are ⓡ above hydrogen (H₂) will react with acids to produce hydrogen gas and a salt. Thus, magnesium will react with hydrochloric acid, whereas copper will not.
- *Acids cause acid-base indicators to change color.* Indicators are substances that have different colors when mixed in acidic and basic solutions. Table M of the *Reference Tables for Physical Setting/Chemistry* lists several ⓡ common indicators and the color changes that they undergo.

## Characteristic Properties of Bases

- *Bases have a bitter taste.*
- *Bases have a slippery or soapy feeling.*
- *Bases conduct an electric current.* Note that the terminology used to describe the strength of a base is the same as that used for acids. Thus, a solution of a base with a high concentration of ions that conducts electricity is called a strong base. Weak bases are poor conductors of electricity and are not highly ionized.
- *Bases react with acids to produce water and a salt.*
- *Bases cause acid-base indicators to change color.*

## Arrhenius Theory

There have been several attempts to develop explanations for the observable properties of acids and bases. Svante Arrhenius, a Swedish chemist, proposed a commonality of all acids to explain their similar properties. An **Arrhenius acid** is defined as a substance whose water solution contains the hydrogen ion as the only positive ion. For example, hydrochloric acid ionizes in water to form hydrogen and chloride ions.

$$HCl \rightarrow H^+ + Cl^-$$

Not all substances that contain hydrogen are acids. Methane (CH₄) is an organic compound containing hydrogen, yet it is not an acid. The hydrogen atoms in methane are bonded to the carbon by covalent bonds. These hydrogen atoms do not ionize in solution: rather, they remain attached to the molecule. Because the hydrogen atoms do not form ions, methane is neither an electrolyte nor an acid.

### The Nature of the Hydrogen Ion

A hydrogen atom consists of a single electron orbiting a nucleus that contains a single proton. As shown in Figure 10-1, when the hydrogen atom becomes a positive ion, the electron is lost, leaving behind the proton. Thus, a positive **hydrogen ion** is a proton.

Chemists believe that this proton cannot exist in a water solution as an isolated proton. The positively charged proton is attracted to an unshared pair of electrons in the water molecule. See Figure 10-2. The proton covalently bonds with

**Figure 10-1. An H⁺ ion is a proton.**

**Figure 10-2. Acids react with water to produce the hydronium ion.**

the water forming $H_3O^+$, the **hydronium ion.** Acids dissolve in water and react to produce hydronium and negative ions.

$$HCl + H_2O \rightarrow H_3O^+ + Cl^-$$
$$H^+ + H_2O \rightarrow H_3O^+$$

According to the Arrhenius theory, the properties of acids are properties of the hydrogen (hydronium) ion.

As shown in the first equation above, each molecule of hydrochloric acid (HCl) that ionizes in water produces a single hydrogen ion. Hydrochloric acid and other acids that produce a single hydrogen ion are called monoprotic acids. Sulfuric acid ($H_2SO_4$), however, ionizes in two steps.

$$H_2SO_4 \rightarrow H^+ + HSO_4^-$$
$$HSO_4^- \rightarrow H^+ + SO_4^{2-}$$

Each molecule of $H_2SO_4$ that ionizes produces two hydrogen ions. Sulfuric acid and other acids that produce two hydrogen ions are called diprotic acids. Similarly, an $H_3PO_4$ molecule ionizes to yield three hydrogen ions and is called a triprotic acid.

## Digging Deeper

Some organic compounds that are acids have chemical formulas that are somewhat misleading. These compounds contain a carboxyl group (−COOH) that gives them the appearance of a base. However, the hydrogen atom in the carboxyl group does ionize in water, thus defining these compounds as acids.

$$CH_3COOH \rightarrow H^+ + CH_3COO^-$$

## The Nature of the Hydroxide Ion

In a parallel manner to acids, the properties of bases are explained as properties of the hydroxide ion ($OH^-$) in solution. Each **Arrhenius base** produces hydroxide ions when dissolved in water. The presence of the hydroxide ion makes the base an electrolyte. It is also the presence of the hydroxide ion that produces the slippery feel and bitter taste common to Arrhenius bases.

Ammonia ($NH_3$) and organic compounds called amines are bases, though at first glance their chemical formulas do not show the presence of hydroxide ions. However, ammonia reacts with water to form the ammonium and hydroxide ions.

$$NH_3 + H_2O \rightarrow NH_4^+ + OH^-$$

Amines are compounds containing carbon and nitrogen that are related to ammonia. Amines also react with water to produce hydroxide ions.

$$CH_3NH_2 + H_2O \rightarrow CH_3NH_3^+ + OH^-$$

There are also other compounds whose formulas do contain an –OH group but which are not bases. The hydroxyl group is composed of an oxygen atom and a hydrogen atom covalently bonded to a carbon chain. This group of organic compounds, called alcohols, are not bases as they do not ionize in water. Thus, they are nonelectrolytes and do not have the characteristics of bases. $CH_3OH$ and $CH_3CH_2OH$ are examples of alcohols, and they do not ionize to produce the hydroxide ion.

## Strength of Acids and Bases

Hydrochloric acid is a dangerous acid that can cause severe injury to your skin. Citric acid is present in citrus and other fruits that we commonly eat. Even more surprising, boric acid is used as an eye-washing solution. How can we explain that these substances are all acids, yet have such different effects? The answer involves the strength of each acid.

When one hundred molecules of hydrochloric acid dissolve in water, all one hundred molecules ionize and form ions. When an acid completely ionizes, it is called a strong acid. Other acids ionize to a much smaller degree. Perhaps only one molecule out of one hundred ionizes. Acids that ionize only slightly are called weak acids.

The degree of ionization is a function of the number of ions that are produced. Highly ionized (strong) acids and bases produce large numbers of ions. These strong acids and bases are strong electrolytes, and hence good conductors of electricity.

## Naming Acids and Bases

Binary acids are composed of hydrogen and one other element. Hydrogen chloride (HCl) is a molecular gas, but becomes an Arrhenius acid when it reacts with water to produce hydrogen ions. The names of binary acids begin with *hydro-* followed by the name of the other element modified to end with *−ic*. Thus, hydrogen chloride gas becomes hydrochloric acid when dissolved in water. Other binary acids are named in the same fashion.

| Table 10-1. Names of Several Acids and Their Ions | | |
|---|---|---|
| Acid Name | Formula of Acid | Anion Name |
| Hydrochloric | HCl | chloride |
| Sulfuric | $H_2SO_4$ | sulfate |
| Sulfurous | $H_2SO_3$ | sulfite |
| Nitric | $HNO_3$ | nitrate |
| Nitrous | $HNO_2$ | nitrite |

Ternary acids are also molecular substances that produce hydrogen ions when dissolved in water. They consist of a polyatomic ion containing oxygen such as nitrate ($NO_3^-$) or sulfate ($SO_4^{2-}$). To name a ternary acid, the anion suffixes *−ate* and *−ite* usually are replaced by the suffixes *−ic* and *−ous* respectively. For example, $HNO_3$ is nitric acid. Sometimes the names are modified slightly, as in $H_2SO_4$, sulfuric acid. Table 10-1 lists the names of several common acids.

Bases are quite simple to name. The name of the positive ion is not modified, and the name of the base ends with hydroxide. For example, $Ca(OH)_2$ is named calcium hydroxide.

# Review Questions

1. According to the Arrhenius theory, when an acidic substance is dissolved in water it will produce a solution containing only one kind of positive ion. To which ion does the theory refer?

   (1) acetate     (3) chloride
   (2) hydrogen     (4) sodium

2. When an Arrhenius base is dissolved in $H_2O$, the only negative ion present in the solution is

   (1) $OH^-$     (3) $H^-$
   (2) $H_3O^-$     (4) $O^{2-}$

3. According to the Arrhenius theory of acids, citric acid in oranges and acetic acid in vinegar are classified as acids because their aqueous solutions contain

(1) hydrogen ions      (3) hydroxide ions
(2) hydrogen atoms     (4) hydroxide atoms

4. In an aqueous solution, which substance yields hydrogen ions as the only positive ion?

(1) $C_2H_5OH$         (3) KH
(2) $CH_3COOH$         (4) KOH

5. Which compound is an electrolyte?

(1) $C_6H_{12}O_6$         (3) $CH_3CH_2OH$
(2) $C_{12}H_{22}O_{11}$        (4) $CH_3COOH$

6. If 1 mol of each of the following substances were dissolved in 1 L of water, which solution would contain the highest concentration of $OH^-$ ions?

(1) $H_2SO_4$    (2) $NH_4Cl$    (3) $KNO_3$    (4) NaOH

7. If 1 mol of each of the following substances were dissolved in 1 L of water, which solution would contain the highest concentration of $H_3O^+$ ions?

(1) $CH_3COOH$         (3) KBr
(2) NaCl               (4) $Ba(OH)_2$

8. When substance X is dissolved in water, the only positive ions in the solution are hydrogen ions. Substance X could be

(1) NaOH    (2) NaH    (3) $H_2S$    (4) $NH_3$

9. Which species is classified as an Arrhenius base?

(1) $CH_3OH$  (2) LiOH   (3) $PO_4^{3-}$   (4) $CO_3^{2-}$

10. As 1 g of sodium hydroxide dissolves in 100 g of water, the conductivity of the water

(1) decreases          (3) remains the same
(2) increases

11. A solution of a base differs from a solution of an acid in that the solution of a base

(1) is able to conduct electricity
(2) is able to cause an indicator color change
(3) has a greater $[H_3O^+]$
(4) has a greater $[OH^-]$

12. A solution of hydrochloric acid is a stronger acid than a solution of acetic acid of the same concentration because

(1) it has more hydrogen ions in solution
(2) it has more hydroxide ions in solution
(3) it has fewer hydrogen ions in solution
(4) it has fewer hydroxide ions in solution.

13. When an Arrhenius acid is dissolved in water, it produces

(1) $H^+$ as the only positive ion in solution
(2) $NH_3^+$ as the only positive ion in solution
(3) $OH^-$ as the only negative ion in solution
(4) $HCO_3^-$ as the only negative ion in solution

14. What would be the name of $ClO_3^-$ if the name of $HClO_3$ is chloric acid?

15. Name the following acids and bases.

(a) $H_2S$
(b) HBr
(c) LiOH
(d) $Mg(OH)_2$

16. A student tests the conductivity of an unknown substance and determines it to be a good conductor of electricity. Based on this he decides that it is an acid. Criticize the student's conclusion. Is there enough evidence to warrant the conclusion? What additional test or tests could be performed to confirm the conclusion? For each test, indicate the result that would verify the substance to be an acid.

## Reactions Involving Acids and Bases

Chemical reactions involving acids and bases are common in industrial and consumer applications, natural processes, and in classroom experiments. Acids and bases undergo many reactions because they are able to react with each other as well as with other compounds and elements.

### Reactions of Acids with Metals

You may recall that any element in the Activity Series of the *Reference* ®  *Tables for Physical Setting/Chemistry* will react with the ion of any element below it. Note that hydrogen ($H_2$) is found near the bottom of the table. Thus, any metal above hydrogen in the table will react with the hydrogen ions in acids to produce $H_2$ and a salt. The reaction between zinc and hydrochloric acid is an example.

$$Zn(s) + 2HCl(aq) \rightarrow H_2(g) + ZnCl_2(aq)$$

Copper, which is below hydrogen in the table, will not react with hydrogen ions in acids.

## Neutralization Reactions

In a neutralization reaction, an Arrhenius acid reacts with an Arrhenius base to produce water and a salt. There are several ways that these reactions can be expressed. For example, consider the neutralization reaction between hydrochloric acid (HCl) and sodium hydroxide (NaOH).

This reaction can be expressed as a word equation:

Hydrochloric acid + Sodium hydroxide → Water + Sodium chloride

Substituting the chemical formulas for words yields the formula equation:

$$HCl(aq) + NaOH(aq) \rightarrow H_2O(\ell) + NaCl(aq)$$

Writing the equation to take the ions in solution into account yields the ionic equation:

$$H^+(aq) + Cl^-(aq) + Na^+(aq) + OH^-(aq) \rightarrow H_2O(\ell) + Na^+(aq) + Cl^-(aq)$$

Note that the sodium and chloride ions are present on both sides of the reaction arrow. Because they have not taken part in the reaction, they are called spectator ions and can be omitted.

$$H^+(aq) + \cancel{Cl^-(aq)} + \cancel{Na^+(aq)} + OH^-(aq) \rightarrow H_2O(\ell) + \cancel{Na^+(aq)} + \cancel{Cl^-(aq)}$$

Omitting the spectator ions yields the net ionic equation:

$$H^+(aq) + OH^-(aq) \rightarrow H_2O(\ell)$$

Because hydrogen ions exist in solution as hydronium ions ($H_3O^+$), this equation can also be written as the reaction between hydronium and hydroxide ions.

$$H_3O^+(aq) + OH^-(aq) \rightarrow 2H_2O(\ell)$$

All neutralization reactions have the same net equation. The Arrhenius definition is able to explain the process of neutralization as a reaction between hydrogen (hydronium) ions and hydroxide ions to form water with the spectator ions forming a salt.

**Writing Neutralization Reactions** Writing neutralization reactions is not a difficult task, as shown in the following Sample Problem.

**Memory Jogger**

Single-replacement reactions have the general formula:

$$A + BC \rightarrow AC + B$$

**Memory Jogger**

When writing equations, first write correct formulas using charges and subscripts. Then, balance the equation using coefficients.

**Memory Jogger**

When writing the formula of the salt in a neutralization reaction, check the charge on both ions. If the ionic charges are not equal and opposite, write the charge of one ion as the subscript of the other.

Write the equation for the neutralization reaction between dilute nitric acid and potassium hydroxide.

**SOLUTION:** Identify the known and unknown values.

*Known*
reactant 1 = nitric acid ($HNO_3$)

reactant 2 = potassium hydroxide (KOH)

*Unknown*
neutralization equation = ?

1. Write a simple word equation for the neutralization reaction.

   acid + base → water + salt

2. Substitute the known compounds into the general word equation.

   $HNO_3$ + KOH → water + salt

3. Picture a box enclosing the hydroxide ($OH^-$) of the base and the hydrogen ($H^+$) of the acid. These particles combine to form water ($H_2O$).

   $HNO_3$ + KOH → $H_2O$ + salt

The remaining $K^+$ and $NO_3^-$ ions combine to form the salt $KNO_3$.

$HNO_3$ + KOH → $H_2O$ + $KNO_3$

4. Now check to see that the equation is balanced. Because the hydroxide and hydrogen ions combine in a 1:1 ratio to form water molecules, they must be present in equal numbers. If needed, the coefficients of the acid and the base are adjusted to balance these ions. In this example, there is one hydroxide ion and one hydrogen ion, so the coefficients are both 1. A coefficient of 1 is not written; the above equation is balanced. Note that the spectator ions form the salt.

## Digging Deeper

Because salts are produced by neutralization, it would seem logical that a salt would be neutral, that is, neither acidic nor basic. There are, however, acidic, basic, and neutral salts. Salts that were formed from a strong acid and a strong base are neutral salts. If the salt was formed by the reaction of a strong acid and a weak base, it will be acidic. If the opposite is the case, that is, a salt formed from a strong base and a weak acid, the salt will be basic. The acidity or basicity of a salt formed from a weak acid and a weak base must be evaluated on a case-by-case basis.

When a diprotic acid reacts with a dihydroxy base, there are two hydrogen ions and two hydroxide ions. These will combine to form two molecules of water. The remaining ions will form the salt.

$$Ca(OH)_2 + H_2SO_4 \rightarrow 2H_2O + CaSO_4$$

Combinations of acids and bases that do not have an equal number of hydroxide and hydrogen ions are also easy to balance. Consider the following unbalanced equation:

$$Mg(OH)_2 + HCl \rightarrow H_2O + MgCl_2$$

Note that there are two hydroxide ions but only one hydrogen ion. Placing a 2 in front of the HCl balances the hydroxide and hydrogen ions that form two molecules of water. The 2 coefficient also supplies the two chloride ions needed to form the salt. The equation is now balanced:

$$Mg(OH)_2 + 2HCl \rightarrow 2H_2O + MgCl_2$$

## Salts

As you learned earlier, when a metal reacts with an acid, hydrogen gas and a salt are formed. In a neutralization reaction, an acid and a base react to form water and a salt. The salts in these reactions are ionic substances composed of positively charged metallic or polyatomic ions, and negative ions other than hydroxide ions. Sodium chloride (NaCl) and ammonium phosphate (($NH_4$)$_3PO_4$) are examples of salts. Salts are named by using the name of the positive ion of the base, and the negative ion of the acid.

**17.** According to the *Reference Tables for Physical Setting/Chemistry,* which metal would react spontaneously with hydrochloric acid?

(1) gold    (2) silver    (3) copper    (4) zinc

**18.** According to the *Reference Tables for Physical Setting/Chemistry,* which of the following metals will react most readily with HCl to release hydrogen gas?

(1) aluminum     (3) silver
(2) copper       (4) gold

**19.** Which metal will release $H_2(g)$ when it reacts with HCl?

(1) Au(s)    (2) Zn(s)    (3) Hg(ℓ)    (4) Ag(s)

**20.** The reaction between one mole of hydrogen ions and one mole of hydroxide ions is called

(1) oxidation     (3) hydrolysis
(2) reduction     (4) neutralization

**21.** Which type of reaction occurs when equal volumes of 0.1M HCl and 0.1M NaOH are mixed?

(1) neutralization     (3) electrolysis
(2) ionization       (4) hydrolysis

**22.** Which type of reaction occurs when 50-mL quantities of 1 M $Ba(OH)_2(aq)$ and $H_2SO_4(aq)$ are combined?

(1) hydrolysis     (3) hydrogenation
(2) ionization     (4) neutralization

**23.** Which compound reacts with an acid to produce water and a salt?

(1) $CH_3Cl$       (3) KCl
(2) $CH_3COOH$    (4) KOH

**24.** How much water is formed when 1.0 mol of HCl reacts completely with 1.0 mol of NaOH?

(1) 1.0 mol     (3) 0.50 mol
(2) 2.0 mol     (4) 0.25 mol

**25.** A water solution contains 0.50 mol of HCl. How much NaOH should be added to the HCl solution to exactly neutralize it?

(1) 1.0 mol     (3) 0.25 mol
(2) 2.0 mol     (4) 0.50 mol

**26.** Which is the net ionic equation for a neutralization?

(1) $H^+ + H_2O \rightarrow H_3O^+$
(2) $H^+ + NH_3 \rightarrow NH_4^+$
(3) $2H^+ + 2O^{2-} \rightarrow 2OH^-$
(4) $H^+ + OH^- \rightarrow H_2O$

**27.** Which substance is always produced by a neutralization reaction?

(1) water
(2) acid
(3) ester
(4) base

**28.** Which products are formed when an acid reacts with a base?

(1) an alcohol and carbon dioxide
(2) an ester and water
(3) a soap and glycerin
(4) a salt and water

**29.** Which compound is a salt?

(1) $Na_3PO_4$
(2) $H_3PO_4$
(3) $CH_3COOH$
(4) $Ca(OH)_2$

**30.** Which compound is classified as a salt?

(1) $CH_3COOH$
(2) $C_2H_5OH$
(3) NaOH
(4) $NaC_2H_3O_2$

**31.** Which formula represents a salt?

(1) KOH
(2) KCl
(3) $CH_3OH$
(4) $CH_3COOH$

**32.** The diagram below shows an acid being added to a base.

A
50 mL of I M HCl

B
50 mL of I M NaOH

As the acid in beaker A is added to the base in flask B, the number of $OH^-$ ions in flask B

(1) decreases and the number of $Na^+$ ions decreases
(2) increases and the number of $Na^+$ ions decreases
(3) decreases and the number of $Na^+$ ions remains the same
(4) increases and the number of $Na^+$ ions remains the same

**33.** The diagram below illustrates an apparatus used to test the conductivity of various solutions.

Switch

Electrode — solution

Electrode

Battery

When the switch is closed, which of the following 1-molar solutions would cause the bulb to glow most brightly?

(1) ammonia
(2) acetic acid
(3) carbonic acid
(4) sulfuric acid

**34.** Which salt is formed when hydrochloric acid is neutralized by a potassium hydroxide solution?

(1) potassium chloride
(2) potassium chlorate
(3) potassium chlorite
(4) potassium perchlorate

**35.** In the neutralization reaction between hydrochloric acid and sodium hydroxide, the spectator ions are

(1) $H^+$ and $OH^-$
(2) $Cl^-$ and $OH^-$
(3) $Na^+$ and $H^+$
(4) $Na^+$ and $Cl^-$

**36.** When NaOH(*aq*) reacts completely with HCl(*aq*) and the resulting solution is evaporated to dryness, the solid remaining is

(1) an ester
(2) an alcohol
(3) a salt
(4) a metal

**37.** Name each of the following.

(a) HF
(b) $H_2Se$
(c) HI

**38.** Consult the Activity Series in the *Reference Tables for Physical Setting/Chemistry* to determine if the following reactions actually occur. If a reaction does occur, write the correctly balanced equation. If the reaction does not occur, write "No reaction."

(a) calcium and hydrochloric acid
(b) zinc and dilute nitric acid
(c) lead and carbonic acid
(d) aluminum and acetic acid
(e) copper and phosphoric acid

**39.** Write the balanced equation for each of the following neutralization reactions, and write the name of the salt formed.

(a) nitric acid and sodium hydroxide
(b) nitric acid and magnesium hydroxide
(c) sulfuric acid and magnesium hydroxide
(d) sulfuric acid and potassium hydroxide
(e) phosphoric acid and lithium hydroxide
(f) phosphoric acid and calcium hydroxide

## Acid–Base Titration

**Titration** is the process of adding measured volumes of an acid or a base of known concentration to an acid or a base of unknown concentration until neutralization occurs. The solution of known concentration is called the standard solution. Knowing the volumes of acid and base used in the titration, together with the known concentration of the standard solution, it is possible to calculate the concentration of the unknown solution.

In all neutralization reactions there must be a 1:1 ratio between the moles of hydrogen ions ($H^+$) and the moles of hydroxide ions ($OH^-$). The equation for concentration shows the relationship among number of moles, volume in liters, and molarity.

$$\text{molarity} = \frac{\text{moles}}{\text{volume}}$$

or

$$\text{moles} = \text{molarity} \times \text{volume}$$

In a neutralization reaction, the number of moles of $H^+$ ions must equal the number of moles of $OH^-$ ions. Thus, equating mol $H^+$ and mol $OH^-$ yields the following equation.

$$\text{molarity } H^+ \times \text{volume}_{acid} = \text{molarity } OH^- \times \text{volume}_{base}$$

or

$$M_A \times V_A = M_B \times V_B$$

In the above equation, $M_A$ = molarity of $H^+$, $V_A$ = volume of acid in milliliters, $M_B$ = molarity of $OH^-$, and $V_B$ = volume of base in milliliters.

To solve any titration problem, the molarity of the acid and base must be expressed as the molarity of the hydrogen ion ($H^+$) and the molarity of the hydroxide ion ($OH^-$), respectively. In the case of monoprotic acids such as HCl, the molarity of the $H^+$ is the same as the molarity of the acid. Thus, a 2.0 M HCl solution has a 2.0 M $H^+$ concentration. The same applies to monohydroxy bases. That is, a 2.5 M NaOH solution has a 2.5 M $OH^-$ concentration.

The case is different for diprotic and triprotic acids. Consider the complete ionization of a 1.0 M solution of sulfuric acid ($H_2SO_4$).

$$H_2SO_4(aq) \rightarrow 2H^+(aq) + SO_4{}^{2-}(aq)$$

One liter of 1.0 M solution of $H_2SO_4$ yields 2 mol of $H^+$ ions. The molarity of the $H^+$ ions will be twice the molarity of the acid solution. Similarly, a triprotic acid produces an $H^+$ ion molarity three times that of the molarity of the acid solution.

The following examples summarize the relationships between the concentration of an acid or base and the resulting concentration of hydrogen ions ($H^+$) or hydroxide ions ($OH^-$) in solution for mono-, di-, and triprotic acids and mono- and dihydroxy bases.

**Monoprotic Acids** The $H^+$ molarity equals the molarity of the acid solution. Hydrochloric acid is an example.

$$\text{2.5 M HCl} = \text{2.5 M } H^+$$

**Diprotic Acids** The $H^+$ molarity is twice the molarity of the acid solution. Sulfuric acid is an example.

$$\text{2.5 M } H_2SO_4 = \text{5.0 M } H^+$$

**Triprotic Acids** The $H^+$ molarity is three times the molarity of the acid solution. Phosphoric acid is an example.

$$\text{2.0 M } H_3PO_4 = \text{6.0 M } H^+$$

**Monohydroxy Bases** The $OH^-$ molarity equals the molarity of the base solution. Sodium hydroxide is an example.

$$\text{3.0 M NaOH} = \text{3.0 M } OH^-$$

**Dihydroxy Bases** The $OH^-$ molarity is twice the molarity of the base solution. Barium hydroxide is an example.

$$\text{0.5 M } Ba(OH)_2 = \text{1.0 M } OH^-$$

## SAMPLE PROBLEM

What is the concentration of a hydrochloric acid solution if 50.0 mL of a 0.250 M KOH are needed to neutralize 20.0 mL of the HCl solution of unknown concentration?

**SOLUTION:** Identify the known and unknown values.

*Known*
molarity of KOH = 0.250 M
$V_B$ = volume of KOH = 50.0 mL
$V_A$ = volume of HCl = 20.0 mL

*Unknown*
$M_A$ = molarity of HCl = ? M

1. Write the balanced equation for the neutralization reaction

$$KOH + HCl \rightarrow H_2O + KCl$$

2. Determine the molarity of the hydroxide ion. Because KOH is a monohydroxy base, the molarity of the hydroxide ion is the same as the molarity of the base solution.

$$M_B = \text{molarity KOH} = 0.250 \text{ M}$$

3. Solve the neutralization reaction equation for $M_A$, substitute the known values, and solve.

$$M_A \times V_A = M_B \times V_B$$
$$M_A = (M_B \times V_B)/ V_A$$
$$M_A = \frac{(0.250 \text{ M})(50.0 \text{ mL})}{20.0 \text{ mL}}$$
$$M_A = 0.625 \text{ M}$$

The molarity of the hydrogen ion is 0.625 M. Because HCl is a monprotic acid, the molarity of the acid is also 0.625 M.

## SAMPLE PROBLEM

What is the concentration of a sulfuric acid solution if 50. mL of a 0.25 M KOH are needed to neutralize 20. mL of the $H_2SO_4$ solution of unknown concentration?

**SOLUTION:** Identify the known and unknown values.

*Known*
molarity of KOH = 0.25 M
$V_B$ = volume of KOH = 50. mL
$V_A$ = volume of $H_2SO_4$ = 20. mL

*Unknown*
$M_A$ = molarity of $H_2SO_4$ = ? M

1. Write the balanced equation for the neutralization reaction.

$$2KOH + H_2SO_4 \rightarrow 2H_2O + K_2SO_4$$

2. Determine the molarity of the hydroxide ion. Because KOH is a monohydroxy base, the molarity of the hydroxide ion is the same as the molarity of base solution.

$$M_B = \text{molarity KOH} = 0.25 \text{ M}$$

3. Solve the neutralization reaction equation for $M_A$, substitute the known values, and solve.

$$M_A \times V_A = M_B \times V_B$$
$$M_A = (M_B \times V_B)/ V_A$$
$$M_A = \frac{(0.250 \text{ M})(50.0 \text{ mL})}{20.0 \text{ mL}}$$
$$M_A = 0.625 \text{ M}$$

4. To determine the molarity of the $H_2SO_4$, adjust for the fact that the acid is diprotic. That is, the molarity of the acid is only half that of the hydrogen ion.

$$\text{molarity } H_2SO_4 = \frac{[H^+]}{2} = \frac{0.625 \text{ M}}{2} = 0.31 \text{ M}$$

**40.** Which compound reacts with an acid to form a salt and water?

(1) $CH_3F$      (3) LiCl
(2) $C_2H_5COOH$      (4) LiOH

**41.** To neutralize 1 mol of sulfuric acid, 2 mol of sodium hydroxide are required. How many liters of 1 M NaOH are needed to exactly neutralize 1 L of 1 M $H_2SO_4$?

(1) 1      (2) 2      (3) 0.5      (4) 4

**42.** How many moles of sodium hydroxide (NaOH) are required to completely neutralize 2 mol of nitric acid ($HNO_3$)?

(1) 1      (2) 2      (3) 40      (4) 60

**43.** During an acid-base neutralization, how many moles of hydroxide ions will react with one mole of hydrogen ions?

(1) 1.0 mol      (3) 17.0 mol
(2) 0.5 mol      (4) 22.4 mol

**44.** How many moles of KOH are needed to exactly neutralize 500. mL of 1.0 M HCl?

(1) 1.0 mol      (3) 0.25 mol
(2) 2.0 mol      (4) 0.50 mol

**45.** One liter of 1 M NaOH will completely neutralize one liter of

(1) 1 M $H_2SO_4$      (3) 2 M $H_2SO_4$
(2) 0.5 M $H_2SO_4$      (4) 1.5 M $H_2SO_4$

**For questions 46–54, show all of your work.**

**46.** Consider the following reaction.

$$KOH + HCl \rightarrow H_2O + HOH$$

How many milliliters of 2.0 M KOH are necessary to neutralize 50. mL of 1.0 M HCl?

**47.** How many milliliters of 2.5 M HCl are required to exactly neutralize 1.5 L of 5.0 M NaOH?

**48.** How many milliliters of 0.20 M $H_2SO_4$ are required to completely neutralize 40. mL of 0.10 M $Ca(OH)_2$?

**49.** How many milliliters of 0.200 M NaOH are needed to neutralize 100. mL of 0.100 M HCl?

**50.** A 2.0-mL sample of NaOH solution is exactly neutralized by 4.0 mL of 3.0 M HCl solution. What is the concentration of the NaOH solution?

**51.** A 10.-mL sample of hydrochloric acid neutralizes 15 mL of a 0.40 M solution of NaOH. What is the molarity of the hydrochloric acid?

**52.** How many mL of 0.20 M hydrochloric acid is required to neutralize 100. mL of 0.80 M potassium hydroxide?

**53.** A 3.0-mL sample of $HNO_3$ solution is exactly neutralized by 6.0 mL of 0.50 M KOH. What is the molarity of the $HNO_3$ solution?

**54.** What is the molarity of hydrogen ions in a 2.7 M solution of the strong acid HCl?

**55.** Write the electron dot diagram of a hydrogen chloride molecule.

**56.** Write the electron dot diagram for the hydronium ion ($H_3O^+$).

**57.** Write the electron dot diagram for the hydroxide ion ($OH^-$).

**58.** Write the word equation form of the net ionic equation for all neutralization equations.

**59.** Write the electron dot diagram for the net ionic equation for a neutralization reaction. Be sure to include the charge on any ionic substance.

**60.** Phosphoric acid is neutralized by a solution of sodium hydroxide. What is the name of the salt formed from the neutralization?

# Acidity and Alkalinity of Solutions

Although water is a covalently bonded substance, it does ionize to a very small extent as shown by the equation below.

$$HOH \leftrightarrow H^+ + OH^-$$

It can be seen that in pure water $[H^+] = [OH^-]$. Le Châtelier's principle tells us that if one of these factors increases, the other decreases. When HCl is added to pure water, the concentration of the hydrogen ion increases, and the concentration of the hydroxide ion decreases. When $[H^+] > [OH^-]$, the solution is acidic. If the reverse is true, and the concentration of $OH^-$ is greater than the concentration of the H$^+$, the solution is alkaline, or basic. The terms **acidity** and **alkalinity** (or basicity) refer to the relative strength of the acid or base in terms of their H$^+$ and OH$^-$ concentrations.

## pH Scale

A scale, called the **pH scale,** has been developed to express [H$^+$] as a number from 0 to 14. A pH of 0 is strongly acidic, a pH of 7 is neutral, and a pH of 14 is strongly basic. The pH scale is logarithmic. Each change of a single pH unit signifies a tenfold change in the concentration of the hydrogen ion. Thus the [H$^+$] is ten times greater in a solution with a pH of 5 as in a solution with a pH of 6.

Because [H$^+$] and [OH$^-$] are directly related, a pH change of one unit represents a tenfold increase or decrease of both the hydrogen ion and hydroxide ion concentration. As the concentration of the hydrogen ion increases, the concentration of the hydroxide ion decreases.

| HIn | H$^+$ + In$^-$ |
|-----|-----|
| (colorless) $\rightarrow$ | (pink) |

**Figure 10-3. Color change in phenolphthalein:** Indicators are weak acids that have different colors depending on the presence or absence of hydrogen. In the diagram above, HIn represents the indicator phenolphthalein.

## Acid-Base Indicators

An **indicator** is a substance that changes its color when it gains or loses a proton. Phenolphthalein is a common indicator that is colorless when it is protonated, that is, when it contains a hydrogen atom. When a base is gradually added to an acid containing phenolphthalein, the solution is initially colorless. Once the acid has been neutralized by the addition of the base, the base then reacts with the hydrogen atom of the indicator. As the phenolphthalein loses its hydrogen (proton), it turns pink. This color change is why phenolphthalein is an indicator; the color change in the phenolphthalein shows (indicates) when a titration has reached an end point.

Other indicators react in a similar way to phenolphthalein, but each has a unique color change that occurs over a specific pH range. Common Acid-Base Indicators in the *Reference Tables for Physical Setting/Chemistry* lists several common indicators, the color changes they undergo, and the pH range over which the color change occurs.

Another example of an indicator is methyl orange. An acid solution with a pH of 2.0 containing methyl orange is red in color. As a base is added to the acid solution, the pH slowly increases. Between pH 3.2 and 4.4, the solution contains both the red and the yellow forms of the indicator, resulting in an orange color. When a pH of 4.4 is achieved, there is no longer an appreciable number of red molecules present, and the solution appears yellow. This same process occurs in other indicators as well. That is, indicators tend to have a distinct color at each end of their useful pH range and pass through an intermediate color region that is a mixture of these two colors.

61. Which pH value indicates the most basic solution?

    (1) 7      (2) 8      (3) 3      (4) 11

62. Which pH value represents a solution with the lowest $OH^-$ ion concentration?

    (1) 1      (2) 7      (3) 10      (4) 14

63. When tested, a solution turns red litmus to blue. This indicates that the solution contains more

    (1) $H^+$ ions than $OH^-$ ions
    (2) $H_3O^+$ ions than $OH^-$ ions
    (3) $OH^-$ ions than $H_3O^+$ ions
    (4) $H^+$ and $OH^-$ ions than $H_2O$ molecules

64. Pure water at 25°C has a pH of

    (1) 1      (2) 5      (3) 7      (4) 14

65. If an aqueous solution turns blue litmus red, which relationship exists between the hydronium ion and hydroxide ion?

    (1) $[H_3O^+] < [OH^-]$
    (2) $[H_3O^+] = [OH^-]$
    (3) $[H_3O^+] > [OH^-]$
    (4) neither ion is present

66. The pH of a 0.1 M $CH_3COOH$ solution is

    (1) less than 1
    (2) greater than 1, but less than 7
    (3) equal to 7
    (4) greater than 7 but less than 14

67. As 0.1 M HCl is added to 0.1 M KOH, the pH of the basic solution

    (1) decreases and the basicity decreases
    (2) decreases and the acidity decreases
    (3) increases and the basicity decreases
    (4) increases and the acidity decreases

68. As an acidic solution is added to a basic solution, the pH of the basic solution

    (1) decreases
    (2) increases
    (3) remains the same

69. An indicator was used to test a water solution with a pH of 12. Which indicator color would be observed?

    (1) colorless phenolphthalein
    (2) red litmus
    (3) colorless litmus
    (4) pink phenolphthalein

70. As a strong acid is added to a beaker containing NaOH, the number of $OH^-$ ions in the beaker

    (1) decreases and the number of $Na^+$ ions decreases
    (2) decreases and the number of $Na^+$ ions remains the same
    (3) increases and the number of $Na^+$ ions decreases
    (4) increases and the number of $Na^+$ ions remains the same

**Answer questions 71–74 using complete sentences.**

71. A blue solution containing an acid-base indicator was tested with a pH meter and found to have a pH of 5.5. Which of the indicators on Common Acid-Base Indicators in the *Reference Tables for Physical Setting/Chemistry* could be this indicator?

72. A solution was yellow in bromthymol blue and blue in bromcresol green. According to Common Acid-Base Indicators in the *Reference Tables for Physical Setting/Chemistry*, what could be the pH of the solution?

73. A solution was tested with a pH meter and found to have a pH of 7.8. What color would the solution have if the following indicators were added?

    (a) bromthymol blue      (b) thymol blue

74. Acid was added to a solution containing an indicator until the solution turned from blue to yellow. Which of the following would be most acidic?

    (a) a yellow solution containing bromthymol blue
    (b) a yellow solution containing bromcresol green
    (c) a yellow solution containing thymol blue

75. As the $H_3O^+$ ion concentration of a solution increases, the pH of the solution

    (1) decreases
    (2) increases
    (3) remains the same

# Brønsted-Lowry Acids and Bases

There are other acid-base definitions that expand upon the Arrhenius definition of acids and bases. One of these, the Brønsted-Lowry theory, defines an acid as any substance that donates a hydrogen ion ($H^+$). As you know, a hydrogen ion is a hydrogen atom without an electron, that is, it is simply a proton. Thus, a Brønsted-Lowry acid is defined as a proton donor. All Arrhenius acids are also Brønsted-Lowry acids. Brønsted-Lowry theory expands upon the Arrhenius concept by including proton donors that are not in aqueous solution.

The Brønsted-Lowry theory defines a base as any substance that accepts a proton ($H^+$). Like the Arrhenius definition, the Brønsted-Lowry definition treats the hydroxide ion ($OH^-$) as a base. Compared with the Arrhenius definition, however, the Brønsted-Lowry definition greatly expands the number of substances that are considered bases.

**Conjugate Acid-Base Pairs**  When an acid loses a proton, the remaining portion of the acid has an unshared pair of electrons that can act as a base. Consider the following reaction.

$$HCl \rightarrow H^+ + Cl^-$$

HCl is an acid because it donates a proton. The chloride ion is a base because it is capable of accepting a proton to form HCl. Note that HCl and $Cl^-$ differ only by a hydrogen ion ($H^+$). A pair of chemical formulas that differ only by the presence of a hydrogen ion are known as a <u>conjugate acid-base pair.</u> HCl cannot donate a proton unless there is a proton acceptor (base) available to accept the proton.

The reaction between $HNO_3$ and water illustrates the reaction between a Brønsted acid and a Brønsted base.

$$
\begin{array}{cccc}
\vdash & \text{Conjugate pair} & \longrightarrow \\
\vdash & \text{Conjugate pair} & \dashv \\
HNO_3 + & H_2O \rightarrow & H_3O^+ + & NO_3^- \\
\text{acid} & \text{base} & \text{acid} & \text{base}
\end{array}
$$

The $HNO_3$ acts as an acid, donating its proton to the water (which acts as a base) producing the hydronium and nitrate ions. If the reaction is reversed, the hydronium ion acts as an acid, donating its proton to the nitrate ion (which acts as a base) to produce nitric acid and water. Note that $HNO_3$ and $NO_3^-$ are a conjugate acid-base pair because they differ by a hydrogen ion. Likewise, $H_2O$ and $H_3O^+$ are also a conjugate acid-base pair.

## Directions
Review the Test–Taking Strategies section of this book. Then answer the following questions. Read each question carefully and answer with a correct choice or response.

## Part A

1 According to the Arrhenius theory, the only negative ions in an aqueous solution of a base are
   (1) $OH^-$ ions
   (2) $HS^-$ ions
   (3) $H^-$ ions
   (4) $HCO_3^-$ ions

2 Which statement best describes the solution produced when an Arrhenius acid is dissolved in water?
   (1) The only negative ion in solution is $OH^-$.
   (2) The only negative ion in solution is $HCO_3^-$.
   (3) The only positive ion in solution is $H^+$.
   (4) The only positive ion in solution is $NH_4^+$.

3 Which substance can act as an Arrhenius acid in aqueous solution?
   (1) NaI
   (2) HI
   (3) LiH
   (4) $NH_3$

4 Unlike an acid, an aqueous solution of a base
   (1) causes some indicators to change color
   (2) conducts electricity
   (3) contains more $H^+$ than $OH^-$
   (4) contains more $OH^-$ than $H^+$

5 According to the Arrhenius theory, when a base is dissolved in water it will produce a solution containing only one kind of negative ion. To which ion does the theory refer?
   (1) hydride
   (2) hydroxide
   (3) hydrogen
   (4) hydronium

6 Acidic solutions are those that contain an excess of
   (1) $H_2$ molecules
   (2) $H_2O$ molecules
   (3) $H^+$ ions
   (4) $OH^-$ ions

7 What are the relative ion concentrations in an acid solution?
   (1) more $H^+$ ions than $OH^-$ ions
   (2) fewer $H^+$ ions than $OH^-$ ions
   (3) an equal number of $H^+$ ions and $OH^-$ ions
   (4) $H^+$ ions, but no $OH^-$ ions

8 What color is phenolphthalein in a basic solution?
   (1) blue
   (2) pink
   (3) yellow
   (4) colorless

9 Which substance is always produced by a neutralization reaction?
   (1) water
   (2) acid
   (3) ester
   (4) base

10 The reaction between one mole of hydrogen ions and one mole of hydroxide ions is called
   (1) oxidation
   (2) reduction
   (3) hydrolysis
   (4) neutralization

11 Pure water has a pH of
   (1) 1        (3) 10
   (2) 7        (4) 4

## Part B

12 Which substance is classified as a salt?
   (1) $Ca(OH)_2$
   (2) $C_2H_4OH$
   (3) $CCl_4$
   (4) $CaCl_2$

13 Consider this neutralization reaction.
   $$H_2SO_4 + 2KOH \rightarrow K_2SO_4 + 2HOH$$

   Which compound is a salt?
   (1) KOH
   (2) $H_2SO4$
   (3) $K_2SO_4$
   (4) HOH

**14** An aqueous solution turns litmus red. The pH of the solution could be
(1) 14
(2) 11
(3) 8
(4) 4

**15** If equal volumes of 0.1 M NaOH and 0.1 M HCl are mixed, the resulting solution will contain a salt and
(1) HCl
(2) NaOH
(3) $H_2O$
(4) NaCl

**16** If equal volumes of 0.1 M NaOH and 0.1 M $H_2SO_4$ are mixed, the resulting solution will contain water,
(1) $H_2SO_4$ and $Na_2SO_4$
(2) $H_2SO_4$ and NaOH
(3) NaOH and $Na_2SO_4$
(4) and $Na_2SO_4$

**17** A sample of a solution with a pH of 10 is tested separately with phenolphthalein and litmus. The colors of the indicators are as follows:
(1) litmus is blue; phenolphthalein is pink
(2) litmus is red; phenolphthalein is pink
(3) litmus is blue; phenolphthalein is colorless
(4) litmus is red; phenolphthalein is colorless

**18** A student observes that an unknown solution conducts electricity and turns blue litmus red. The student should be able to conclude that the unknown solution is most likely
(1) an acid
(2) a base
(3) an ester
(4) an alcohol

**19** An aqueous solution of an ionic compound turns red litmus blue, conducts electricity, and reacts with an acid to form a salt and water. This compound could be
(1) HCl
(2) NaI
(3) $KNO_3$
(4) LiOH

**20** What will be the concentration of 150. mL of a 2.4 M NaOH solution if it is diluted to form 200. mL of solution?
(1) 1.6 M
(2) 1.8 M
(3) 2.0 M
(4) 3.2 M

**21** Both $HNO_3$ and $CH_3COOH$ can be classified as
(1) Arrhenius acids that turn blue litmus red
(2) Arrhenius bases that turn blue litmus red
(3) Arrhenius acids that turn red litmus blue
(4) Arrhenius bases that turn red litmus blue

**22** A substance is added to a water solution containing phenolphthalein, causing the solution to turn pink. Which substance would produce this result?
(1) $HC_2H_3O_2$
(2) $H_2CO_3$
(3) KOH
(4) $CH_3OH$

**23** A student accidentally spills an unknown chemical on her hand. She quickly washes it off, and notices that her skin feels slippery. She has a electrical conductivity tester at her lab station and tests the conductivity of the solution. It is a good conductor of electricity. She then places a strip of litmus paper in a sample of the liquid and it turns blue. She can conclude that the liquid is
(1) a strong base
(2) a weak base
(3) a strong acid
(4) a weak acid

**24.** How are $HNO_3(aq)$ and $CH_3COOH(aq)$ similar?
(1) They are Arrhenius acids and they turn red litmus blue.
(2) They are Arrhenius acids and they turn blue litmus red.
(3) They are Arrhenius bases and they turn red litmus blue.
(4) They are Arrhenius bases and they turn blue litmus red.

**25** Sulfuric acid, $H_2SO_4(aq)$ can be used to neutralize barium hydroxide, $Ba(OH)_2(aq)$. What is the formula of the salt produced by this neutralization?
(1) BaS
(2) $BaSO_2$
(3) $BaSO_3$
(4) $BaSO_4$

# Part C

Use the following information to answer questions 26 through 30.

(A) KCl  (B) $CH_3OH$  (C) $Ba(OH)_2$  (D) $CH_3COOH$

Four flasks each contain 100 milliliters of aqueous solutions of equal concentrations at 25°C and 1 atm.

26 Which solutions contain electrolytes? [1]

27 Which solution has the lowest pH? [1]

28 What causes some solutions to have a low pH? [1]

29 Which solution is most likely to react with an acid to form salt and water? [1]

30 Which solution has the lowest freezing point? [1]

---

31 A student recorded the following buret readings during the titration of a base with an acid:

### Titration Readings

|  | Standard 0.100 M HCl | Unknown KOH |
|---|---|---|
| Initial reading | 9.08 mL | 0.55 mL |
| Final reading | 19.09 mL | 5.56 mL |

Calculate the molarity of the KOH. [1]

32 Calcium hydroxide is commonly known as agricultural lime and is used to adjust the soil pH. Before the lime was added to a field, the soil pH was 5. After the lime was added, the soil underwent a 100-fold decrease in hydronium ion concentration. What was the new pH of the soil in the field? [1]

Use the following information to answer questions 33 and 34.

A student titrates 60.0 mL of $HNO_3(aq)$ with 0.30 M NaOH. Phenolphthalein is used as the indicator. After adding 42.2 mL of NaOH($aq$) a color change remains for 25 seconds, and the student stops the titration.

33 What color change does the phenolphthalein undergo during this titration?

34 What is the molarity of the $HNO_3$?

Base your answers to questions 35 and 36 on the information below.

In a titration experiment, a student use a 1.4 M HBr($aq$) solution and the indicator phenolphthalein to determine the concentration of a KOH($aq$) solution. The data for trial 1 is recorded in the table below.

### Trial 1 Data

| Buret readings | HBr($aq$) | KOH($aq$) |
|---|---|---|
| Initial volume (mL) | 7.50 | 11.00 |
| Final volume (mL) | 22.90 | 33:10 |
| Volume used (mL) | 15.40 | 22.10 |

35 Calculate the molarity of the KOH. [1]

36 Why is it better to use several trials of a titration rather than one trial to determine the concentration of a solution of unknown concentration? [1]

---

37 Quicklime, CaO, can be added to soil to increase the pH. When CaO is added to water it reacts to form $Ca(OH)_2$. Write a balanced neutralization equation for the reaction between $Ca(OH)_2$ and $H_2SO_4$.

38 A sample of wet soil has a pH of 4.0. After the addition of quicklime, the $H^+$ ion concentration of the soil is 1/100 of the original $H^+$ ion concentration of the soil. What is the new pH of the soil?

39 Samples of acid rain are brought to a laboratory for analysis. Several titrations are performed and it is determined that a 20.0 milliliter sample of acid rain is neutralized with 6.50 milliliters of 0.010M NaOH. What is the molarity of the $H^+$ ions in the acid rain?

Use the information below to answer questions 40 and 41.

Using burets, a student titrated a sodium hydroxide solution of unknown concentration with a standard solution of 0.10 M hydrochloric acid. The data are recorded in the table below.

### Titration Data

| Solution | HCl($aq$) | NaOH($aq$) |
|---|---|---|
| Initial buret reading (mL) | 15.50 | 5.00 |
| Final buret reading (mL) | 25.00 | 8.80 |

40 Determine both the total volume of HCl(*aq*) and the total volume of NaOH(*aq*) [1]

41 What is the molarity of the NaOH solution.

---

42 Identify two indicators from Reference Table M that are yellow in solutions with a pH of 5.5 [1]

43 Two samples of the same rainwater are tested using two indicators. Methyl Orange is yellow in one sample. Litmus is red in the other. Identify a possible pH value for the rainwater that was tested. [1]

**Consider the following information to answer question 44.**

A truck carrying concentrated nitric acid overturns and spills its contents. The acid drains into a nearby pond. The pH of the pond water was 8.0 before the spill. After the spill, the pH is 1000 times more acidic.

44 What color will bromthymol blue be at this new pH? [1]

# Organic Chemistry

## What You Know About Organic Chemistry

### ? What does organic *mean?* ?

Although your grocery store might have a special "organic section" with specially grown foods, chances are more than just the food is organic! To chemists, *organic* refers to substances containing the element carbon. So in this picture the plastic racks, rubber hose, polyester shirt, and even the man are organic as well! Look around your classroom to see how many organic substances you can identify.

# 11 Organic Chemistry

## Vocabulary

| | | |
|---|---|---|
| addition reaction | esterification | organic acid |
| alcohol | ester | organic halide |
| aldehyde | ether | polymer |
| alkane | fermentation | polymerization |
| alkene | functional group | saponification |
| alkyne | hydrocarbon | saturated |
| amide | isomer | substitution reaction |
| amine | ketone | unsaturated |
| amino acid | | |

## Topic Overview

Organic chemistry is the study of carbon and most carbon compounds. The name *organic* is a remnant of a time when it was thought that carbon compounds could only be made by living things; hence the term *organic*. Today it is widely recognized that organic chemistry contains far more compounds than only those made by living things. The number of organic compounds is enormous. Tens of thousands of new organic compounds are discovered every year, and there seems to be no end in sight to future discoveries.

The number of carbon compounds far exceeds the number of inorganic compounds. Why can carbon form so many compounds? The answer lies in the ability of carbon atoms to bond with other carbon atoms to form chains, rings, and networks. In this topic you will be introduced to the wide variety of organic compounds and the types of reactions that they undergo.

## Bonding of Carbon Atoms

The ability of carbon to form many different compounds is based, to a large extent, on the tendency of carbon atoms to covalently bond with other carbon atoms and form chains. This process can be continued indefinitely, leading to chains of thousands of carbon atoms. Figure 11-1 shows electron dot diagrams of the ground state and the bonded state of a carbon atom and a three-dimensional representation of a tetrahedron with a carbon atom at its center. Note that when carbon bonds, the formerly paired electrons occupy separate orbitals, enabling carbon atoms to form four covalent bonds.

Study the diagram of carbon in Figure 11-1. Note that when carbon is in the bonded state it has four potential sites for covalent bonds. Although the

### Memory Jogger

Substances that are covalently bonded form molecules. They generally have low melting and boiling points, and are poor conductors of heat and electricity. They are generally nonpolar and tend to dissolve in nonpolar solvents. Covalently bonded substances tend to react more slowly than ionic compounds.

angle between adjacent electrons appears to be 90°, the atom is actually three dimensional, and the electrons are located at the corners of a tetrahedron with an angle of 109.5° between each pair of electrons.

Figure 11-2 shows carbon atoms sharing electrons to form a chain. In such diagrams, a single line is often used to represent the pair of shared electrons (C–C). When one pair of electrons is shared between two carbon atoms, the bond is called a <u>single covalent bond</u> (Figure 11-2A). Organic compounds containing only single bonds are said to be **saturated.**

Sometimes carbon atoms can share two pairs of electrons, forming a <u>double covalent bond</u> (Figure 11-2B) or even three pairs of electrons in a <u>triple</u> <u>covalent bond</u> (Figure 11-2C). Compounds containing one or more double or triple covalent bonds are called **unsaturated** compounds. In Figure 11-2, double and triple covalent bonds are represented by double and triple lines, respectively.

The chains of carbon atoms can be open or closed. Figure 11-3 shows six carbon atoms in both an open chain and a closed chain.

Carbon atoms can also bond with other carbon atoms forming three-dimensional networks. Diamonds are made of networks of carbon atoms in which each carbon atom is bonded to four other carbon atoms in a characteristic network structure. As recent discoveries have shown, carbon atoms can be arranged in large networks in which each carbon atom is bonded with a single bond to two other carbon atoms and with a double bond to one other carbon atom. The most common of these forms is buckminsterfullerene, also called a buckyball, which contains 60 carbon atoms forming a pattern similar to that on a soccer ball. The carbon atoms form a framework, and the inside of the network is empty space.

**Structural Formulas** The molecular formula shows the kind and number of atoms in a compound. For example, the molecular formula $C_3H_8$ tells the reader that the compound contains three carbon atoms and eight hydrogen atoms. Structural formulas attempt to show not only the kinds and numbers of atoms but also the bonding patterns and approximate shapes of molecules. Figure 11-4 shows the molecular formulas and structural formulas for two organic compounds. It is important to remember that these structural formulas are two-dimensional representations of three-dimensional molecules. Each carbon atom can be pictured as the center of a tetrahedron, and a short line can represent each of its covalent bonds.

# Hydrocarbons

Although there exists an extremely large number of organic compounds, the study of these compounds is simplified because they can be classified into groups called homologous series, the members of which have related

**Figure 11-1. Lewis diagrams of carbon and bonded carbon:** Carbon forms four equivalent covalent bonds. The tetrahedral molecular shape allows for equal spacing between these bonds.

| A Single covalent bonds | B A double covalent bond | C A triple covalent bond |
|---|---|---|
| ·C̈:C̈:C̈:C̈· | C̈::C̈:C̈:C̈· | ·C̈:::C̈:C̈:C̈· |
| C–C–C–C | C=C–C–C | C≡C–C–C |

**Figure 11-2. Carbon atoms share electrons in covalent bonds to form chains**

Open chain

Closed chain

**Figure 11-3: Open and closed carbon chains**

| | Methane | Ethane |
|---|---|---|
| Molecular Formula | $CH_4$ | $C_2H_6$ |
| Structural Formula | $\begin{array}{c} H \\ | \\ H-C-H \\ | \\ H \end{array}$ | $\begin{array}{c} H \quad H \\ | \quad | \\ H-C-C-H \\ | \quad | \\ H \quad H \end{array}$ |
| Condensed Structural Formula | $CH_4$ | $CH_3CH_3$ |
| Ball-and-Stick Model | | |
| Space-Filling Model | | |

**Figure 11-4. Various formulas and models of two organic compounds**

**Figure 11-5. The first five members of the alkane family**

Methane
$CH_4$

$\begin{array}{c} H \\ | \\ H-C-H \\ | \\ H \end{array}$

Ethane
$C_2H_6$

$\begin{array}{c} H \quad H \\ | \quad | \\ H-C-C-H \\ | \quad | \\ H \quad H \end{array}$

Propane
$C_3H_8$

$\begin{array}{c} H \quad H \quad H \\ | \quad | \quad | \\ H-C-C-C-H \\ | \quad | \quad | \\ H \quad H \quad H \end{array}$

Butane
$C_4H_{10}$

$\begin{array}{c} H \quad H \quad H \quad H \\ | \quad | \quad | \quad | \\ H-C-C-C-C-H \\ | \quad | \quad | \quad | \\ H \quad H \quad H \quad H \end{array}$

Pentane
$C_5H_{12}$

$\begin{array}{c} H \quad H \quad H \quad H \quad H \\ | \quad | \quad | \quad | \quad | \\ H-C-C-C-C-C-H \\ | \quad | \quad | \quad | \quad | \\ H \quad H \quad H \quad H \quad H \end{array}$

structures and properties. A homologous series of compounds is a group of related compounds in which each member differs from the one before it by the same additional unit.

**Hydrocarbons** are organic compounds that contain only atoms of hydrogen and carbon. These compounds are the parent compounds from which many other organic compounds are derived. Alkanes, alkenes, and alkynes are three important homologous series of hydrocarbons. By studying these series you will more easily understand other organic series closely related to them.

## Alkanes

The **alkanes** are a homologous series of saturated hydrocarbons that release energy when burned. Methane ($CH_4$), the first member of the series, comprises about 90% of natural gas, which is used to heat many homes. The second member, ethane ($C_2H_6$), accounts for most of the rest of natural gas. Propane ($C_3H_8$) is familiar as a home heating fuel and is also used for outdoor grills and camping equipment. The fourth alkane, butane ($C_4H_{10}$), is found in disposable lighters.

As the number of carbons increases in the alkane series, the boiling point increases. Chains of five to 12 carbon atoms are found in gasoline. Home heating oils contain 10 to 16 carbon atoms in chains. Paraffin wax, common in candles, contains 20 or more carbon atoms per chain, while road tar (asphalt) may contain 40 carbons in a chain. The names and molecular and structural formulas of the first five members of this series are found in Figure 11-5.

Study the formulas for the members of the alkane series shown in Figure 11-5. Notice that there is a constant relationship between each succeeding member. Ethane has one more carbon atom and two more hydrogen atoms than the preceding member, methane. The same relationship exists between propane and ethane, and butane and propane. This relationship, in which each successive member differs by one carbon atom and two hydrogen atoms ($CH_2$), from the previous member, defines the nature of a homologous series.

## Alkenes

The same relationship between successive members can be found in the homologous series of alkenes. Each member of the **alkene** series contains one double covalent bond.

Because there must be at least two carbon atoms to form a double bond, there is no alkene corresponding to methane of the alkane series. Ethene, the first member of the alkene series, has the formula $C_2H_4$. The addition of $CH_2$ to ethene produces propene ($C_3H_6$), the second member of the series. Note that the names of the members of the alkene series are derived from the names of the alkane chains with the same number of carbon atoms. The alkenes are named from the corresponding alkane by replacing the -*ane* of the alkane name to -*ene*. For example, the four carbon chain of the alkane series is butane, while butene is the four carbon chain of the alkene series. The first two alkenes are shown in Figure 11-6.

Alkenes provide chemists with starting materials to make other organic compounds. Probably the most important of these is ethene, whose common name is ethylene. When ethylene units are attached to each other to make very long chains, the product is polyethylene, a common plastic.

**Figure 11-6. Some members of the alkene and alkyne families**

## Alkynes

The **alkynes** are a homologous series of unsaturated hydrocarbons that contain one triple bond. The naming of the alkyne series repeats the pattern observed in the alkenes. To find the alkyne name, use the corresponding name from the alkane series, and change the -*ane* ending to -*yne*. Thus the first member of the series is ethyne ($C_2H_2$), as shown in Figure 11-6.

The alkynes, like the alkenes, provide chemists with starting materials to make other organic compounds. The first member of the series, ethyne, is commonly known as acetylene, used as a fuel in welding torches.

## General Formulas

In every homologous series there is a definite relationship between the number of carbon and hydrogen atoms. Note that in the alkene series, there are always twice as many hydrogen atoms as carbon atoms. Hence it is possible to show this by writing $C_nH_{2n}$, the general formula of alkenes. If it is known that a certain alkene contains 10 carbon atoms, then it will contain 20 hydrogen atoms.

Each corresponding member of the alkane series has two more hydrogen atoms than found in the alkenes. $C_4H_8$ is the formula of butene, but $C_4H_{10}$ is the formula of butane. The general formula of the alkanes shows this change by adding two hydrogen atoms to the general formula, $C_nH_{2n+2}$. Ethyne ($C_2H_2$) has two fewer hydrogens than are present in ethene ($C_2H_4$). In a similar way, all alkynes have two fewer hydrogen atoms than the corresponding alkenes. This is shown in the general formula of the alkynes, $C_nH_{2n-2}$. These relationships are summarized in Table Q of the *Reference Tables for Physical Setting/Chemistry*.

Ⓡ

# Review Questions

1. All organic compounds must contain the element

   (1) hydrogen      (3) carbon
   (2) nitrogen      (4) oxygen

2. Which element is composed of atoms that can form more than one covalent bond with one another?

   (1) hydrogen      (3) carbon
   (2) helium        (4) calcium

3. What is the total number of valence electrons in a carbon atom in the ground state?

   (1) 12     (2) 2     (3) 6     (4) 4

4. Which property is generally characteristic of an organic compound?

   (1) low melting point
   (2) high melting point
   (3) soluble in polar solvents
   (4) insoluble in nonpolar solvents

5. In general, which property do organic compounds share?

   (1) high melting point
   (2) high electrical conductivity
   (3) readily soluble in water
   (4) slow reaction rate

6. A hydrocarbon molecule containing one triple covalent bond is classified as an

   (1) alkene         (3) alkyne
   (2) alkane         (4) alkadiene

7. What is the total number of hydrogen atoms in a molecule of butene?

   (1) 10     (2) 6     (3) 8     (4) 4

8. By how many carbon atoms does each member of a homologous series differ from the previous member?

   (1) 1     (2) 2     (3) 3     (4) 4

9. Which of the following is a saturated hydrocarbon?

   (1) ethene        (3) propene
   (2) ethyne        (4) propane

10. What is the total number of pairs of electrons shared between the two adjacent carbon atoms in an ethyne molecule?

    (1) 1     (2) 2     (3) 3     (4) 4

11. Which compound is a member of the same homologous series as $C_3H_6$?

    (1) $C_2H_4$        (3) $C_3H_4$
    (2) $C_2H_6$        (4) $C_3H_8$

12. Which hydrocarbon is a member of the series with the general formula $C_nH_{2n-2}$?

    (1) ethyne        (3) butane
    (2) ethene        (4) benzene

13. Which compound belongs to the alkene series?

    (1) $C_2H_2$        (3) $C_6H_6$
    (2) $C_2H_4$        (4) $C_6H_{14}$

14. Which type of bond occurs in a saturated hydrocarbon molecule?

    (1) single covalent     (3) triple covalent
    (2) double covalent     (4) ionic

15. Which type of bonds and solids are characteristic of organic compounds?

    (1) ionic bonds and ionic solids
    (2) ionic bonds and molecular solids
    (3) covalent bonds and ionic solids
    (4) covalent bonds and molecular solids

16. The four single bonds of a carbon atom are directed in space toward the corners of a

    (1) regular tetrahedron
    (2) regular octahedron
    (3) square plane
    (4) trigonal bipyramid

17. In which group could the hydrocarbons all belong to the same homologous series?

    (1) $C_2H_2$, $C_2H_4$, $C_2H_6$     (3) $C_2H_4$, $C_2H_6$, $C_3H_6$
    (2) $C_2H_4$, $C_3H_4$, $C_4H_8$     (4) $C_2H_4$, $C_3H_6$, $C_4H_8$

18. Which formula represents butane?

    (1) $CH_3CH_3$        (3) $CH_3CH_2CH_2CH_3$
    (2) $CH_3CH_2CH_3$     (4) $CH_3CH_2CH_2CH_2CH_3$

## Isomers

Each of the alkanes listed on Figure 11-5 is composed of a continuous chain of carbon atoms. However, beginning with butane there is more than one way of combining the carbon and hydrogen atoms. In Figure 11-7, structural formulas show two different ways in which four carbon atoms and 10 hydrogen atoms can be combined. Not only can the carbon atoms be attached to each other in a continuous chain of four atoms, but they can also be arranged in a chain of three carbon atoms, with the fourth attached to the middle carbon. When a molecular formula can be represented by more than one structural arrangement, the compounds are called **isomers**. Isomers, while having the same molecular formula, have different chemical and physical properties. The boiling point of *n*-butane is 0.5°C, while its isomer boils at −10°C.

As the number of carbon atoms increases, so does the number of possible isomers. While butane has two isomers, octane ($C_8H_{18}$) has 18, and decane ($C_{10}H_{22}$) has 75. It is this ability to form isomers that is largely responsible for the large number of organic compounds.

## Naming Organic Compounds

When carbon atoms are attached to each other in one continuous chain, the compounds are called straight-chain hydrocarbons. This arrangement is called the normal form, and the letter *n-* precedes the name (*n*-butane). Compounds with branched chains must be given names that are different from the straight-chain name because they have different chemical and physical properties. The rules for naming organic compounds are governed by the International Union of Pure and Applied Chemistry (IUPAC). The following rules will produce names of branched compounds that are approved by the IUPAC.

Figure 11-7. Isomers of butane

1. Each compound is named by finding the longest continuous chain of carbon atoms. In the structure on the top in Figure 11-8, the longest chain consists of three carbon atoms, and, hence the compound is named as a derivative of propane, the third alkane. In the second example, the longest continuous chain consists of six carbon atoms, and the compound will be named as a hexane. Note that the chain does not have to appear as a straight chain, but it must be continuous.

2. While the name for the longest chain in the first example is propane, there is a $CH_3$ group attached to the chain. How should it be named? A group that contains one less hydrogen atom than an alkane with the same number of carbon atoms is classified as one of the <u>alkyl groups,</u> with a group name derived from the name of its corresponding alkane. Thus, the $CH_3$ that is attached to the propane belongs to the methyl group, so called because, like methane, it has one carbon atom. Table 11-1 shows the relationship between the alkanes and the common alkyl groups. The compound in the first example is called methyl propane. There is no need to identify the location of the methyl group because it can only be attached to the central carbon.

3. If necessary, the location of the alkyl group is shown by assigning numbers to the carbon atoms in the longest chain. The carbon chain must be numbered from the end that will give the lowest number for the attached group. In the second example, the compound should be named 2-methyl hexane rather than 5-methyl hexane.

4. There may be more than one of the same type of group attached to the parent chain. A prefix is used to indicate the number of attached groups of each type that are present. If two methyl groups are attached, the prefix *di-* will be used. *Tri-* will indicate three, and *tetra-*, four. In addition, commas are used to indicate the specific carbon to which each group is attached. For example, if two methyl groups are attached to the second carbon atom in a five-carbon chain, and another methyl

Methyl propane
$CH_3CH(CH_3)CH_3$

2-methyl hexane
$CH_3CH_2CH_2-CH_2-CH(CH_3)CH_3$

Figure 11-8. Naming organic compounds

group is attached to the third carbon atom, the compound would be 2,2,3-trimethyl pentane. When more than one group is attached to the parent chain, the chain must be numbered in such a way to produce the smaller total value of the attached chains.

### Table 11-1. Relationship of Alkanes and Alkyl Groups

| Alkane | | Alkyl Group | |
|---|---|---|---|
| Name | Formula | Name | Formula |
| methane | $CH_4$ | methyl | $CH_3$ |
| ethane | $C_2H_6$ | ethyl | $C_2H_5$ |
| *n*-propane | $C_3H_8$ | *n*-propyl | $C_3H_7$ |

# Review Questions

19. Which compound is an isomer of $C_4H_9OH$?

    (1) $C_3H_7CH_3$
    (2) $C_2H_5OC_2H_5$
    (3) $C_2H_5COOC_2H_5$
    (4) $CH_3COOH$

20. Which compound is an isomer of $CH_3CH_2OH$?

    (1) $CH_3COOH$
    (2) $CH_3CH_2CH_3$
    (3) $CH_3OCH_3$
    (4) $CH_3COCH_3$

21. Which formula represents an isomer of the compound propanoic acid ($CH_3CH_2COOH$)?

    (1) $CH_3CH_2CH_2OH$
    (2) $CH_3CH_2CH_2COOH$
    (3) $CH_3CH(OH)CH_2OH$
    (4) $CH_3COOCH_3$

22. Given the compound:

    H H H
    | | |
    H—C—C—C—Cl
    | | |
    H H Cl

    Which structural formula represents an isomer?

    (1)
    H H H H
    | | | |
    H—C—C—C—C—Cl
    | | | |
    H H H Cl

    (3)
    H H H
    | | |
    H—C—C—C—Cl
    | | |
    H H H

    (2)
    H H H H
    | | | |
    Cl—C—C—C—C—Cl
    | | | |
    H H H Cl

    (4)
    H H H
    | | |
    Cl—C—C—C—H
    | | |
    H Cl H

23. Which compounds are isomers?

    (1) $CH_3Br$ and $CH_2Br_2$
    (2) $CH_3OH$ and $CH_3CH_2OH$
    (3) $CH_3OH$ and $CH_3CHO$
    (4) $CH_3OCH_3$ and $CH_3CH_2OH$

24. An −*ol* suffix indicates that an −OH group has been added to a hydrocarbon. Which formula represents 1,2-ethanediol?

    (1) $C_2H_4(OH)_2$
    (2) $C_3H_5(OH)_3$
    (3) $Ca(OH)_2$
    (4) $Co(OH)_3$

25. Which structural formula represents 1,1-dibromopropane?

    (1)
    H H
    | |
    H—C—C—H
    | |
    Br Br

    (3)
    H H H
    | | |
    H—C—C—C—H
    | | |
    Br Br H

    (2)
    Br H
    | |
    H—C—C—H
    | |
    Br H

    (4)
    Br H H
    | | |
    H—C—C—C—H
    | | |
    Br H H

26. Which is an isomer of ?

    (1)
    H H
    | |
    H—C—O—C—H
    | |
    H H

    (3)
    H O
    | ‖
    H—C—C—H
    |
    H

    (2)
    H H
    | |
    HO—C—C—H
    | |
    H H

    (4)
    H H H
    | | |
    H—C—C—O—C—H
    | | |
    H H H

27. Which compound has the molecular formula $C_5H_{12}$?

    (1) butane
    (2) pentane
    (3) 2,2-dimethyl butane
    (4) 2,2-dimethyl pentane

**28.** Which is the correct IUPAC name for the hydrocarbon with the structural formula shown below?

(1) 1-methyl-2-ethylenethane     (3) *n*-propane
(2) 1-propylethane              (4) *n*-pentane

**29.** Write the structural formula for 3-methyl pentane.

**30.** Write the structural formula for 2, 2-dimethyl hexane.

**31.** Write the structural formula for 2-methyl, 3-ethyl hexane.

**32.** Write the structural formula for 2,2,3-trimethyl heptane.

**33.** Write the structural formula for 3,3-dimethyl, 4-ethyl octane.

---

# Functional Groups

Although hydrocarbons are the most basic organic compounds, many other organic compounds form when other atoms replace one or more hydrogen atoms in a hydrocarbon. These atoms or groups of atoms, called **functional groups,** replace hydrogen atoms in a hydrocarbon and give the compound distinctive physical and chemical properties. The naming of these compounds is made easy because they derive their names from the hydrocarbon with the corresponding number of carbon atoms.

## Halides

When any of the halogens (F, Cl, Br, or I) replaces a hydrogen atom in an alkane, the compound is called an **organic halide,** or halocarbon. The functional group of an organic halide is the halogen that is attached to the chain. Organic halides are often used as organic solvents and are found in some pesticides. They are named by citing the location of the halogen attached to the chain. Figure 11-9 shows some examples of halocarbons and shows how the chain is numbered when necessary to show the location of the halogen.

## Alcohols

**Alcohols** are organic compounds in which one or more hydrogen atoms of a hydrocarbon are replaced by an –OH group. The –OH group is called a hydroxyl group and is the functional group that gives alcohols their specific chemical and physical properties. Although the –OH group resembles the hydroxide ion of inorganic bases, it does not form an ion in water. Hence, alcohols are nonelectrolytes and do not turn indicators characteristic acid or basic colors. While these hydroxyl groups do not form ions in solution, they are quite polar. This polarity allows alcohols to be soluble in water, which is also polar.

There are several different types of alcohols. The type is dependent on the number of hydroxyl groups in the compound and on the position of each hydroxyl group on the main carbon chain.

**Classification of Alcohols** Alcohols are classified as primary, secondary, or tertiary based on whether the hydroxyl group is attached to a primary,

Chloromethane
$CH_3Cl$

2-fluoropropane
$CH_3CHFCH_3$

2,2,3-trichlorobutane
$CH_3-CCl_2CHClCH_3$

**Figure 11-9. Some typical organic halides**

Figure 11-10. **Some representative alcohols**

Primary
1-butanol
(monohydroxy)

Secondary
2-butanol
(monohydroxy)

Tertiary
2-methyl, 2-propanol
(monohydroxy)

1,2-ethanediol
(dihydroxy)

1,2,3-propanetriol
(trihydroxy)

secondary, or tertiary carbon atom. Primary carbon atoms are attached directly to only one other carbon atom and are located at the end of a chain or branch. Secondary carbon atoms are directly attached to two other carbon atoms. Tertiary carbon atoms are attached directly to three other carbon atoms.

Alcohols are classified according to the carbon atom to which the hydroxyl group is attached. A <u>primary alcohol</u> has a hydroxyl group attached to a primary carbon atom at the end of the chain. Primary alcohols are represented by $R$–OH or $RCH_2OH$, where the $R$ represents a hydrocarbon chain in which a hydrogen atom is replaced by the functional group shown.

A <u>secondary alcohol</u> has a hydroxyl group attached to a secondary carbon atom. Secondary alcohols can be represented by $R$–CH(OH)–$R'$, where $R$ and $R'$ represent two hydrocarbon chains.

A <u>tertiary alcohol</u> has a hydroxyl group attached to a tertiary carbon atom. A tertiary alcohol can be represented by $R_1R_2R_3COH$.

**Dihydroxy and Trihydroxy Alcohols** Alcohols can also be classified by the number of hydroxyl groups that are attached to the carbon chain. In addition to alcohols that have one hydroxyl group (monohydroxy), there are families of alcohols with two or more attached groups. Ethylene glycol, also known as antifreeze, is the common name for a dihydroxy (two hydroxyl groups) alcohol. Its proper name is 1,2-ethanediol. 1,2,3-propanetriol is another common substance, glycerol, which is used as a moistening agent in cosmetics. Figure 11-10 shows examples of the various types of alcohols.

## Other Substituted Hydrocarbons

**Aldehydes** When an oxygen atom is attached to a carbon chain by a double covalent bond, it is called a carbonyl group (–C=O). **Aldehydes** are organic compounds in which the carbonyl group is found on the end carbon (a primary carbon), as shown in Figure 11-11. Aldehydes are named by substituting –*al* in place of the final –*e* of the corresponding alkane name. The first member of the series has the IUPAC name methanal. Its common name is formaldehyde, and it is used as a preservative. An aldehyde can be recognized from

Propanal,
an
aldehyde

Propanone,
a
ketone

Figure 11-11. **An aldehyde and a ketone:** Both aldehydes and ketones contain the carbonyl group.

its structural formula by the presence of a double bonded oxygen atom together with a hydrogen atom attached to an end carbon.

**Ketones** A **ketone** is formed when the carbonyl group (–C=O) is found on an interior carbon atom that is attached to two other carbon atoms, as shown in Figure 11-11. Ketones are named by replacing the final –*e* from the corresponding alkane name with –*one*. The first ketone is formed by a carbonyl group attached to the central carbon atom of a chain of three carbon atoms. Its IUPAC name is propanone. The common name of propanone is acetone. Ketones are often used as solvents. The carbonyl group is quite polar, allowing the ketone to dissolve in water. The remainder of the molecule causes the ketone to be soluble in other organic compounds.

**Ethers** **Ethers** are a series of organic compounds in which two carbon chains are joined together by an oxygen atom bonded between two carbon atoms. The general formula is written R–O–R' to show the oxygen bridge between the two carbon chains. Structures and common and IUPAC names for some ethers are shown in Figure 11-12.

**Organic Acids** **Organic acids** are a homologous series of organic compounds whose functional group is a carboxyl group (–COOH). Organic acids derive their names from the corresponding hydrocarbons by replacing the –*e* with –*oic acid*. Thus the two-carbon hydrocarbon is ethane, while the corresponding acid is ethanoic acid. Ethanoic acid is commonly known as acetic acid, which is found in vinegar. Although most organic compounds are nonelectrolytes, organic acids are generally weak electrolytes.

**Esters** **Esters** are organic compounds whose type formula is R–CO–OR'. The R–CO–O– part of the formula comes from an organic acid, and the R' part of the formula comes from an alcohol. Esters have strong, fragrant aromas and are responsible for the odors of many foods and flavorings, such as pineapples, bananas, wintergreen, and oranges.

**Amines** Perhaps the easiest way to understand amines is as a derivative of ammonia. An **amine** is formed when one or more of the hydrogen atoms of ammonia are replaced by an alkyl group. To name an amine, the –*e* ending of the alkane name is changed to end in –*amine*, and the alkane chain is numbered to show the location of the amine group. Figure 11-13 shows the relation of amines to ammonia. Amines are important biological chemicals present in the B vitamins, hormones, and anesthetics. They are also used commercially in the preparation of dyes.

**Amino Acids** Like all organic acids, **amino acids** contain the carboxylic group (–COOH) but also contain an amine group. The amine group is attached to the carbon atom that is adjacent to the acid group (Figure 11-14). The remainder of the molecule is represented by R, which indicates the side chain. There are ten essential amino acids that the body must obtain through diet because it cannot synthesize them. The remaining amino acids can be synthesized. Amino acids are the building blocks of protein.

**Figure 11-12. Some common ethers**

**Figure 11-13. The relation of amines and ammonia**

**Figure 11-14. An amino acid:** Amino acids have both an acid group and an amine group.

## Digging Deeper

Proteins are extremely long chains of amino acids. They have molecular masses well over 100 000 atomic mass units. These proteins are different sequences of 20 different amino acids, providing an almost infinite variety of combinations. Proteins compose the tendons and contractile myosin of our muscles, the hemoglobin in our blood, and many essential enzymes and hormones.

**Figure 11-15. Formation of an amide:** Two amino acids combine to form an amide (peptide).

**Amides** When one of the hydrogen atoms of the amino group reacts with the –OH of an organic acid, a condensation reaction occurs. This reaction produces water and an **amide**, which is a compound formed by the combination of the two amino acids. Look at Figure 11-15. Peptide bonding holds amino acid molecules together, forming long protein chains. While organic chemists call this linkage an amide, biologists refer to it as a peptide link. Additional condensation reactions occur, first producing a polypeptide. Eventually the chain is long enough to be a protein.

# Review Questions

**34.** When the name of an alcohol is derived from the corresponding alkane, the final –e of the name of the alkane should be replaced by the suffix

(1) –al    (2) –ol    (3) –one    (4) –ole

**35.** In a secondary alcohol, the carbon bonded to the –OH group must also be bonded to

(1) one carbon atom    (3) three carbon atoms
(2) two carbon atoms    (4) four carbon atoms.

**36.** Which class of compounds has the general formula R–O–R'?

(1) esters    (3) ethers
(2) alcohols    (4) aldehydes

**37.** The formula $C_5H_{11}OH$ represents an

(1) acid    (3) ether
(2) ester    (4) alcohol

**38.** The general formula R–COOH represents a class of compounds called

(1) alkanes    (3) acids
(2) alkenes    (4) alcohols

**39.** Which structural formula represents a secondary alcohol?

**40.** Which is the general formula for an aldehyde?

**41.** Which structural formula represents a tertiary alcohol?

**42.** Which structural formula represents a tertiary alcohol?

**43.** Which functional group is found in all organic acids?

**44.** Which general formula represents a ketone?

(1) $R-\overset{\overset{O}{\|}}{C}-R'$

(3) $R-OH$

(2) $R-\overset{\overset{O}{\|}}{C}-O-R'$

(4) $R-\overset{O}{\underset{OH}{C}}$

**45.** Which structural formula represents a monohydroxy alcohol?

**46.** The molecule $CH_3-\overset{\overset{O}{\|}}{C}-CH_3$ is a member of a class of organic compounds called

(1) ethers      (3) alcohols
(2) ketones     (4) aldehydes

**47.** Which is the structural formula for 2-propanol?

**48.** Which is the general formula for organic acids?

---

## Organic Reactions

Organic reactions generally occur more slowly than inorganic reactions. When covalently bonded substances react, they must first break relatively strong existing bonds before making new bonds.

### Combustion

Perhaps the most common type of organic reaction is <u>combustion</u>. Almost all organic compounds will burn. When sufficient oxygen is present, hydrocarbons will burn to produce water and carbon dioxide. Propane, commonly used in outdoor grills, burns according to the following equation.

$$C_3H_8(g) + 5O_2(g) \rightarrow 3CO_2(g) + 4H_2O(g)$$

When the supply of oxygen is limited, carbon monoxide may be produced instead of carbon dioxide.

$$2C_3H_8(g) + 7O_2(g) \rightarrow 6CO(g) + 8H_2O(g)$$

When carbon dioxide is produced the reaction is called complete combustion, while incomplete combustion describes the production of carbon monoxide and water.

### Substitution

A **substitution reaction** involves the replacement of one or more of the hydrogen atoms in a saturated hydrocarbon with another atom or group. For example, halogen atoms can replace hydrogen atoms in saturated hydrocarbons. When ethane reacts with chlorine in a substitution reaction, the products of the reaction are chloroethane and hydrogen chloride.

$$C_2H_6 + Cl_2 \rightarrow C_2H_5Cl + HCl$$

Because all of the bonding sites on a saturated hydrocarbon are filled, chlorine must first remove a hydrogen atom from the hydrocarbon chain, forming hydrogen chloride. The removal of a hydrogen atom from the chain provides an open bond site where a chlorine atom can then attach itself.

### Addition

**Addition reactions** involve adding one or more atoms at a double or triple bond. When ethene and chlorine react, the double bond of the ethene is opened and a chlorine atom is added to each carbon atom.

$$C_2H_4 + Cl_2 \rightarrow C_2H_4Cl_2$$

Unsaturated hydrocarbons can also react with hydrogen by addition reactions. In this case, the final product is a saturated hydrocarbon.

$$C_2H_4 + H_2 \rightarrow C_2H_6$$

## Esterification

**Esterification** is the reaction between an organic acid and an alcohol to produce an ester plus water. An example of an esterification reaction between acetic acid and ethanol to produce the ester ethyl ethanoate is shown in Figure 11-16. Sulfuric acid is used as a dehydrating agent. It removes two hydrogen atoms and an oxygen atom to form water, with the remaining fragments combining to form the ester. Esters are named by using the alkyl name of the alcohol followed by the acid group modified to end in −*oate*. The ester produced by the reaction of methanol with ethanoic acid is methyl ethanoate.

## Saponification

When an ester reacts with an inorganic base to produce an alcohol and a soap, the reaction is called a **saponification** reaction (Figure 11-17). One of the most common saponification reactions involves the reaction of a fat with a strong base such as sodium hydroxide. The products of this reaction are soap and glycerol.

## Fermentation

**Fermentation** is a chemical process in which yeast cells secrete the enzyme zymase and break the six-carbon chain of sugars into carbon dioxide and two-carbon fragments of alcohol. The following equation shows what happens during fermentation.

$$C_6H_{12}O_6 \rightarrow 2C_2H_5OH + 2CO_2$$

**Figure 11-16. Esterification:** An acid and an alcohol react to produce water and an ester.

**Figure 11-17. Saponification:** A fat and an alkali react to produce glycerol and a soap, which is a salt of a fatty acid.

## Polymerization

**Polymers** are organic compounds made up of chains of smaller units covalently bonded together. The formation of these large polymer molecules is called **polymerization,** and each individual unit of a polymer is called a <u>monomer.</u> Synthetic plastics such as nylon, rayon, and polyethylene, are the best-known polymers. There are also many naturally occurring polymers, such as proteins, starches, and cellulose.

**Addition Polymerization** <u>Addition polymerization</u> reactions involve the joining of monomers of unsaturated compounds. When the double bond between the carbon atoms of ethene breaks, the resulting bond site is called a free radical because of the two unbonded electrons. These electrons can bond with similar open bonds of adjacent molecules to form long chains. A typical addition polymerization reaction can be shown as follows.

$$n C_2H_2 \rightarrow (C_2H_2)_n$$

**Condensation Polymerization** Condensation polymerization reactions result from the bonding of monomers by removing water from hydroxyl groups and joining the monomers by an ether or ester linkage.

# Review Questions

**49.** Which type of reaction do ethane molecules and ethene molecules undergo when they react with chlorine?

(1) Ethane and ethene both react by addition.
(2) Ethane and ethene both react by substitution.
(3) Ethane reacts by substitution and ethene reacts by addition.
(4) Ethane reacts by addition and ethene reacts by substitution.

**50.** Which type of reaction is represented by the following equation?

H-O-C-C-O-H + H-O-C-C-O-H ⟶

H-O-C-C-O-C-C-O-H + $H_2O$

(1) condensation polymerization
(2) addition polymerization
(3) esterification
(4) saponification

**51.** Which substance is made up of monomers joined together in long chains?

(1) ketone          (3) ester
(2) protein         (4) acid

**52.** Which equation represents a substitution reaction?

(1) $CH_4 + 2O_2 \rightarrow CO_2 + 2H_2O$
(2) $C_2H_4 + Br_2 \rightarrow C_2H_4Br_2$
(3) $C_3H_6 + H_2 \rightarrow C_3H_8$
(4) $C_4H_{10} + Cl_2 \rightarrow C_4H_9Cl + HCl$

**53.** When $C_3H_8$ burns completely in an excess of oxygen, the products formed are

(1) CO and $H_2O$
(2) $CO_2$ and $H_2O$
(3) CO and $H_2$
(4) $CO_2$ and $H_2$

**54.** Molecules of propene combine in a chemical reaction to produce a single molecule. The reaction is called

(1) substitution
(2) saponification
(3) polymerization
(4) esterification

**55.** The reaction represented by

$CH_3CHCH_2 + Br_2 \rightarrow CH_3CHBrCH_2Br$

is an example of

(1) fermentation
(2) addition
(3) substitution
(4) saponification

56. What are the products of a fermentation reaction?

    (1) an ester and water
    (2) a salt and water
    (3) an alcohol and carbon dioxide
    (4) a soap and glycerol

57. Which equation represents an addition reaction?

    (1) $CH_4 + O_2 \rightarrow CO_2 + 2H_2O$
    (2) $C_2H_6 + Br_2 \rightarrow C_2H_5Br + HBr$
    (3) $C_3H_6 + Cl_2 \rightarrow C_3H_6Cl_2$
    (4) $C_4H_{10} + Cl_2 \rightarrow C_4H_9Cl + HCl$

58. Which hydrocarbon will undergo a substitution reaction with chlorine?

    (1) methane
    (2) ethyne
    (3) propene
    (4) butene

59. The equation

    $$CH_3OH + CH_3OH \rightarrow CH_3OCH_3 + H_2O$$

    illustrates the

    (1) oxidation of alcohols to form a ketone
    (2) oxidation of alcohols to form an acid
    (3) dehydration of alcohols to form a polymer
    (4) dehydration of alcohols to form an ether

60. Which type of reaction is represented by the following equation?

    $$C_6H_{12}O_6 \rightarrow 2C_2H_5OH + 2CO_2$$

    (1) saponification
    (2) polymerization
    (3) esterification
    (4) fermentation

61. Which process usually produces water as one of the products?

    (1) cracking
    (2) hydrolysis
    (3) addition polymerization
    (4) condensation polymerization

62. Esterification is the reaction of an acid with

    (1) water
    (2) an alcohol
    (3) a base
    (4) a salt

63. (a) Write the structure of two different amino acids.

    (b) Show how these two acids would combine to become an amide (show a peptide linkage).

64. Write a word equation for a saponification reaction.

65. Explain the difference between a substitution reaction and a replacement reaction.

**For each substance in questions 66 through 70, write the number of the organic reaction, chosen from the list below, that will produce this substance.**

### Organic Reactions

    (1) esterification
    (2) saponification
    (3) polymerization
    (4) fermentation
    (5) substitution
    (6) halogen addition

66. ethanol

67. glycerol

68. methyl acetate

69. polyethylene

70. dichloromethane

## Directions

Review the Test–Taking Strategies section of this book. Then answer the following questions. Read each question carefully and answer with a correct choice or response.

## Part A

1 In the alkane series, each molecule contains
  (1) only one double bond
  (2) two double bonds
  (3) one triple bond
  (4) all single bonds

2 Which kind of bond is most common in organic compounds?
  (1) covalent         (3) hydrogen
  (2) ionic            (4) metallic

3 A carbon atom in an alkane has a total of
  (1) two covalent bonds   (3) four covalent bonds
  (2) two ionic bonds      (4) four ionic bonds

4 What is the maximum number of covalent bonds that a carbon atom can form?
  (1) 1        (2) 2        (3) 3        (4) 4

5 A hydrocarbon molecule is saturated if the molecule contains
  (1) single covalent bonds only
  (2) only one double covalent bond
  (3) a triple covalent bond
  (4) single and double covalent bonds

6 Which statement explains why the element carbon forms so many compounds?
  (1) Carbon atoms combine readily with oxygen.
  (2) Carbon atoms have a high electronegativity value.
  (3) Carbon atoms readily form ionic bonds with other carbon atoms.
  (4) Carbon atoms readily form covalent bonds with other carbon atoms.

7 In the alkane family, each member differs from the preceding member by one carbon atom and two hydrogen atoms. Such a series of hydrocarbons is called
  (1) a homologous series
  (2) a periodic series
  (3) an actinide series
  (4) a lanthanide series

8 A molecule of ethane and a molecule of ethene both have the same
  (1) empirical formula
  (2) molecular formula
  (3) number of carbon atoms
  (4) number of hydrogen atoms

9 The products of condensation polymerization are a polymer and
  (1) carbon dioxide        (3) ethanol
  (2) water                 (4) glycerol

10 Which type of compound is represented by the structural formula shown below?

  (1) a ketone          (3) an ester
  (2) an aldehyde       (4) an ether

11 If a hydrocarbon molecule contains a triple bond, its IUPAC name ends in
  (1) *-ane*    (2) *-ene*    (3) *-one*    (4) *-yne*

12 Which compound is an organic acid?
  (1) $CH_3OH$              (3) $CH_3COOH$
  (2) $CH_3OCH_3$           (4) $CH_3COOCH_3$

13 Which is the structural formula of an aldehyde?

14 Which general formula represents an ether?
  (1) *R*–OH               (3) *R*–O–*R'*
  (2) *R*–CHO              (4) *R*–COOH

15 What are the products of a fermentation reaction?
  (1) an alcohol and carbon monoxide
  (2) an alcohol and carbon dioxide
  (3) a salt and water
  (4) a salt and an acid

# Part B

**16** Which compounds are isomers?
(1) 1-propanol and 2-propanol
(2) methanoic acid and ethanoic acid
(3) methanol and methanal
(4) ethane and ethanol

**17** Which is the correct structural formula for 2, 2-dimethylpropane?

(1)

(2)

(3)

(4)

**18** What is the chemical process illustrated by the following equation?

$$C_6H_{12}O_6 \rightarrow 2C_2H_5OH + 2CO_2$$

(1) fermentation       (3) esterification
(2) saponification     (4) polymerization

**19** Which reaction is used to produce polyethylene $(C_2H_4)_n$ from ethylene?
(1) addition polymerization
(2) substitution
(3) condensation polymerization
(4) reduction

**20** Which structural formula represents the product formed from the reaction of $Cl_2$ and $C_2H_4$?

(1)
```
    H  H
    |  |
H — C — C — H
    |  |
    Cl Cl
```

(2)
```
    Cl Cl
    |  |
H — C = C — H
```

(3)   H — C ≡ C — Cl

(4)
```
    H  H
    |  |
H — C — C — Cl
    |  |
    H  H
```

**21** Methanol is classified as a
(1) monohydroxy alcohol
(2) secondary alcohol
(3) tertiary alcohol
(4) dihydroxy alcohol

**22** What is the total number of pairs of electrons that one carbon atom shares with the other carbon atom in the molecule $C_2H_4$?
(1) 1        (3) 3
(2) 2        (4) 4

**23** To be classified as a tertiary alcohol, the functional —OH group is bonded to a carbon atom that must be bonded to how many other carbon atoms?
(1) 1        (3) 3
(2) 2        (4) 4

24 A student investigated four different substances in the solid phase. The table below is a record of the characteristics (marked with an X) exhibited by each substance. Which substance has characteristics most like those of an organic compound?

| Characteristic Tested | Substance | | | |
|---|---|---|---|---|
| | A | B | C | D |
| High melting point | X | | X | |
| Low melting point | | X | | X |
| Soluble in water | X | | | X |
| Insoluble in water | | X | X | |
| Decomposed under high heat | | X | | |
| Stable under high heat | X | | X | X |
| Electrolyte | X | | | X |
| Nonelectrolyte | | X | X | |

(1) A          (2) B          (3) C          (4) D

25 Which hydrocarbon is a member of the alkene family?
(1) $C_2H_2$
(2) $C_3H_6$
(3) $C_4H_{10}$
(4) $C_5H_{12}$

26 Which structural formula represents a dihydroxy alcohol?

(1)

(2)

(3)

(4)

27 Which organic compound will dissolve in water to produce a solution that will turn blue litmus red?

28 The compound 1,2-ethanediol is a
(1) monohydroxy alcohol
(2) dihydroxy alcohol
(3) primary alcohol
(4) secondary alcohol

29 Which formula represents a ketone?
(1) $CH_3COOH$
(2) $C_2H_5OH$
(3) $CH_3COCH_3$
(4) $CH_3COOCH_3$

30 Which condensed structural formula represents a saturated hydrocarbon?
(1) $CH_3CH_2CH_2OH$
(2) $CH_3CHOHCH_3$
(3) $CH_3CH_2CH_3$
(4) $CH_2CHCH_3$

# Part C

**Base your answers to questions 31 and 32 on the condensed structural formula below.**

$$CH_3CH_2CHCH_2$$

31 Draw the structural formula for this compound. [1]

32 The formula below represents a product formed when HCl reacts with $CH_3CH_2CHCH_2$

```
    H   H   H   H
    |   |   |   |
H — C — C — C — C — H
    |   |   |   |
    H   Cl  H   H
```

What is the IUPAC name for this product? [1]

33 Given the equation:

Butanoic acid + 1-pentanol → water + X

To which class of compounds does product X belong? [1]

34 Identify the homologous series to which $CH_2CHCH_2$ belongs. [1]

**Base your answers to questions 35 and 36 on the information below.**

35 Given the reaction between 1-butene and chlorine gas:

$$C_4H_8 + Cl_2 \rightarrow C_4H_8Cl_2$$

Which type of chemical reaction is represented by this equation? [1]

36 Draw the structural formula of the product, 1,2-dichlorobutane. [1]

37 The condensed structural formula for n-pentane is $CH_3CH_2CH_2CH_2CH_3$. Draw the structural formula of an isomer of *n*-pentane. [1]

**Base your answers for questions 38 and 39 on the information below.**

Given the balanced equation for an organic reaction between butane and chlorine:

$$C_4H_{10} + Cl_2 \rightarrow C_4H_9Cl + HCl$$

38 Identify the type of organic reaction shown. [1]

39 Draw a structural formula for the organic product. [1]

**Base your answers to questions 40 and 41 on the information below.**

Many esters have distinctive odors, which lead to their widespread use as artificial flavorings and fragrances. For example, methyl butanoate has an odor similar to pineapple and ethyl methanoate has an odor similar to raspberry.

40 Draw a structural formula for the ester that has an odor similar to pineapple. [1]

41 What is the chemical name for the alcohol that reacts with methanoic acid to produce the ester that has an odor similar to raspberry? [1]

42 Draw a structural formula for 2,2,4-trimethylpentane.

**Base your answers to questions 43 through 45 on the information below.**

The incomplete equation below represents an esterification reaction. The alcohol is represented by X.

```
    H O                        H O     H H H
    | ||                       | ||    | | |
H — C — C — OH  +  X  catalyst→  H — C — C — O — C — C — C — H  +  H₂O
    |                          |       | | |
    H                          H       H H H
```

43 Circle only the acid functional group. [1]

44 Write the IUPAC name for the reactant represented by its structural formula in this equation. [1]

45 Draw the structural formula for the alcohol represented in this equation. [1]

# Nuclear Chemistry

## What **You Know** **About** Nuclear Chemistry

**?** *Are you ready for a debate?* **?**

Danger! Danger! Nuclear radiation! Or is it so dangerous? In addition to generating power, scientists make daily use of nuclear energy in industry, medicine, and research. As you study this topic, think about the pros and cons of nuclear power.

- **What makes nuclear power unique?**

- **How are nuclear reactions different from ordinary chemical reactions?**

- **Is nuclear chemistry a natural or human-made phenomenon?**

- **What are the uses and dangers of nuclear chemistry?**

# 12 Nuclear Chemistry

## Vocabulary

| | | |
|---|---|---|
| alpha particle | fusion | radioisotope |
| artificial transmutation | gamma ray | tracer |
| beta particle | half-life | transmutation |
| fission | natural transmutation | |

## Topic Overview

Most chemical reactions involve either the exchange or sharing of electrons between atoms. Nuclear chemistry is quite different in nature because it involves changes in the nucleus. When the atomic nucleus of one element is changed into the nucleus of a different element, the reaction is called a **transmutation.** In this topic you will study various types of transmutations and learn about properties of radioactive substances.

## Stability of Nuclei

Nuclei are composed of combinations of protons and neutrons. Hydrogen, with one proton, is the only element that does not contain one or more neutrons. Most nuclei are stable; that is, they are found within the "belt of stability" shown in Figure 12-1. It is the ratio of neutrons to protons that determines the stability of a given nucleus. The ratio in all nuclei with atomic numbers greater than 83 makes those nuclei unstable.

Because of this instability, all nuclei with atomic numbers greater than 83 are also radioactive, as explained in the next paragraph. For any element, an isotope that is unstable and thus radioactive is called a **radioisotope.**

An unstable nucleus decays in a series of steps which eventually produce a stable nucleus in the belt of stability. When an unstable nucleus decays, it emits radiation in the form of alpha particles, beta particles, positrons, and/or gamma radiation. An **alpha particle** is a helium nucleus composed of two protons and two neutrons. It is represented by the symbol $^4_2He$ or the symbol $\alpha$, which is the Greek letter alpha. A **beta particle** $(\beta^-)$ is an electron whose source is an atomic nucleus, while a positron $(\beta^+)$ is identical to an electron except that it has a positive charge. Almost all nuclear decay also releases some energy in the

Figure 12-1. **Composition of stable nuclei**

form of **gamma rays** ($\gamma$), which are similar to X rays but have greater energy.

Figure 12-2 shows how alpha particles, beta particles and gamma rays react to an electric field. Table 12-1 summarizes information about each type of radiation.

Radiation can be harmful when it interacts with living things. Serious damage occurs when radioactivity causes ionization of normal tissue. When molecules in a cell are ionized, they may no longer carry on their normal functions and thus may cause the death of the cell. Other interactions of radioactivity with the DNA of a cell may cause mutations to occur. When these mutations occur in sperm or egg cells, they can cause mutations to be transmitted from generation to generation.

## Alpha Decay

When an unstable nucleus emits an alpha particle, the nucleus is called an alpha emitter. Alpha emission is characteristic of heavy nuclei, especially of atoms with atomic numbers greater than 82. As a nucleus emits an alpha particle, its atomic number decreases by two (the two protons of the alpha particle), and its mass number decreases by four (the two protons and two neutrons of the alpha particle). For example, when radium-226 emits an alpha particle, its atomic number decreases by two, from 88 to 86. It is then no longer an atom of radium; it has become an atom of radon (atomic number 86). During the process, the nucleus has lost a total of 4 amu, and the new radon nucleus has a total mass of 222. The alpha decay of radium-226 is shown in Figure 12-3. The process is a transmutation because the atom undergoes a change in its atomic number and becomes a different element.

Alpha decay can be summarized as follows.

- atomic number decreases by two
- number of protons decreases by two
- number of neutrons decreases by two
- mass number decreases by four

## Beta Decay

A nucleus that emits a beta particle as a result of nuclear disintegration is said to undergo beta decay and is called a beta emitter. Beta decay is interpreted as the emission of an

**Figure 12-2. Separation of radioactive emissions:** Because they are positively charged, alpha particles are attracted to the negative plate. Because they are negatively charged, beta particles are attracted to the positively charged plate. Because they have no charge, gamma rays are undeflected in an electrical field. Alpha particles are not deflected as much as beta particles because alpha particles are more massive.

| Table 12-1. Some Common Forms of Radiation | | | | |
|---|---|---|---|---|
| Particle | Mass | Charge | Symbol | Penetrating Power |
| Alpha | 4 amu | 2+ | $^{4}_{2}He$, $\alpha$ | low |
| Beta | 0 amu | 1− | $^{0}_{-1}e$, $\beta^-$ | moderate |
| Positron | 0 amu | 1+ | $^{0}_{+1}e$, $\beta^+$ | moderate |
| Gamma | 0 amu | none | $\gamma$ | high |

$$^{226}_{88}Ra \longrightarrow \,^{222}_{86}Rn \;+\; ^{4}_{2}He$$

**Figure 12-3. Alpha decay:** In alpha decay, a nucleus ejects an alpha particle and becomes a smaller nucleus with less positive charge.

**Figure 12-4. Beta decay:** Beta decay has the effect of turning a neutron in the nucleus into a proton and an electron.

electron during the conversion of a neutron to a proton.

$$_0^1 n \rightarrow {}_1^1 p + {}_{-1}^0 e$$

When a nucleus emits a beta particle, which has a charge of 1−, the charge on the nucleus increases by one, which also means that the atomic number increases by one. The beta decay of lead-214 to bismuth-214 is shown in Figure 12-4.

Beta decay can be summarized as follows.

- atomic number increases by one
- number of protons increases by one
- number of neutrons decreases by one
- mass number remains the same

### Positron Emission

Positron emission is interpreted as the production of a positron during the conversion of a proton to a neutron.

$$_1^1 p \rightarrow {}_0^1 n + {}_{+1}^0 e$$

When a nucleus emits a positron, which has a charge of 1+, the charge on the nucleus decreases by one, and thus the atomic number decreases by one. For example the positron emission of potassium-37 to argon-37 is represented by the following equation.

$$_{19}^{37} K \rightarrow {}_{18}^{37} Ar + {}_{+1}^0 e$$

Positron emission can be summarized as follows.

- atomic number decreases by one
- number of protons decreases by one
- number of neutrons increases by one
- mass number remains the same

## Nuclear Equations

As you have seen in this section, nuclear reactions can be represented by equations. As in chemical equations, mass and charge must balance on both sides of the equation.

For example, the following equation is balanced because the sum of charges and the sum of mass numbers are the same on both sides of the equation. For this equation, the sum of the charges of reactants equals 9 and so does the sum of the charges of the products. The sum of the mass numbers of the reactants is 18, which balances the sum of the mass numbers of the products.

$$_7^{14} N + {}_2^4 He \rightarrow {}_8^{17} O + {}_1^1 H$$

By using the concept of the conservation of charge and mass number, you can identify a missing particle in an equation.

## SAMPLE PROBLEM

What particle is represented by X in the following equation?

$$^{27}_{13}Al + ^{1}_{0}n \rightarrow ^{24}_{11}Na + X$$

**SOLUTION:** Identify the known and unknown values.

*Known*
charge and mass numbers
for Al, neutron, and Na

*Unknown*
identity of X = ?

**1.** Balance charge on both sides of the equation:

The sum of the charges on the left is 13. Therefore, the sum on the right must also be 13. Na accounts for 11, so X must have a charge of 2.

**2.** Balance mass numbers on both sides of the equation:

The sum of the mass numbers on the left is 28, so the sum on the right must also be 28. Na accounts for 24, so X must have a mass number of 4.

The particle with an atomic number of 2 and a mass number of 4 is the alpha particle ($^{4}_{2}He$). X is an alpha particle.

# Review Questions

**1.** Which particle has the greatest mass?

(1) an alpha particle   (3) an electron
(2) a beta particle   (4) a neutron

**2.** In the following equation, which particle is represented by the letter X?

$$^{14}_{6}C \rightarrow ^{14}_{7}N + X$$

(1) an alpha particle   (3) a neutron
(2) a beta particle   (4) a proton

**3.** Which radioactive emanations have a charge of 2+?

(1) alpha particles   (3) gamma rays
(2) beta particles   (4) neutrons

**4.** Which species has a negative charge?

(1) a lithium ion   (3) an aluminum ion
(2) an alpha particle   (4) a beta particle

**5.** According to Reference Table N in the *Reference Tables for Physical Setting/Chemistry*, a product of the radioactive decay of Ra-226 is

(1) $^{4}_{2}He$  (2) $^{226}_{89}U$  (3) $^{0}_{-1}e$  (4) $^{230}_{90}U$

**6.** Which equation represents nuclear disintegration resulting in release of a beta particle?

(1) $^{220}_{87}Fr + ^{4}_{2}He \rightarrow ^{224}_{89}Ac$
(2) $^{239}_{94}Pu \rightarrow ^{235}_{92}U + ^{4}_{2}He$
(3) $^{32}_{15}P + ^{0}_{-1}e \rightarrow ^{32}_{14}Si$
(4) $^{198}_{79}Au \rightarrow ^{198}_{80}Hg + ^{0}_{-1}e$

**7.** In the nuclear equation $^{232}_{90}Th \rightarrow ^{228}_{88}Ra + X$, the letter X represents

(1) an alpha particle   (3) a gamma ray
(2) a beta particle   (4) a neutron

**8.** In the reaction $^{238}_{92}U \rightarrow X + ^{4}_{2}He$, the particle represented by X is

(1) $^{234}_{90}Th$  (2) $^{234}_{92}U$  (3) $^{238}_{93}Np$  (4) $^{242}_{94}Pu$

**9.** Which nuclear equation represents beta decay?

(1) $^{27}_{13}Al + ^{4}_{2}He \rightarrow ^{30}_{15}P + ^{1}_{0}n$
(2) $^{238}_{92}U \rightarrow ^{234}_{90}Th + ^{4}_{2}He$
(3) $^{14}_{6}C \rightarrow ^{14}_{7}N + ^{0}_{-1}e$
(4) $^{37}_{18}Ar + ^{0}_{-1}e \rightarrow ^{37}_{17}Cl$

**10.** In which reaction does the letter X represent an alpha particle?

(1) $^{226}_{88}Ra \rightarrow {}^{222}_{86}Rn + X$    (3) $^{230}_{90}Th \rightarrow {}^{230}_{88}Ra + X$

(2) $^{234}_{90}Th \rightarrow {}^{235}_{91}Pa + X$    (4) $^{234}_{92}U \rightarrow {}^{234}_{90}Th + X$

**11.** What does the X represent in the following reaction?

$$^{2}_{1}H + {}^{3}_{1}H \rightarrow {}^{4}_{2}He + {}^{1}_{0}n + X$$

(1) a released electron
(2) another neutron
(3) energy converted from mass
(4) mass converted from energy

**12.** Which of the following nuclear reactions is classified as alpha decay?

(1) $^{14}_{6}C \rightarrow {}^{14}_{7}N + {}^{0}_{+1}e$    (3) $^{226}_{88}Ra \rightarrow {}^{222}_{86}Rn + {}^{4}_{2}He$

(2) $^{42}_{19}K \rightarrow {}^{42}_{20}Ca + {}^{0}_{-1}e$    (4) $^{3}_{1}H \rightarrow {}^{0}_{-1}e + {}^{4}_{2}He$

**13.** Which isotope is represented by the X when the following equation is correctly balanced?

$$^{14}_{7}N + {}^{4}_{2}He \rightarrow {}^{1}_{1}H + X$$

(1) $^{17}_{2}O$    (2) $^{17}_{8}O$    (3) $^{17}_{9}F$    (4) $^{19}_{9}F$

**14.** Which element has no stable isotopes?

(1) $_{27}Co$    (2) $_{51}Sb$    (3) $_{90}Th$    (4) $_{82}Pb$

**15.** Write balanced nuclear equations for each of the following:

(a) beta decay of Pb-210
(b) beta decay of Cs-137
(c) alpha decay of Rn-222
(d) alpha decay of Au-185
(e) positron emission of Fe-53
(f) positron emission of Ca-37

---

# Transmutations

Nuclear reactions can be either naturally occurring or artificial. Alpha, beta, and positron decay are **natural transmutations** that occur as a result of unstable neutron-to-proton ratios. When bombarding the nucleus with high-energy particles brings about the change, the process is given the name of **artificial transmutation**. Scientists in research and commercial settings perform artificial transmutations.

**Types of Transmutations**  There are two types of artificial transmutations. The first type involves the collision of a charged particle with a target nucleus. If charged particles such as protons or alpha particles are to react with atomic nuclei, they must have sufficient energy to overcome the repulsive forces that exist between positively charged objects. Scientists can supply this energy by accelerating charged particles in devices called cyclotrons and synchrotrons, which use magnetic or electrostatic fields to speed up protons and other charged particles.

A second type of artificial transmutation occurs when a neutron collides with a target nucleus. Neutrons can be obtained as by-products of nuclear reactors similar to those used to generate electricity. Because the neutron does not possess a charge, it is not repelled by the target nucleus and can be captured by the "strong" force that holds protons and neutrons in the nucleus. These reactions are used to prepare radioactive nuclei from stable nuclei. Listed below are a few examples.

$$^{238}_{92}U \rightarrow {}^{1}_{0}n + {}^{239}_{92}U$$

$$^{59}_{27}Co \rightarrow {}^{1}_{0}n + {}^{60}_{27}Co$$

$$^{32}_{16}S \rightarrow {}^{1}_{0}n + {}^{32}_{15}P + {}^{1}_{1}H$$

It is easy to tell the difference between natural and artificial transmutation. Natural transmutation consists of a single nucleus undergoing decay. Artificial transmutation will have two reactants, a fast-moving particle and a target material.

16. The nuclear reaction

$$^{4}_{2}He + ^{27}_{13}Al \rightarrow ^{30}_{15}P + ^{1}_{0}n$$

is an example of

(1) nuclear fusion
(2) nuclear fission
(3) natural transmutation
(4) artificial transmutation

17. Which particle is represented by X in the following transmutation?

$$^{234}_{90}Th \rightarrow ^{234}_{91}Pa + X$$

(1) $^{0}_{-1}e$  (2) $^{4}_{2}He$  (3) $^{1}_{1}H$  (4) $^{0}_{+1}e$

18. Which equation represents a nuclear reaction that is an example of an artificial transmutation?

(1) $^{43}_{21}Sc \rightarrow ^{43}_{20}Ca + ^{0}_{+1}e$  (3) $^{10}_{4}Be \rightarrow ^{10}_{5}B + ^{0}_{-1}e$

(2) $^{14}_{7}N + ^{4}_{2}He \rightarrow ^{17}_{8}O + ^{1}_{1}H$  (4) $^{14}_{6}C \rightarrow ^{14}_{7}N + ^{0}_{-1}e$

19. Which particle is represented by X in the following transmutation?

$$^{131}_{53}I \rightarrow ^{131}_{54}Xe + X$$

(1) alpha  (2) beta  (3) neutron  (4) proton

20. What is the charge of the element represented by X in the following transmutation?

$$^{1}_{0}n + ^{235}_{92}U \rightarrow ^{141}_{56}Ba + X + 3^{1}_{0}n$$

(1) 36  (2) 89  (3) 92  (4) 93

21. Which species is represented by X in the following transmutation?

$$^{9}_{4}Be + ^{1}_{1}H \rightarrow ^{4}_{2}He + X$$

(1) $^{8}_{3}Li$  (2) $^{6}_{3}Li$  (3) $^{8}_{5}B$  (4) $^{10}_{5}B$

22. Which species is represented by X in the following transmutation?

$$^{7}_{3}Li + X \rightarrow ^{8}_{4}Be$$

(1) $^{1}_{1}H$  (2) $^{2}_{1}H$  (3) $^{3}_{2}He$  (4) $^{4}_{2}He$

23. What is the identity of particle X in the following transmutation?

$$^{9}_{4}Be + X \rightarrow ^{6}_{3}Li + ^{4}_{2}He$$

(1) $^{1}_{1}H$  (2) $^{2}_{1}H$  (3) $^{0}_{-1}e$  (4) $^{1}_{0}n$

# Fission and Fusion

A **fission** reaction involves the splitting of a heavy nucleus to produce lighter nuclei. A **fusion** reaction involves the combining of light nuclei to produce a heavier nucleus. In both types of reactions, the total mass of the products is less than the total nuclear mass of the reactants.

## Conversion of Matter to Energy

At first glance this loss of mass seems to contradict our concept that matter (mass) can neither be created nor destroyed. Properly expressed, the law states that the total amount of matter and energy cannot be destroyed. The loss of mass in these nuclear reactions represents a conversion of some matter into energy. The relationship was expressed by Albert Einstein in his famous equation

$$E = mc^2$$

where $E$ is energy, $m$ is mass, and c is the speed of light, which is $3.00 \times 10^8$ m/s. Because the speed of light is such a large number, you can see that the conversion of a minute amount of matter produces an extremely large amount of energy.

The energy produced by nuclear reactions is far greater than that of ordinary chemical reactions. The conversion of 1.00 g of matter into energy yields $9.00 \times 10^{13}$ J. When 1.00 g of methane is burned in an ordinary chemical reaction, there is a release of $5.56 \times 10^4$ J of energy.

**Figure 12-5. Fission:** Fission involves the splitting of a large nucleus into middle-weight nuclei and neutrons.

Gram for gram, the nuclear reaction gives off over a billion times as much energy.

This conversion of matter into energy occurs when protons and neutrons are combined into nuclei. The total mass of the nucleus is less than the sum of the masses of the individual protons and neutrons. The matter that has been converted into energy is called the <u>mass defect.</u>

## Fission Reactions

A fission reaction begins with the capture of a neutron by the nucleus of a heavy element such as uranium-235 or plutonium-239. The nucleus produced by the capture is unstable. It immediately splits, undergoing the process of fission. The products of fission are two middle-weight nuclei, one or more neutrons, and a large amount of energy. A small amount of matter from the original atom of uranium or plutonium is converted into energy.

$$\ce{^1_0}n + \ce{^{235}_{92}U} \rightarrow \ce{^{142}_{56}Ba} + \ce{^{91}_{36}Kr} + 3\ce{^1_0}n + \text{energy}$$

The products shown in this equation are only two of more than 200 different radioactive products that may be produced by the fission process. Some other possible products are shown in Figure 12-5.

## Fusion Reactions

Fusion reactions involve the combining of light nuclei to form heavier ones. The most common example of fusion occurs in the sun where hydrogen nuclei react in a series to produce helium nuclei. These fusion reactions produce the huge amounts of energy released by the sun. One of the possible series of reactions involving the fusion of hydrogen nuclei to form helium and release energy is given by the following sequence.

$$\ce{^1_1H} + \ce{^1_1H} \rightarrow \ce{^2_1H} + \ce{^0_{+1}}e$$

$$\ce{^1_1H} + \ce{^2_1H} \rightarrow \ce{^3_2He}$$

$$\ce{^3_2He} + \ce{^3_2He} \rightarrow \ce{^4_2He} + 2\ce{^1_1H}$$

$$\ce{^3_2He} + \ce{^1_1H} \rightarrow \ce{^4_2He} + \ce{^0_{+1}}e$$

While these reactions produce the energy from the sun, they are not yet available to produce energy here on Earth. Extremely high temperatures and pressures are needed to allow the positively charged hydrogen nuclei to fuse into helium. When methods are developed that will contain a reaction such as these and make it practical, an important new energy source will have been developed. One major advantage of fusion as an energy source is that the products are not highly radioactive, like the products of fission reactions.

# Review Questions

24. High energy is a requirement for fusion reactions to occur because the nuclei involved
    (1) attract each other because they have like charges
    (2) attract each other because they have unlike charges
    (3) repel each other because they have like charges
    (4) repel each other because they have unlike charges

25. When a uranium nucleus breaks up into fragments, which type of nuclear reaction occurs?
    (1) fusion          (3) replacement
    (2) fission         (4) redox

26. Which pair of nuclei can undergo a fusion reaction?
    (1) potassium-40 and cadmium-113
    (2) zinc-64 and calcium-44
    (3) uranium-238 and lead-208
    (4) hydrogen-2 and hydrogen-3

27. What process is represented by the following reaction?

    $$_1^2H + _1^2H \rightarrow _2^4He + energy$$

    (1) fission
    (2) fusion
    (3) artificial transmutation
    (4) alpha decay

28. During a fission reaction, which type of particle is captured by a nucleus?
    (1) deuteron        (3) neutron
    (2) electron        (4) proton

29. What is the primary result of a fission reaction?
    (1) conversion of mass to energy
    (2) conversion of energy to mass
    (3) binding together of two heavy nuclei
    (4) binding together of two light nuclei

30. Compared to an ordinary chemical reaction, a fission reaction will
    (1) release smaller amounts of energy
    (2) release larger amounts of energy
    (3) absorb smaller amounts of energy
    (4) absorb larger amounts of energy

31. Which type of reaction produces energy and intensely radioactive waste products?
    (1) fusion of tritium and deuterium
    (2) fission of uranium
    (3) burning of heating oil
    (4) burning of wood

32. Which process occurs in a controlled fusion reaction?
    (1) Light nuclei collide to produce heavier nuclei.
    (2) Heavy nuclei collide to produce lighter nuclei.
    (3) Neutron bombardment splits light nuclei.
    (4) Neutron bombardment splits heavy nuclei.

33. Consider this reaction.

    $$_{92}^{235}U + _0^1n \rightarrow _{56}^{138}Ba + _{36}^{95}Kr + 3 _0^1n + energy$$

    This equation can best be described as
    (1) fission         (3) natural decay
    (2) fusion          (4) endothermic

# Half-Life

Radioactive substances decay at a constant rate that is not dependent on factors such as temperature, pressure, or concentration. It is also a random event. That is, it is impossible to predict when a given unstable nucleus will decay. However, the number of unstable nuclei that will decay in a given time in a sample of the element can be predicted. The time it takes for half of the atoms in a given sample of an element to decay is called the **half-life** of the element. Each isotope has its own half-life. The shorter the half-life of an isotope, the less stable it is. Table N in *Reference Tables for Physical Setting/Chemistry* lists various isotopes together with their half-lives and the mode by which they decay. Figure 12-6 shows the decay of carbon-14.

If radioactive substance X has a half-life of 5 s, each five seconds will result in the amount of X present at the beginning of the time being reduced by half. If 20 g of X begins to decay, after 5 s only 10 g will remain. Five seconds later, only 5 g of the original 20 g will remain. $(1/2 \times 1/2 = 1/4)$. The fraction remaining after a given number of half-lives is calculated using the relationship

**Figure 12-6. The half-life of C-14**

$$\text{fraction remaining} = (1/2)^n$$

where $n$ is equal to the number of half-lives. The number of half-lives is calculated by dividing the total time that the substance has decayed by the half-life of the isotope.

## SAMPLE PROBLEM

Most chromium atoms are stable, but Cr-51 is an unstable isotope with a half-life of 28 days.
**(a)** What fraction of a sample of Cr-51 will remain after 168 days?
**(b)** If a sample of Cr-51 has an original mass of 52.0 g, what mass will remain after 168 days?

**SOLUTION:** Identify the known and unknown values.

*Known*
half-life of Cr-51 = 28 days
time = 168 days
original mass = 52.0 g

*Unknown*
fraction of Cr-51 remaining after 168 days = ?
mass of Cr-51 remaining after 168 days = ? g

**1.** Determine how many half-lives elapse during 168 days.

$$\text{Number of half-lives} = \frac{\text{time elapsed } (t)}{\text{half-life } (T)}$$

$$= \frac{168 \text{ days}}{28 \text{ days/half-life}}$$

$$= 6 \text{ half-lives}$$

**2.** Calculate the fraction remaining.

$$\text{Fraction remaining} = (1/2)^{t/T}$$
$$= (1/2)^6$$
$$= 1/64$$

The fraction of Cr-51 remaining after 168 days will be 1/64 of the original.

**3.** Calculate the mass remaining.

mass remaining = original mass × fraction remaining
$$= 52.0 \text{ g} \times 1/64 = 0.813 \text{ g}$$

Mass remaining can also be calculated by dividing the current mass by 2 at the end of each half-life.

After 1 half-life, mass = 52.0 g/2 = 26.0 g
After 2 half-lives, mass = 26.0 g/2 = 13.0 g
After 3 half-lives, mass = 13.0 g/2 = 6.50 g
After 4 half-lives, mass = 6.50 g/2 = 3.25 g
After 5 half-lives, mass = 3.25 g/2 = 1.63 g
After 6 half-lives, mass = 1.63 g/2 = 0.815 g

## SAMPLE PROBLEM

How much was present originally in a sample of Cr-51 if 0.75 mg remains after 168 days?

**SOLUTION:** Identify the known and unknown values.

| Known | Unknown |
|---|---|
| half-life of Cr-51 = 28 days | original mass = ? g |
| time = 168 days | |
| final mass = 0.75 mg | |

From the previous sample problem, 168 days represents 6 half-life periods for Cr-51. The sample will double for each half-life period. Multiply the remaining amount by a factor of 2 for each half-life.

$$\text{original mass} = \text{final mass} \times 2^n$$

$$= 0.75 \text{ mg} \times 2^6$$

$$= 48 \text{ mg}$$

The initial amount of a substance can be determined from the half-life, the amount remaining, and the time passed. When determining an original amount, each half-life represents a doubling of the amount present.

**Graphing Half-Life Data** As a radioactive substance decays, a Geiger counter can be used to record the individual decay events. When this data is graphed, it provides a way to measure the half-life of an isotope. Figure 12-7 is a graph of the data of the decay of a hypothetical radioisotope. To determine the half-life, select a convenient count on the y-axis (1). Draw a vertical line to a value of half of the original (2). In this case the line extends from 6000 counts to 3000 counts. The half-life is represented by the time segment on the x-axis (2 to 3), or 15 minutes. It does not matter where you begin, the half-life will still be the same. Simply draw a line to reduce the count by half, and then read the half-life.

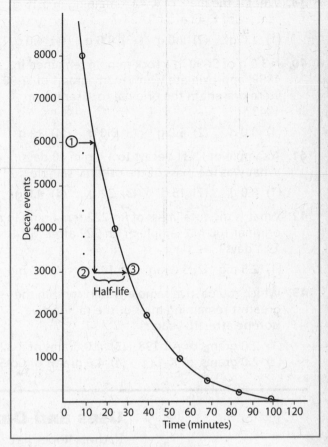

**Figure 12-7. A hypothetical half-life**

# Review
## Questions

Refer to Table N in *Reference Tables for Physical Setting/Chemistry* for half-life values as needed.

**34.** After 62.0 hours, 1.0 g remains unchanged from a sample of $^{42}$K. How much $^{42}$K was in the original sample?

(1) 8.0 g    (2) 16 g    (3) 32 g    (4) 64 g

**35.** If 80 mg of a radioactive element decays to 10 mg in 30 min, what is the element's half-life in minutes?

(1) 10    (2) 20    (3) 30    (4) 40

**36.** In 6.20 h, a 100.-g sample of Ag-112 decays to 25.0 g. What is the half-life of Ag-112?

(1) 1.60 h    (2) 3.10 h    (3) 6.20 h    (4) 12.4 h

**37.** Which of the following 10-g samples of a radio-isotope will decay to the greatest extent in 28 days?

(1) P-32    (2) Kr-85    (3) Fr-220    (4) I-131

**38.** How many hours are required for potassium-42 to undergo three half-life periods?

(1) 6.2 h    (2) 12.4 h    (3) 24.8 h    (4) 37.2 h

**39.** What is the mass of K-42 remaining in a 16-g sample of K-42 after 37.2 h?

(1) 1.0 g    (2) 2.0 g    (3) 8.0 g    (4) 4.0 g

**40.** If 3.0 g of Sr-90 in a rock sample remained in 1999, approximately how many grams of Sr-90 were present in the original rock sample in 1943?

(1) 9.0 g    (2) 6.0 g    (3) 3.0 g    (4) 12 g

**41.** A sample of I-131 decays to 1.0 g in 40 days. What was the mass of the original sample?

(1) 8.0 g    (2) 16 g    (3) 32 g    (4) 4.0 g

**42.** What is the total mass of Rn-222 remaining in an original 160-mg sample of Rn-222 after 19.1 days?

(1) 2.5 mg   (2) 5.0 mg   (3) 10 mg   (4) 20 mg

**43.** Which radioactive sample would contain the greatest remaining mass of the radioactive isotope after 10 years?

(1) 2.0 grams of Au-198    (3) 4.0 grams of P-32
(2) 2.0 grams of K-42     (4) 4.0 grams of Co-60

**44.** A radioactive element has a half-life of 2 days. Which fraction represents the amount of an original sample of this element remaining after 6 days?

(1) $\frac{1}{8}$               (3) $\frac{1}{3}$

(2) $\frac{1}{2}$               (4) $\frac{1}{4}$

**45.** Which of the following radioisotopes has the shortest half-life?

(1) $^{14}C$            (3) $^{37}K$
(2) $^{3}H$             (4) $^{32}P$

**46.** As the temperature of a sample of a radioactive element decreases, the half-life of the element

(1) decreases       (3) remains the same
(2) increases        (4) varies with the pressure

**47.** If one-eighth of the mass of the original sample of a radioisotope remains unchanged after 4800 years, the isotope could be

(1) H-3             (3) Sr-90
(2) K-42           (4) Ra-226

---

# Uses and Dangers of Radioisotopes

Radioisotopes have many practical applications in industry, medicine, and research. They also have potential dangers because of harm that could be done by the radiation released.

## Uses of Radioisotopes

The following applications represent just a few of the many uses of radioisotopes. Although they must be used with proper precautions, certain radioisotopes provide information that could not be determined from isotopes that are not radioactive.

**Dating** Carbon-14 is perhaps best known for its use in dating previously living materials. There is an extremely small amount of C-14 in the atmosphere. When an organism is alive, it uses this radioactive carbon in the same way as it uses stable C-12. When the organism dies, it no longer takes in any carbon.

Each gram of carbon in a living organism emits about 15 disintegrations per minute (dpm). After the organism dies and time passes, the radioactive C-14 continues to decay, but it is not replaced. Therefore the dpm decreases with time. Because the half-life of C-14 is 5730 years, after that time period there will only be about 7 dpm for each gram of carbon in the organism. Therefore, a reading of 7 dpm/g carbon indicates the remains are about 5700 years old, while a reading of 3.5 dpm would show a material to be about twice as old, about 11,000 years. After about four half-lives, C-14 becomes ineffective as a method for dating materials because too little C-14 remains to be accurately measured.

U-238 is a radioactive material that spontaneously decays through a series of steps until it forms stable Pb-206. As time passes, the amount of lead in the sample will increase as the amount of uranium decreases. Scientists can use the ratio of U-238/Pb-206 to date rocks and other geological formations.

**Chemical Tracers** The ability to detect radioactive materials and their decay products makes it possible to determine their presence or absence in a substance. Any radioisotope used to follow the path of a material in a system is called a **tracer.** If radioactive P-31 is present in fertilizer administered to a plant, the uptake of the phosphorus can be traced by detectors. Scientists can then determine the proper amounts and timing of fertilizer applications. C-14 is another tracer used to map the path of carbon in metabolic processes.

**Industrial Applications** Radioactive isotopes and gamma rays are absorbed in varying amounts by different materials. The thicker the material, the more radiation that will be absorbed. Thus, radiation products can be used to measure the thickness of materials such as a plastic wrap or aluminum foil or to test the strength of a weld.

**Medical Applications** Certain radioisotopes that are quickly eliminated from the body and have short half-lives are important as tracers in medical diagnosis. Many are also used in treatment of various disorders and diseases. Others might be used to make materials free from bacteria or other disease-causing organisms.

I-131 has uses both in the detection and treatment of thyroid conditions. Because iodine accumulates in the thyroid gland, small amounts of I-131 can be administered to a patient and a radiogram made of the thyroid to diagnose a disorder. When a person has an overactive thyroid (hyperthyroidism), I-131 can be given in large enough doses to destroy some of the thyroid and reduce its production of thyroxin.

Cobalt-60 emits large amounts of gamma radiation as it decays. These rays can be aimed at cancerous tumors. The rapidly growing cells of the tumor are more likely to be killed than normal cells by the gamma rays.

Intense beams of gamma radiation can be used to irradiate foods to kill bacteria. Certain types of foods, such as spices, are irradiated on a regular basis. Irradiation of produce and meats has also been approved in many locations. By killing the bacteria present, the food lasts longer without spoiling and causes fewer bacterial infections in those who consume it. Other destruction of bacteria by radiation is also important. Co-60 and Cs-137 are two of the sources of gamma radiation currently being used to destroy anthrax bacilli.

Technetium, atomic number 43, is a radioactive element that is rapidly absorbed by cancerous cells. When Tc-99 is given to patients with cancerous tumors, it accumulates in the tumor and can easily be detected by a scan. When radioisotopes are used for diagnostic purposes, it is advantageous if they have a short half-life and are quickly eliminated by the body so that they do not damage healthy tissue.

## Radiation Risks

The uses of radiation are not without risks. While radioisotopes can be used to kill cancerous cells, they also have the potential of damaging normal tissue. High doses of radiation can cause serious illness and death. Radiation can cause mutations that could potentially be passed from generation to generation.

Nuclear power plants are a particular problem. After the fuel rods no longer have enough uranium to make them useful in the reactor, they contain many decay products, many with long half-lives. It is difficult to store and dispose of these waste products.

Of major concern to many people is the overall safety issue of nuclear power plants themselves. While the plants are designed to protect the public, there is still a danger of a nuclear accident that might release radioactivity into the air or water. The 1986 accident at Chernobyl in Ukraine destroyed farmland that will probably be unusable for generations.

# Review Questions

**48.** Which radioisotope is used for diagnosing thyroid disorders?

(1) cobalt-60　　　(3) lead-206
(2) uranium-238　　(4) iodine-131

**49.** Which procedure is based on the half-life of a radioisotope?

(1) accelerating to increase kinetic energy
(2) radiation to kill cancer cells
(3) counting to determine a level of radioactivity
(4) dating to determine age

**50.** Radiated food can be safely stored for a longer time because radiation

(1) prevents air oxidation
(2) prevents air reduction
(3) kills bacteria
(4) causes bacteria to mutate

**51.** A radioactive-dating procedure to determine the age of a mineral compares the mineral's remaining amounts of U-238 and the isotope

(1) Pb-206　　　(3) Pb-214
(2) Bi-206　　　(4) Bi-214

**52.** Which isotopic ratio needs to be determined when the age of ancient wooden objects is investigated?

(1) U-235 to U-238　　(3) N-16 to N-14
(2) H-2 to H-3　　　　(4) C-14 to C-12

**53.** Which two characteristics do radioisotopes have that are useful in medical diagnosis?

(1) long half-lives and slow elimination from the body
(2) long half-lives and quick elimination from the body
(3) short half-lives and slow elimination from the body
(4) short half-lives and quick elimination from the body

**54.** A radioisotope is called a tracer when it is used to

(1) kill bacteria
(2) kill cancerous tissue
(3) determine the age of animal skeletal remains
(4) determine the path of an element in an organism

**55.** Which radioactive isotope is used in geological dating?

(1) U-238　(2) I-131　(3) Co-60　(4) Tc-99

**56.** Which isotope can be used as a tracer to study the age of organic material?

(1) C-12　(2) C-14　(3) Sr-88　(4) Sr-90

**57.** Brain tumors can be located by using an isotope of

(1) C-14　(2) I-131　(3) Tc-99　(4) U-238

## Directions

Review the Test–Taking Strategies section of this book. Then answer the following questions. Read each question carefully and answer with a correct choice or response.

## Part A

**1** Samples of elements that are radioactive must contain atoms
(1) with stable nuclei
(2) with unstable nuclei
(3) in the excited state
(4) in the ground state

**2** Organic molecules react to form a product. These reactions can be studied using
(1) Sr-90    (2) Co-60    (3) N-16    (4) C-14

**3** Radiation used in the processing of food is intended to
(1) increase the rate of nutrient decomposition
(2) kill microorganisms that are found in food
(3) convert ordinary nutrients to more stable forms
(4) replace chemical energy with nuclear energy

**4** The age of certain minerals can be determined if they contain the nuclide
(1) P-32          (3) U-238
(2) Co-60       (4) Au-198

**5** The course of a chemical reaction can be traced by using a
(1) polar molecule     (3) stable isotope
(2) diatomic molecule   (4) radioisotope

**6** Bombarding a nucleus with high-energy particles that change it from one element into another is called
(1) a half-reaction
(2) a breeder reaction
(3) artificial transmutation
(4) natural transmutation

**7** An alpha decay results in the formation of a new element with the atomic number
(1) increased by two    (3) decreased by two
(2) increased by four   (4) decreased by four

**8** When a radioactive nucleus emits a beta particle, the atom's
(1) mass number is increased by 1
(2) mass number is decreased by 1
(3) atomic number is increased by 1
(4) atomic number is decreased by 1

**9** As the temperature increases, pressure remaining constant, the half-life of a radioactive element
(1) decreases           (3) remains the same
(2) increases           (4) depends on the mass

**10** Which of the following is not deflected by an electric field?
(1) alpha          (3) positron
(2) beta           (4) gamma ray

## Part B

**11** Which statement explains why fusion reactions are difficult to initiate?
(1) Positive nuclei attract each other.
(2) Positive nuclei repel each other.
(3) Neutrons prevent nuclei from getting close enough to fuse.
(4) Electrons prevent nuclei from getting close enough to fuse.

**12** Which particle has the greatest chance of overcoming the electrostatic forces surrounding the nucleus of an atom?
(1) an alpha particle    (3) a proton
(2) a beta particle      (4) a neutron

**13** The diagram below shows a nuclear reaction in which a neutron is captured by a heavy nucleus. Which type of reaction is illustrated by the diagram?

(1) an endothermic fission reaction
(2) an exothermic fission reaction
(3) an endothermic fusion reaction
(4) an exothermic fusion reaction

**14** Which equation represents a fusion reaction?

(1) $^{3}_{1}H + ^{1}_{1}H \rightarrow ^{2}_{4}He$

(2) $^{40}_{18}Ar + ^{1}_{1}H \rightarrow ^{40}_{19}K + ^{1}_{0}n$

(3) $^{234}_{91}Pa \rightarrow ^{234}_{92}U + ^{0}_{-1}e$

(4) $^{226}_{88}Ra \rightarrow ^{222}_{86}Rn + ^{4}_{2}He$

**15** Consider this reaction.

$$^{27}_{13}Al + ^{4}_{2}He \rightarrow ^{30}_{15}P + ^{1}_{0}n$$

This reaction can best be described as
(1) beta decay
(2) artificial transmutation
(3) fission
(4) fusion

**16** When I-131 undergoes radioactive decay, which element is formed?

(1) Te-132  (3) I-130
(2) Xe-131  (4) Sb-127

**17** Which is a gaseous radioactive waste product that is released into the atmosphere after it has decayed to a safe radiation level?

(1) radon-222  (3) cesium-137
(2) radium-226  (4) cobalt-60

**18** Which particle is represented by X in the following correctly balanced nuclear equation?

$$^{12}_{6}C + ^{249}_{98}Cf \rightarrow ^{257}_{104}Unq + 4X$$

(1) $^{14}_{7}H$  (2) $^{1}_{0}n$  (3) $^{4}_{2}He$  (4) $^{0}_{-1}e$

**19** The diagram below shows a nuclear reaction in which a neutron is captured by a heavy nucleus.

Which type of reaction is illustrated by the diagram?
(1) an endothermic fission reaction
(2) an exothermic fission reaction
(3) an endothermic fusion reaction
(4) an exothermic fusion reaction

**20** In which list can all particles be accelerated by an electric field?

(1) alpha particles, beta particles, and neutrons
(2) alpha particles, beta particles, and protons
(3) alpha particles, protons, and neutrons
(4) beta particles, protons, and neutrons

**21** In which process is mass converted to energy by the process of fission?

(1) $^{14}_{7}N + ^{1}_{0}n \rightarrow ^{14}_{6}C + ^{1}_{1}H$

(2) $^{235}_{92}U + ^{1}_{0}n \rightarrow ^{87}_{35}Br + ^{146}_{57}La + 3^{1}_{0}n$

(3) $^{226}_{88}Ra \rightarrow ^{222}_{86}Rn + ^{4}_{2}He$

(4) $^{2}_{1}H + ^{2}_{1}H \rightarrow ^{4}_{2}He$

**22** Write a balanced nuclear equation for the positron emission of Al-24.

**23** Write a balanced nuclear equation for the beta decay of Si-35.

**24** Write a balanced nuclear equation for the alpha decay of Ra-226.

**25** How many grams of a 20-g sample of C-14 would remain after 17,190 years?

**26** Complete the equation:

$$^{1}_{0}n + ^{235}_{92}U \rightarrow ^{72}_{30}Zn + X + 4^{1}_{0}n$$

Neutron  Heavy nucleus  Neutron captured in nucleus

Nuclear deformation

Products

# Part C

27 Write an equation for the alpha decay of $^{214}_{84}$Po, followed by a beta decay of the product. [2]

28 Using Figure 12-1 as a guide, indicate whether each of the following nuclei is stable or unstable. [3]

(a) $^{110}_{40}$X  (c) $^{110}_{60}$X

(b) $^{90}_{60}$X

29 Explain why it is more difficult to cause an artificial transmutation with an alpha particle than with a neutron. [2]

30 Plot the following data and determine the half-life of the isotope. [3]

| Time (min) | Counts (per min) |
|---|---|
| 0 | 12 000 |
| 2 | 7 000 |
| 4 | 4 000 |
| 8 | 1 400 |
| 10 | 800 |
| 12 | 450 |

31 Points X and Y lie outside the zone of stability on the graph shown below. Write a beta decay equation for X and a positron emission equation for Y. Plot the positions of the products of the decay of X and Y on the graph. [4]

32 Carbon dating presumes that the amount of C-14 has been constant in the atmosphere over many thousands of years. Suppose that 5700 years ago, the amount of C-14 in the atmosphere were only half the amount that is currently in the atmosphere. How would this affect carbon dating? [1]

33 The elements with atomic numbers greater than 92 are all human-made. What element was produced when Es-253 was bombarded with an alpha particle, producing a new element and a neutron? Include the atomic number, symbol, and mass number. [2]

34 State one possible advantage of using nuclear power instead of burning fossil fuels. [1]

35 State one possible risk of using nuclear power. [1]

36 If animals feed on plants that have taken up Sr-90, the Sr-90 can find its way into their bone structures. Explain one danger to the animals. [1]

**Base your answers to questions 37 and 38 on the following.**

Given the nuclear equation:

$$^{235}_{92}U + ^1_0n \rightarrow ^{142}_{56}Ba + ^{91}_{36}Kr + 3^1_0n$$

37 State the type of nuclear reaction represented by the equation. [1]

38 The sum of the masses of the products is slightly less than the sum of the masses of the reactants. Explain this loss of mass. [1]

39 This process releases greater energy than an ordinary chemical reaction does. Name another type of nuclear reaction that releases greater energy than an ordinary chemical reaction. [1]

40 How can particles emitted from radioactive nuclei damage human tissue? [1]

41 Americium-241 is an alpha emitter used in smoke detectors. Write the equation for the alpha decay of Am-241. [1]

42 How is the radioactive decay of Krypton-85 different from the radioactive decay of Americium-241. [1]

43 Given the nuclear equation: $^{58}_{29}Cu \rightarrow ^{58}_{28}Ni + X$ What nuclear particle is represented by X? [1]

44 Write an equation for the radioactive decay of $^{137}_{55}$Cs. [1]

**45** If 12.5 grams of cesium-137 remained after 90.69 years, what was the mass of the original sample? [1]

**Base your answers to questions 46 and 47 on the information below.**

In living organisms, the ratio of the naturally occurring isotopes of carbon, C-12 to C-13 to C-14 is fairly consistent. When an organism such as a woolly mammoth died, it stopped taking in carbon, and the amount of C-14 present in the mammoth began to decrease. For example, one fossil of a woolly mammoth is found to have 1/32 of the amount of C-14 found in living organisms.

**46** Identify the type of nuclear reaction that caused the amount of C-14 in the woolly mammoth to decrease after the organism died. [1]

**47** Determine the total time that has elapsed since this woolly mammoth died. [1]

**48** Suppose a 40-gram sample of iondine-131 and a 40-gram sample of cesium-137 were both abandoned in 1987. Explain why iodine-131 would not be as great a radiation risk today as the sample of cesium-137 would. [1]

**Base your answers on questions 49 and 50 on the information below.**

The radioisotopes carbon-14 and nitrogen-16 are present in a living organism. Carbon-14 is commonly used to date a once-living organism.

**49** Write a nuclear equation to show the decay of C-14. [1]

**50** Explain why N-16 is a poor choice for the radioactive dating of bones. [1]

**51** A sample of wood is found to contain 1/8 as much C-14 as is present in the wood of a living tree. What is the approximate age, in years, of the wood? [1]

**Base your answers to questions 52 and 53 on the information below.**

Some radioisotopes used as tracers make it possible for doctors to see the images of internal body parts and observe their functions. The table below lists information about three radioisotopes and the body part each radioisotope is used to study.

| Medical Uses of Some Radioisotopes | | | |
|---|---|---|---|
| Radioisotopes | Half-Life | Decay Mode | Body Part |
| $24_{Na}$ | 15 hours | Beta | Circulatory system |
| $59_{Fe}$ | 44.5 days | Beta | Red blood cells |
| $131_I$ | 8.1 days | Beta | thyroid |

**52** Write the equation for the nuclear decay of the radioisotope used to study red blood cells. [1]

**53** It could take up to 60. hours for a radioisotope to be delivered to a hospital from the laboratory where it was produced. What fraction of an original sample of Na-24 remains unchanged after 60. hours? [1]

# Appendix 1:
# Reference Tables for Physical Setting/Chemistry

## Using the Reference Tables

You should become thoroughly familiar with all details of these tables.

Look for the (R) on the topic pages to see where the content is enhanced by the reference tables.

Some of the ways these reference tables are used in Regents Examination questions include:

- Finding a specific fact, such as the value of the heat of vaporization of water.

- Using an equation to determine the concentration of an unknown solution in a titration.

- Determining the solubility of various compounds in water.

- Assessing the relative activity of representative metals and halogens.

- Interpreting the symbols of radioisotopes to determine mode of decay and length of half-life.

- Using the Periodic Table to determine the properties of elements.

- Interpreting the color changes of indicators to determine acidity or alkalinity.

# Reference Tables for Physical Setting/CHEMISTRY
## 2002 Edition

### Table A
### Standard Temperature and Pressure

| Name | Value | Unit |
|---|---|---|
| Standard Pressure | 101.3 kPa / 1 atm | kilopascal / atmosphere |
| Standard Temperature | 273 K / 0°C | kelvin / degree Celsius |

### Table B
### Physical Constants for Water

| | |
|---|---|
| Heat of Fusion | 334 J/g |
| Heat of Vaporization | 2260 J/g |
| Specific Heat Capacity of $H_2O$ ($\ell$) | 4.18 J/g•°C |

### Table C
### Selected Prefixes

| Factor | Prefix | Symbol |
|---|---|---|
| $10^3$ | kilo- | k |
| $10^{-1}$ | deci- | d |
| $10^{-2}$ | centi- | c |
| $10^{-3}$ | milli- | m |
| $10^{-6}$ | micro- | $\mu$ |
| $10^{-9}$ | nano- | n |
| $10^{-12}$ | pico- | p |

### Table D
### Selected Units

| Symbol | Name | Quantity |
|---|---|---|
| m | meter | length |
| g | gram | mass |
| Pa | pascal | pressure |
| K | kelvin | temperature |
| mol | mole | amount of substance |
| J | joule | energy, work, quantity of heat |
| s | second | time |
| L | liter | volume |
| ppm | part per million | concentration |
| M | molarity | solution concentration |

### Table E
### Selected Polyatomic Ions

| | | | | |
|---|---|---|---|---|
| $H_3O^+$ | hydronium | | $CrO_4^{2-}$ | chromate |
| $Hg_2^{2+}$ | dimercury (I) | | $Cr_2O_7^{2-}$ | dichromate |
| $NH_4^+$ | ammonium | | $MnO_4^-$ | permanganate |
| $C_2H_3O_2^-$ $CH_3COO^-$ | acetate | | $NO_2^-$ | nitrite |
| $CN^-$ | cyanide | | $NO_3^-$ | nitrate |
| $CO_3^{2-}$ | carbonate | | $O_2^{2-}$ | peroxide |
| $HCO_3^-$ | hydrogen carbonate | | $OH^-$ | hydroxide |
| $C_2O_4^{2-}$ | oxalate | | $PO_4^{3-}$ | phosphate |
| $ClO^-$ | hypochlorite | | $SCN^-$ | thiocyanate |
| $ClO_2^-$ | chlorite | | $SO_3^{2-}$ | sulfite |
| $ClO_3^-$ | chlorate | | $SO_4^{2-}$ | sulfate |
| $ClO_4^-$ | perchlorate | | $HSO_4^-$ | hydrogen sulfate |
| | | | $S_2O_3^{2-}$ | thiosulfate |

# Table F
## Solubility Guidelines for Aqueous Solutions

| Ions That Form *Soluble* Compounds | Exceptions |
|---|---|
| Group 1 ions ($Li^+$, $Na^+$, etc.) | |
| ammonium ($NH_4^+$) | |
| nitrate ($NO_3^-$) | |
| acetate ($C_2H_3O_2^-$ or $CH_3COO^-$) | |
| hydrogen carbonate ($HCO_3^-$) | |
| chlorate ($ClO_3^-$) | |
| perchlorate ($ClO_4^-$) | |
| halides ($Cl^-$, $Br^-$, $I^-$) | when combined with $Ag^+$, $Pb^{2+}$, and $Hg_2^{2+}$ |
| sulfates ($SO_4^{2-}$) | when combined with $Ag^+$, $Ca^{2+}$, $Sr^{2+}$, $Ba^{2+}$, and $Pb^{2+}$ |

| Ions That Form *Insoluble* Compounds | Exceptions |
|---|---|
| carbonate ($CO_3^{2-}$) | when combined with Group 1 ions or ammonium ($NH_4^+$) |
| chromate ($CrO_4^{2-}$) | when combined with Group 1 ions, $Ca^{2+}$, $Mg^{2+}$, or ammonium ($NH_4^+$) |
| phosphate ($PO_4^{3-}$) | when combined with Group 1 ions or ammonium ($NH_4^+$) |
| sulfide ($S^{2-}$) | when combined with Group 1 ions or ammonium ($NH_4^+$) |
| hydroxide ($OH^-$) | when combined with Group 1 ions, $Ca^{2+}$, $Ba^{2+}$, $Sr^{2+}$, or ammonium ($NH_4^+$) |

## Table G    Solubility Curves

# Table H
## Vapor Pressure of Four Liquids

## Table I
## Heats of Reaction at 101.3 kPa and 298 K

| Reaction | $\Delta H$ (kJ)* |
|---|---|
| $CH_4(g) + 2O_2(g) \longrightarrow CO_2(g) + 2H_2O(\ell)$ | −890.4 |
| $C_3H_8(g) + 5O_2(g) \longrightarrow 3CO_2(g) + 4H_2O(\ell)$ | −2219.2 |
| $2C_8H_{18}(\ell) + 25O_2(g) \longrightarrow 16CO_2(g) + 18H_2O(\ell)$ | −10943 |
| $2CH_3OH(\ell) + 3O_2(g) \longrightarrow 2CO_2(g) + 4H_2O(\ell)$ | −1452 |
| $C_2H_5OH(\ell) + 3O_2(g) \longrightarrow 2CO_2(g) + 3H_2O(\ell)$ | −1367 |
| $C_6H_{12}O_6(s) + 6O_2(g) \longrightarrow 6CO_2(g) + 6H_2O(\ell)$ | −2804 |
| $2CO(g) + O_2(g) \longrightarrow 2CO_2(g)$ | −566.0 |
| $C(s) + O_2(g) \longrightarrow CO_2(g)$ | −393.5 |
| $4Al(s) + 3O_2(g) \longrightarrow 2Al_2O_3(s)$ | −3351 |
| $N_2(g) + O_2(g) \longrightarrow 2NO(g)$ | +182.6 |
| $N_2(g) + 2O_2(g) \longrightarrow 2NO_2(g)$ | +66.4 |
| $2H_2(g) + O_2(g) \longrightarrow 2H_2O(g)$ | −483.6 |
| $2H_2(g) + O_2(g) \longrightarrow 2H_2O(\ell)$ | −571.6 |
| $N_2(g) + 3H_2(g) \longrightarrow 2NH_3(g)$ | −91.8 |
| $2C(s) + 3H_2(g) \longrightarrow C_2H_6(g)$ | −84.0 |
| $2C(s) + 2H_2(g) \longrightarrow C_2H_4(g)$ | +52.4 |
| $2C(s) + H_2(g) \longrightarrow C_2H_2(g)$ | +227.4 |
| $H_2(g) + I_2(g) \longrightarrow 2HI(g)$ | +53.0 |
| $KNO_3(s) \xrightarrow{H_2O} K^+(aq) + NO_3^-(aq)$ | +34.89 |
| $NaOH(s) \xrightarrow{H_2O} Na^+(aq) + OH^-(aq)$ | −44.51 |
| $NH_4Cl(s) \xrightarrow{H_2O} NH_4^+(aq) + Cl^-(aq)$ | +14.78 |
| $NH_4NO_3(s) \xrightarrow{H_2O} NH_4^+(aq) + NO_3^-(aq)$ | +25.69 |
| $NaCl(s) \xrightarrow{H_2O} Na^+(aq) + Cl^-(aq)$ | +3.88 |
| $LiBr(s) \xrightarrow{H_2O} Li^+(aq) + Br^-(aq)$ | −48.83 |
| $H^+(aq) + OH^-(aq) \longrightarrow H_2O(\ell)$ | −55.8 |

*Minus sign indicates an exothermic reaction.

## Table J
## Activity Series**

| Most | Metals | Nonmetals | Most |
|---|---|---|---|
| | Li | $F_2$ | |
| | Rb | $Cl_2$ | |
| | K | $Br_2$ | |
| | Cs | $I_2$ | |
| | Ba | | |
| | Sr | | |
| | Ca | | |
| | Na | | |
| | Mg | | |
| | Al | | |
| | Ti | | |
| | Mn | | |
| | Zn | | |
| | Cr | | |
| | Fe | | |
| | Co | | |
| | Ni | | |
| | Sn | | |
| | Pb | | |
| | **$H_2$ | | |
| | Cu | | |
| | Ag | | |
| Least | Au | | Least |

**Activity Series based on hydrogen standard

*Note:* $H_2$ is *not* a metal

## Table K
## Common Acids

| Formula | Name |
|---------|------|
| $HCl(aq)$ | hydrochloric acid |
| $HNO_3(aq)$ | nitric acid |
| $H_2SO_4(aq)$ | sulfuric acid |
| $H_3PO_4(aq)$ | phosphoric acid |
| $H_2CO_3(aq)$ or $CO_2(aq)$ | carbonic acid |
| $CH_3COOH(aq)$ or $HC_2H_3O_2(aq)$ | ethanoic acid (acetic acid) |

## Table L
## Common Bases

| Formula | Name |
|---------|------|
| $NaOH(aq)$ | sodium hydroxide |
| $KOH(aq)$ | potassium hydroxide |
| $Ca(OH)_2(aq)$ | calcium hydroxide |
| $NH_3(aq)$ | aqueous ammonia |

## Table M
## Common Acid–Base Indicators

| Indicator | Approximate pH Range for Color Change | Color Change |
|-----------|----------------------------------------|--------------|
| methyl orange | 3.2–4.4 | red to yellow |
| bromthymol blue | 6.0–7.6 | yellow to blue |
| phenolphthalein | 8.2–10 | colorless to pink |
| litmus | 5.5–8.2 | red to blue |
| bromcresol green | 3.8–5.4 | yellow to blue |
| thymol blue | 8.0–9.6 | yellow to blue |

## Table N
## Selected Radioisotopes

| Nuclide | Half-Life | Decay Mode | Nuclide Name |
|---------|-----------|------------|--------------|
| $^{198}Au$ | 2.69 d | $\beta^-$ | gold-198 |
| $^{14}C$ | 5730 y | $\beta^-$ | carbon-14 |
| $^{37}Ca$ | 175 ms | $\beta^+$ | calcium-37 |
| $^{60}Co$ | 5.26 y | $\beta^-$ | cobalt-60 |
| $^{137}Cs$ | 30.23 y | $\beta^-$ | cesium-137 |
| $^{53}Fe$ | 8.51 min | $\beta^+$ | iron-53 |
| $^{220}Fr$ | 27.5 s | $\alpha$ | francium-220 |
| $^{3}H$ | 12.26 y | $\beta^-$ | hydrogen-3 |
| $^{131}I$ | 8.07 d | $\beta^-$ | iodine-131 |
| $^{37}K$ | 1.23 s | $\beta^+$ | potassium-37 |
| $^{42}K$ | 12.4 h | $\beta^-$ | potassium-42 |
| $^{85}Kr$ | 10.76 y | $\beta^-$ | krypton-85 |
| $^{16}N$ | 7.2 s | $\beta^-$ | nitrogen-16 |
| $^{19}Ne$ | 17.2 s | $\beta^+$ | neon-19 |
| $^{32}P$ | 14.3 d | $\beta^-$ | phosphorus-32 |
| $^{239}Pu$ | $2.44 \times 10^4$ y | $\alpha$ | plutonium-239 |
| $^{226}Ra$ | 1600 y | $\alpha$ | radium-226 |
| $^{222}Rn$ | 3.82 d | $\alpha$ | radon-222 |
| $^{90}Sr$ | 28.1 y | $\beta^-$ | strontium-90 |
| $^{99}Tc$ | $2.13 \times 10^5$ y | $\beta^-$ | technetium-99 |
| $^{232}Th$ | $1.4 \times 10^{10}$ y | $\alpha$ | thorium-232 |
| $^{233}U$ | $1.62 \times 10^5$ y | $\alpha$ | uranium-233 |
| $^{235}U$ | $7.1 \times 10^8$ y | $\alpha$ | uranium-235 |
| $^{238}U$ | $4.51 \times 10^9$ y | $\alpha$ | uranium-238 |

ms = milliseconds; s = seconds; min = minutes; h = hours; d = days; y = years

## Table O
## Symbols Used in Nuclear Chemistry

| Name | Notation | Symbol |
|---|---|---|
| alpha particle | $^4_2\text{He}$ or $^4_2\alpha$ | $\alpha$ |
| beta particle (electron) | $^0_{-1}\text{e}$ or $^0_{-1}\beta$ | $\beta^-$ |
| gamma radiation | $^0_0\gamma$ | $\gamma$ |
| neutron | $^1_0\text{n}$ | n |
| proton | $^1_1\text{H}$ or $^1_1\text{p}$ | p |
| positron | $^0_{+1}\text{e}$ or $^0_{+1}\beta$ | $\beta^+$ |

## Table P
## Organic Prefixes

| Prefix | Number of Carbon Atoms |
|---|---|
| meth- | 1 |
| eth- | 2 |
| prop- | 3 |
| but- | 4 |
| pent- | 5 |
| hex- | 6 |
| hept- | 7 |
| oct- | 8 |
| non- | 9 |
| dec- | 10 |

## Table Q
## Homologous Series of Hydrocarbons

| Name | General Formula | Examples | |
|---|---|---|---|
| | | Name | Structural Formula |
| alkanes | $C_nH_{2n+2}$ | ethane | H—C—C—H (with H atoms) |
| alkenes | $C_nH_{2n}$ | ethene | C=C (with H atoms) |
| alkynes | $C_nH_{2n-2}$ | ethyne | H—C≡C—H |

$n$ = number of carbon atoms

# Table R
## Organic Functional Groups

| Class of Compound | Functional Group | General Formula | Example |
|---|---|---|---|
| halide (halocarbon) | $-F$ (fluoro-) <br> $-Cl$ (chloro-) <br> $-Br$ (bromo-) <br> $-I$ (iodo-) | $R-X$ ($X$ represents any halogen) | $CH_3CHClCH_3$ <br> 2-chloropropane |
| alcohol | $-OH$ | $R-OH$ | $CH_3CH_2CH_2OH$ <br> 1-propanol |
| ether | $-O-$ | $R-O-R'$ | $CH_3OCH_2CH_3$ <br> methyl ethyl ether |
| aldehyde | $\overset{\displaystyle O}{\overset{\|}{-C-H}}$ | $\overset{\displaystyle O}{\overset{\|}{R-C-H}}$ | $\overset{\displaystyle O}{\overset{\|}{CH_3CH_2C-H}}$ <br> propanal |
| ketone | $\overset{\displaystyle O}{\overset{\|}{-C-}}$ | $\overset{\displaystyle O}{\overset{\|}{R-C-R'}}$ | $\overset{\displaystyle O}{\overset{\|}{CH_3CCH_2CH_2CH_3}}$ <br> 2-pentanone |
| organic acid | $\overset{\displaystyle O}{\overset{\|}{-C-OH}}$ | $\overset{\displaystyle O}{\overset{\|}{R-C-OH}}$ | $\overset{\displaystyle O}{\overset{\|}{CH_3CH_2C-OH}}$ <br> propanoic acid |
| ester | $\overset{\displaystyle O}{\overset{\|}{-C-O-}}$ | $\overset{\displaystyle O}{\overset{\|}{R-C-O-R'}}$ | $\overset{\displaystyle O}{\overset{\|}{CH_3CH_2COCH_3}}$ <br> methyl propanoate |
| amine | $\overset{\|}{\underset{\|}{-N-}}$ | $R-\overset{R'}{\overset{\|}{N}}-R''$ | $CH_3CH_2CH_2NH_2$ <br> 1-propanamine |
| amide | $\overset{\displaystyle O}{\overset{\|}{-C-NH}}$ | $R-\overset{O}{\overset{\|}{C}}-\overset{R'}{\overset{\|}{N}}H$ | $\overset{\displaystyle O}{\overset{\|}{CH_3CH_2C-NH_2}}$ <br> propanamide |

$R$ represents a bonded atom or group of atoms.

# Periodic Table of the Elements

# Table S
## Properties of Selected Elements

| Atomic Number | Symbol | Name | First Ionization Energy (kJ/mol) | Electro-negativity | Melting Point (K) | Boiling* Point (K) | Density** (g/cm³) | Atomic Radius (pm) |
|---|---|---|---|---|---|---|---|---|
| 1 | H | hydrogen | 1312 | 2.1 | 14 | 20 | 0.00009 | 37 |
| 2 | He | helium | 2372 | — | 1 | 4 | 0.000179 | 32 |
| 3 | Li | lithium | 520 | 1.0 | 454 | 1620 | 0.534 | 155 |
| 4 | Be | beryllium | 900 | 1.6 | 1551 | 3243 | 1.8477 | 112 |
| 5 | B | boron | 801 | 2.0 | 2573 | 3931 | 2.340 | 98 |
| 6 | C | carbon | 1086 | 2.6 | 3820 | 5100 | 3.513 | 91 |
| 7 | N | nitrogen | 1402 | 3.0 | 63 | 77 | 0.00125 | 92 |
| 8 | O | oxygen | 1314 | 3.5 | 55 | 90 | 0.001429 | 65 |
| 9 | F | fluorine | 1681 | 4.0 | 54 | 85 | 0.001696 | 57 |
| 10 | Ne | neon | 2081 | — | 24 | 27 | 0.0009 | 51 |
| 11 | Na | sodium | 496 | 0.9 | 371 | 1156 | 0.971 | 190 |
| 12 | Mg | magnesium | 736 | 1.3 | 922 | 1363 | 1.738 | 160 |
| 13 | Al | aluminum | 578 | 1.6 | 934 | 2740 | 2.698 | 143 |
| 14 | Si | silicon | 787 | 1.9 | 1683 | 2628 | 2.329 | 132 |
| 15 | P | phosphorus | 1012 | 2.2 | 317 | 553 | 1.820 | 128 |
| 16 | S | sulfur | 1000 | 2.6 | 386 | 718 | 2.070 | 127 |
| 17 | Cl | chlorine | 1251 | 3.2 | 172 | 239 | 0.003214 | 97 |
| 18 | Ar | argon | 1521 | — | 84 | 87 | 0.001783 | 88 |
| 19 | K | potassium | 419 | 0.8 | 337 | 1047 | 0.862 | 235 |
| 20 | Ca | calcium | 590 | 1.0 | 1112 | 1757 | 1.550 | 197 |
| 21 | Sc | scandium | 633 | 1.4 | 1814 | 3104 | 2.989 | 162 |
| 22 | Ti | titanium | 659 | 1.5 | 1933 | 3580 | 4.540 | 145 |
| 23 | V | vanadium | 651 | 1.6 | 2160 | 3650 | 6.100 | 134 |
| 24 | Cr | chromium | 653 | 1.7 | 2130 | 2945 | 7.190 | 130 |
| 25 | Mn | manganese | 717 | 1.6 | 1517 | 2235 | 7.440 | 135 |
| 26 | Fe | iron | 762 | 1.8 | 1808 | 3023 | 7.874 | 126 |
| 27 | Co | cobalt | 760 | 1.9 | 1768 | 3143 | 8.900 | 125 |
| 28 | Ni | nickel | 737 | 1.9 | 1726 | 3005 | 8.902 | 124 |
| 29 | Cu | copper | 745 | 1.9 | 1357 | 2840 | 8.960 | 128 |
| 30 | Zn | zinc | 906 | 1.7 | 693 | 1180 | 7.133 | 138 |
| 31 | Ga | gallium | 579 | 1.8 | 303 | 2676 | 5.907 | 141 |
| 32 | Ge | germanium | 762 | 2.0 | 1211 | 3103 | 5.323 | 137 |
| 33 | As | arsenic | 944 | 2.2 | 1090 | 889 | 5.780 | 139 |
| 34 | Se | selenium | 941 | 2.6 | 490 | 958 | 4.790 | 140 |
| 35 | Br | bromine | 1140 | 3.0 | 266 | 332 | 3.122 | 112 |
| 36 | Kr | krypton | 1351 | — | 117 | 121 | 0.00375 | 103 |
| 37 | Rb | rubidium | 403 | 0.8 | 312 | 961 | 1.532 | 248 |
| 38 | Sr | strontium | 549 | 1.0 | 1042 | 1657 | 2.540 | 215 |
| 39 | Y | yttrium | 600 | 1.2 | 1795 | 3611 | 4.469 | 178 |
| 40 | Zr | zirconium | 640 | 1.3 | 2125 | 4650 | 6.506 | 160 |

# Table S
## Properties of Selected Elements (cont.)

| Atomic Number | Symbol | Name | First Ionization Energy (kJ/mol) | Electro-negativity | Melting Point (K) | Boiling* Point (K) | Density** (g/cm³) | Atomic Radius (pm) |
|---|---|---|---|---|---|---|---|---|
| 41 | Nb | niobium | 652 | 1.6 | 2741 | 5015 | 8.570 | 146 |
| 42 | Mo | molybdenum | 684 | 2.2 | 2890 | 4885 | 10.220 | 139 |
| 43 | Tc | technetium | 702 | 1.9 | 2445 | 5150 | 11.500 | 136 |
| 44 | Ru | ruthenium | 710 | 2.2 | 2583 | 4173 | 12.370 | 134 |
| 45 | Rh | rhodium | 720 | 2.3 | 2239 | 4000 | 12.410 | 134 |
| 46 | Pd | palladium | 804 | 2.2 | 1825 | 3413 | 12.020 | 137 |
| 47 | Ag | silver | 731 | 1.9 | 1235 | 2485 | 10.500 | 144 |
| 48 | Cd | cadmium | 868 | 1.7 | 594 | 1038 | 8.650 | 171 |
| 49 | In | indium | 558 | 1.8 | 429 | 2353 | 7.310 | 166 |
| 50 | Sn | tin | 709 | 2.0 | 505 | 2543 | 7.310 | 162 |
| 51 | Sb | antimony | 831 | 2.1 | 904 | 1908 | 6.691 | 159 |
| 52 | Te | tellurium | 869 | 2.1 | 723 | 1263 | 6.240 | 142 |
| 53 | I | iodine | 1008 | 2.7 | 387 | 458 | 4.930 | 132 |
| 54 | Xe | xenon | 1170 | 2.6 | 161 | 166 | 0.0059 | 124 |
| 55 | Cs | cesium | 376 | 0.8 | 302 | 952 | 1.873 | 267 |
| 56 | Ba | barium | 503 | 0.9 | 1002 | 1910 | 3.594 | 222 |
| 57 | La | lanthanum | 538 | 1.1 | 1194 | 3730 | 6.145 | 138 |
| Elements 58–71 have been omitted. |||||||||
| 72 | Hf | hafnium | 659 | 1.3 | 2503 | 5470 | 13.310 | 167 |
| 73 | Ta | tantalum | 728 | 1.5 | 3269 | 5698 | 16.654 | 149 |
| 74 | W | tungsten | 759 | 2.4 | 3680 | 5930 | 19.300 | 141 |
| 75 | Re | rhenium | 756 | 1.9 | 3453 | 5900 | 21.020 | 137 |
| 76 | Os | osmium | 814 | 2.2 | 3327 | 5300 | 22.590 | 135 |
| 77 | Ir | iridium | 865 | 2.2 | 2683 | 4403 | 22.560 | 136 |
| 78 | Pt | platinum | 864 | 2.3 | 2045 | 4100 | 21.450 | 139 |
| 79 | Au | gold | 890 | 2.5 | 1338 | 3080 | 19.320 | 146 |
| 80 | Hg | mercury | 1007 | 2.0 | 234 | 630 | 13.546 | 160 |
| 81 | Tl | thallium | 589 | 2.0 | 577 | 1730 | 11.850 | 171 |
| 82 | Pb | lead | 716 | 2.3 | 601 | 2013 | 11.350 | 175 |
| 83 | Bi | bismuth | 703 | 2.0 | 545 | 1833 | 9.747 | 170 |
| 84 | Po | polonium | 812 | 2.0 | 527 | 1235 | 9.320 | 167 |
| 85 | At | astatine | — | 2.2 | 575 | 610 | — | 145 |
| 86 | Rn | radon | 1037 | — | 202 | 211 | 0.00973 | 134 |
| 87 | Fr | francium | 393 | 0.7 | 300 | 950 | — | 270 |
| 88 | Ra | radium | — | 0.9 | 973 | 1413 | 5.000 | 233 |
| 89 | Ac | actinium | 499 | 1.1 | 1320 | 3470 | 10.060 | — |
| Elements 90 and above have been omitted. |||||||||

*Boiling point at standard pressure
**Density at STP

# Table T
## Important Formulas and Equations

| | | |
|---|---|---|
| **Density** | $d = \dfrac{m}{V}$ | $d$ = density<br>$m$ = mass<br>$V$ = volume |
| **Mole Calculations** | number of moles $= \dfrac{\text{given mass (g)}}{\text{gram-formula mass}}$ | |
| **Percent Error** | % error $= \dfrac{\text{measured value} - \text{accepted value}}{\text{accepted value}} \times 100$ | |
| **Percent Composition** | % composition by mass $= \dfrac{\text{mass of part}}{\text{mass of whole}} \times 100$ | |
| **Concentration** | parts per million $= \dfrac{\text{grams of solute}}{\text{grams of solution}} \times 1\,000\,000$ | |
| | molarity $= \dfrac{\text{moles of solute}}{\text{liters of solution}}$ | |
| **Combined Gas Law** | $\dfrac{P_1 V_1}{T_1} = \dfrac{P_2 V_2}{T_2}$ | $P$ = pressure<br>$V$ = volume<br>$T$ = temperature (K) |
| **Titration** | $M_A V_A = M_B V_B$ | $M_A$ = molarity of $H^+$     $M_B$ = molarity of $OH^-$<br>$V_A$ = volume of acid     $V_B$ = volume of base |
| **Heat** | $q = mC\Delta T$<br>$q = mH_f$<br>$q = mH_v$ | $q$ = heat     $H_f$ = heat of fusion<br>$m$ = mass     $H_v$ = heat of vaporization<br>$C$ = specific heat capacity<br>$\Delta T$ = change in temperature |
| **Temperature** | K $=$ °C $+ 273$ | K = kelvin<br>°C = degrees Celsius |
| **Radioactive Decay** | fraction remaining $= \left(\dfrac{1}{2}\right)^{\frac{t}{T}}$<br><br>number of half-life periods $= \dfrac{t}{T}$ | $t$ = total time elapsed<br>$T$ = half-life |

# Appendix 2:
## Graphing and Math Skills

This appendix provides a review of basic graphing skills that will be helpful in answering various types of questions on the Regents Examination for Physical Setting/Chemistry.

## Graphing

A graph of data collected during an experiment provides a single cohesive picture of many separate pieces of data. Graphs often allow you to see patterns and relationships in the data that are not otherwise obvious.

**Variables**  Each of a graph's axes represents a variable. In a typical science experiment, the scientist changes one variable in order to see how a second variable changes in response. The variable that the scientist controls and changes is called the *independent variable*. Normally the independent variable is plotted on the horizontal or *x*-axis. The variable that responds to changes in the independent variable is called the *dependent variable*. The dependent variable is usually plotted on the vertical or *y*-axis.

**Data Tables**  As data is collected during an experiment it is often organized and displayed in the form of a data table. The data table should have a title that briefly describes the experiment or data. This data table title may be the same title used for the graph of the data. Data tables typically have at least two columns, one for the dependent variable and one for the independent variable. The independent variable is placed in the first column, and the dependent variable is placed in the second column. Label each column with the name of the variable being measured.

**Preparing a Graph**  In order to prepare the graph, first look at the data table. Take note of the range of values of each of the variables in the data table. Determine if the origin of the graph will have a value of zero. Although origins with zero values are common, they are not mandatory.

Considering the range of data values, divide each axis into convenient units based on the graph paper's grid. If you are drawing your own axes on blank paper, choose divisions that are convenient for clearly displaying the data.

Be sure that each box represents the same increment. Axis scales should be chosen to spread the data over as much space as possible. Label each axis with the name of the variable being plotted and the units being used.

Now that the blank graph is prepared, the *x-y* data point pairs are plotted. Once the points have been plotted, a best-fit line is drawn to show the trend indicated by the data. The best-fit line does not have to pass through every point. In fact, the chance of that happening is quite small. When a best-fit line is properly drawn, there are often as many points above the line as there are below the line. Remember that the data represents measurements, and that all measurements have some amount of uncertainty. You may want to think of the line as an average relationship between the variables.

### SAMPLE PROBLEM

During a lab period each team was assigned to determine the relationship between the volume and mass of an unknown liquid. Each team was assigned two volumes. They carefully filled graduated cylinders to the assigned volumes and then massed the cylinders and their contents. Knowing the masses of the empty graduated cylinders, they calculated the mass of the liquid. The following data were collected and posted on the blackboard. Prepare a data table to display the data in an organized way, and then graph the data.

**Team A**

| volume 10 mL | mass 9.5 g |
| volume 15 mL | mass 13.0 g |

**Team D**

| volume 40 mL | mass 34.4 g |
| volume 45 mL | mass 37.8 g |

**Team B**

| volume 20 mL | mass 17.0 g |
| volume 25 mL | mass 21.5 g |

**Team C**

| volume 30 mL | mass 25.5 g |
| volume 35 mL | mass 30.1 g |

## Independent and Dependent Variables:
In this case, each team was assigned two specific volumes. Thus, volume is the variable being changed during the experiment; volume is the independent variable. The teams observed how mass changed in response to the change in volume. Thus, mass is the dependent variable.

### 1. Preparing the Data Table:
Prepare the data table by placing the volume data in the first column and the mass data in the second column. Order the volume data from the lowest value to highest value. Give the table a title that reflects the type of data it contains.

**Relationship Between Volume and Mass of an Unknown Liquid**

| Volume (mL) | Mass (g) |
|---|---|
| 10.0 | 9.5 |
| 15.0 | 13.0 |
| 20.0 | 17.0 |
| 25.0 | 21.5 |
| 30.0 | 25.5 |
| 35.0 | 30.1 |
| 40.0 | 34.4 |
| 45.0 | 37.8 |

Note that with the data organized as shown in the data table, there is a clear relationship between the variables. As the volume of the liquid increases, the mass of the liquid also increases.

### 2. Preparing the Graph:
Because the volume is the independent variable, it is plotted on the x-axis. The x-label is Volume (mL). Because the x-axis data ranges from 10.0 mL to 45.0 mL, a range of 0.0 mL to 50.0 mL is chosen for the x-axis. Each box along the axis has a value of 2.0 mL.

Mass is the dependent variable and is plotted on the y-axis. The y-axis label is Mass (g). Because the y-axis data ranges from 9.5 g to 37.8 g, a range of 0.0 g to 40.0 g is chosen for the y-axis. Each box along the axis has a value of 2.0 g.

### 3. Plotting the Data:
Now that the blank graph is prepared, the x-y data point pairs are plotted. For this example, the points are plotted as a solid dot. See Figure A.

**Figure A.** Graph of volume versus mass for an unknown liquid

The graph above shows the plotted data and the data points connected by straight lines. The line on the graph indicates that the relationship between the volume of liquid and the mass of the liquid is not uniform. This is unlikely. Figure B shows why the use of a best-fit line is appropriate in this case. The best-fit straight line can be described by the equation $y = mx + b$. In this case, b (the y-intercept) occurs at the origin, so b has a value of zero. This is logical, for if there is no volume, the mass must be zero.

**Figure B.** Best-fit line drawn of the graph of volume versus mass for an unknown liquid

The slope of the line can be calculated by dividing the rise by the run. The rise over run is equal to $\Delta y / \Delta x$. (Note that the $\Delta$ symbol means "change in.") The units of $\Delta y/\Delta x$ are g/mL, which are the units commonly used for the density of a liquid. Thus the slope of the best-fit line represents the density of the unknown liquid. The density of a liquid should be a constant value.

If students had used their own data points to calculate the slope, there would be four different density calculations. Substituting each team's data in the equation

$$\text{density} = \frac{\text{mass}}{\text{volume}} = \frac{\Delta y}{\Delta x}$$

yields the following results:

Team A
$$\text{density} = \frac{(13.0\text{ g} - 9.5\text{ g})}{(15.0\text{ mL} - 10.0\text{ mL})} = \frac{0.70\text{ g}}{\text{mL}}$$

Team B
$$\text{density} = \frac{(21.5\text{ g} - 17.0\text{ g})}{(25.0\text{ mL} - 20.0\text{ mL})} = \frac{0.90\text{ g}}{\text{mL}}$$

Team C
$$\text{density} = \frac{(30.1\text{ g} - 25.5\text{ g})}{(35.0\text{ mL} - 30.0\text{ mL})} = \frac{0.92\text{ g}}{\text{mL}}$$

Team D
$$\text{density} = \frac{(37.8\text{ g} - 34.4\text{ g})}{(45.0\text{ mL} - 40.0\text{ mL})} = \frac{0.68\text{ g}}{\text{mL}}$$

Constructing the slope using the best-fit line simply involves picking two convenient points on the line and making a calculation using these values. Figure C shows the density to be 0.88 g/mL.

**Figure C. Calculation of slope using data points from the best-fit line**

**Interpolation and Extrapolation** A graph is also useful because it allows you to estimate values that are not part of the data table. When a value is read from the graph's curve that falls within the data table's values, the process in called *interpolation*. Interpolating from the graph in Figure B shows that a volume of 37 mL of the unknown liquid has a mass of approximately 32 g.

When the curve or line on a graph is extended beyond the known plotted values and used to make predictions, the process is called extrapolation. Extrapolating from the graph in Figure B shows that a volume of 8.0 mL of the unknown liquid should have a mass of approximately 7 g.

**Graph Shapes and Relationships** Figure D shows several typical graph shapes. If one variable increases as the other variable increases, the relationship is said to be direct. If one variable increases as the other decreases, the relationship is said to be indirect or inverse.

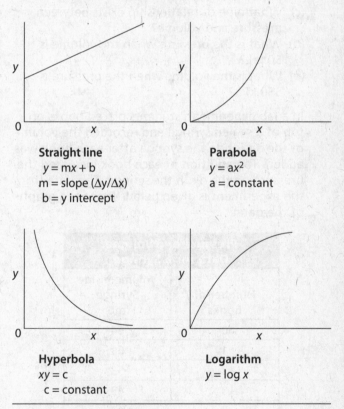

**Figure D. Typical graph shapes**

# Practice Problems

1. In a laboratory experiment, the pressure on a confined gas was increased and the resulting changes in volume were recorded. The temperature of the gas was kept constant during the experiment.

| Pressure and Volume Data for a Confined Gas | |
|---|---|
| Pressure (kPa) | Volume (mL) |
| 100 | 93.0 |
| 200 | 46.5 |
| 300 | 31.0 |
| 400 | 23.2 |
| 500 | 18.6 |
| 600 | 15.5 |

(a) What are the independent and dependent variables?
(b) Plot a graph of the data starting with a pressure of 0 kPa.
(c) What type of relationship exists between pressure and volume?
(d) What is the pressure when the volume is 50 mL?
(e) What is the volume when the pressure is 550 kPa?

2. In a lab experiment, students placed books on top of a sealed syringe and recorded the volume of the air inside the syringe after each book was added. The addition of each book increased the pressure on the air in the syringe. The data from the experiment is given below. Prepare a graph of the data.

| Pressure and Volume Data for a Syringe | |
|---|---|
| Number of Books | Volume Inside Syringe (mL) |
| 0 | 64 |
| 1 | 61 |
| 2 | 53 |
| 3 | 48 |
| 4 | 43 |
| 5 | 39 |
| 6 | 36 |
| 7 | 32 |

3. In a laboratory exercise, the volume of a gas is measured at various temperatures while the pressure is held constant. Data from the experiment is given in the data table below.

| Trial | Temperature (°C) | Volume (cm³) |
|---|---|---|
| A | 0 | 100 |
| B | 50 | 120 |
| C | 100 | 135 |
| D | 150 | 155 |
| E | 200 | 173 |

(a) Graph the data. In preparing the graph, extend the temperature axis out to 300°C. Based on the trend in the behavior of the gas, extend the volume axis so you can extrapolate the volume at a temperature of 300°C. When preparing your graph decide if the axis used for the volume of the gas should begin at 0 cm³ or 100 cm³.
(b) What type of relationship exists between temperature and volume?
(c) Identify the independent and dependent variables.
(d) Extrapolate to determine the volume at 300°C.

4. Consult the *Reference Tables for Physical Setting/Chemistry* and prepare a graph to show the relationship between atomic radii and atomic number for the elements in periods 2 and 3. After you have prepared the graph decide if atomic radius is a periodic function. Write a sentence supporting your opinion.

5. Consult the *Reference Tables for Physical Setting/Chemistry* and prepare a graph showing the relationship between atomic number and boiling point of the noble gases. What type of relationship exists between the atomic number and boiling point of the noble gases? Using your knowledge of chemistry, propose a reason why this relationship exists.

**Base your answers to questions 6 and 7 on the information below.**

In a laboratory experiment, 10.00 grams of an unknown solid is added to 100. milliliters of water and the temperature of the resulting solution is measured over several minutes, as recorded in the table that follows.

| Data Table | |
|---|---|
| Time (minutes) | Temperature (°C) |
| 0 | 24.0 |
| 0.5 | 28.5 |
| 1.0 | 31.0 |
| 1.5 | 34.5 |
| 2.0 | 41.0 |
| 2.5 | 45.5 |
| 3.0 | 46.5 |

**Base your answers to questions 8 through 10 on the information below.**

A substance is a solid at 15°C. A student heated a sample of the solid substance and recorded the temperature at one-minute intervals in the data table below.

| Time (min) | 0 | 1 | 2 | 3 | 4 | 5 | 6 | 7 | 8 | 9 | 10 | 11 | 12 |
|---|---|---|---|---|---|---|---|---|---|---|---|---|---|
| Temp (°C) | 15 | 32 | 46 | 53 | 53 | 53 | 53 | 53 | 53 | 53 | 53 | 60 | 65 |

**Heating Curve**

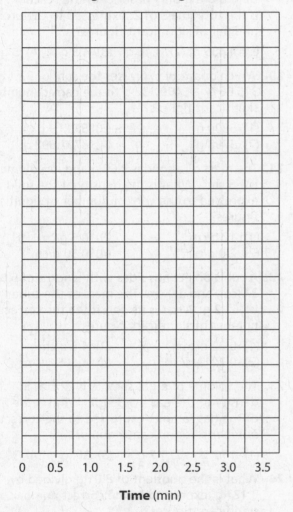

**Change in Temperature During the Dissolving of a Solid**

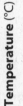

Temperature (°C)

Time (min)

8. On the grid mark an appropriate scale on the axis labeled "Temperature (°C). [1]

9. Plot the data from the table. Circle and connect the points. [1]

10. Based on the data table, what is the melting point of this substance? [1]

6. On the grid mark an appropriate scale on the axis labeled "Temperature °C."

7. Plot the data from the data table. Circle and connect the points.

**Base your answers to questions 11 through 13 on the information below.**

| First Ionization Energy of Selected Elements | | |
|---|---|---|
| Element | Atomic Number | First Ionization Energy (kJ/mol) |
| Lithium | 3 | 520 |
| Sodium | 11 | 496 |
| Potassium | 19 | 419 |
| Rubidium | 37 | 403 |
| Cesium | 55 | 376 |

**First Ionization Energy Versus
Atomic Number of Selected Elements**

First Ionization Energy (kJ/mol)

3   7   11  15  19  23  27  31  35  39  43  47  51  55
**Atomic Number**

11. Mark an appropriate scale on the axis labeled "First Ionization Energy (kJ/mol)." [1]

12. On the grid, plot the data from the table. Circle and connect the points. [1]

13. State the trend in the first ionization energy for the elements in the table as the atomic number increases. [1]

# Significant Figures

You may find some of the rules for determining the number of significant figures in a number a bit confusing. If so, a simple memory aid known as the Atlantic and Pacific rule may help you.

**The Atlantic and Pacific Rule** Imagine a map of the United States, with the Pacific Ocean on the left and the Atlantic Ocean on the right.

- When a decimal is **P**resent in a measurement, start on the **P**acific side (left side of the number) with the first nonzero digit. All the following digits are significant.

- When a decimal is **A**bsent in a measurement, start on the **A**tlantic side (right side of the number) with the first nonzero digit. All the preceding digits are significant.

# Practice Problems

14. Which milligram quantity contains a total of four significant figures?

(1) 0.30310 mg      (3) 3100. mg
(2) 3010 mg         (4) 30,001 mg

15. Which measurement contains three significant figures?

(1) 0.05 g           (3) 0.056 g
(2) 0.050 g          (4) 0.0563 g

16. Which measurement has the greatest number of significant figures?

(1) 6.060 mg         (3) 606 mg
(2) 60.6 mg          (4) 60,600 mg

17. Which mass measurement contains a total of three significant figures?

(1) 22.0 g   (2) 22.00 g   (3) 220 g   (4) 2200 g

18. Which quantity expresses the sum (2.1 g + 33.566 g + 12.22 g) to the proper degree of precision?

(1) 47.886 g         (3) 47.9 g
(2) 47.89 g          (4) 48.0 g

19. When 1.255 g of X reacts completely with 3.2 g of Y, Z is the only product of the reaction. What is the total mass of Z, expressed to the proper number of significant figures?

(1) 4.455 g   (2) 4.46 g   (3) 4.5 g   (4) 5 g

20. Which quantity expresses the sum of 22.1 g + 375.66 g + 5400.132 g to the correct number of significant figures?

(1) 5800 g           (3) 5797.9 g
(2) 5798 g           (4) 5797.892 g

21. The mass of a solid is 3.60 g and its volume is 1.8 $cm^3$. What is the density of the solid, expressed to the correct number of significant figures?

(1) 12 g/$cm^3$      (3) 0.5 g/$cm^3$
(2) 2.0 g/$cm^3$     (4) 0.50 g/$cm^3$

22. A cubic object has sides with lengths of 6.0 cm, 3.0 cm, and 2.0 cm. The mass of the cube is 162.2 g. What is its density to the correct number of significant figures?

(1) 0.22 g/$cm^3$    (3) 4.5 g/$cm^3$
(2) 0.2219 g/$cm^3$  (4) 4.505 g/$cm^3$

23. The volume of a gas sample is 22 L at STP. The density of the gas is 1.35 g/L. What is the mass of the gas sample, expressed to the correct number of significant figures?

(1) 16.7 g   (2) 17 g   (3) 30. g   (4) 30.0 g

24. What is the quotient of 8.01 g divided by 3.127 g, expressed to the correct number of significant figures?

(1) 2.6      (2) 2.56    (3) 2.5562   (4) 2.5616

25. What is the product of 2.324 cm × 1.11 cm expressed to the correct number of significant figures?

(1) 2.58 $cm^2$      (3) 2.5796 $cm^2$
(2) 2.5780 $cm^2$    (4) 2.57964 $cm^2$

26. A solution contains 12.55 grams of a solid dissolved in 50.0 milliliters of water. What is the number of grams of solid dissolved per milliliter of water, rounded to the correct number of significant figures?

(1) 0.25 g/mL      (3) 0.3 g/mL
(2) 0.251 g/mL     (4) 0.2510 g/mL

27. Add the following using the rules for significant figures.

(a) 35.7 g + 432.33 g + 5142.312 g
(b) 0.027 g + 0.0023 g

28. For each of the following, express the answer to the correct number of significant figures.

(a) Determine the density of a substance that has a mass of 21.6 g and a volume of 8.00 $cm^3$.
(b) Determine the mass of an object that has a density of 4.0 g/mL and a volume of 2.55 mL.

29. A student calculates the density of an unknown solid. The mass is 10.04 grams, and the volume is 8.21 cubic centimeters. How many significant figures should appear in the final answer?

(1) 1      (2) 2      (3) 3      (4) 4

**Base your answer to question 30 on the information given below and on the data table.**

In each of two trials, a 0.500 M NaOH(aq) solution is added to a flask containing a volume of HCl(aq) solution of unknown concentration.

| Volumes of Base and Acid Used in Titration Trials | | | |
|---|---|---|---|
| | | Trial 1 | Trial 2 |
| Solution (aq) | Molarity (M) | Volume Used | Volume Used |
| NaOH | 0.500 | 17.03 | 16.87 |
| HCl | ? | 10.22 | 10.12 |

30. Based on the information given in the table, how many significant figures should be shown in the calculated molarity of the HCl(aq) used in trial 2?

**Base your answer to question 31 on the data showing the calculation of a sample of copper sulfate in a crucible.**

| | |
|---|---|
| Mass of $CuSO_4 \cdot 5H_2O$ and crucible: | 21.37 g |
| Mass of crucible: | 19.24 g |
| Mass of $CuSO_4 \cdot 5H_2O$: | 2.13 g |

31. What is the total number of significant figures that should be recorded in the calculated mass of $CuSO_4 \cdot 5H_2O$?

**Base your answer to question 32 on the information provided in the data table below.**

| | Standard 0.100 M HCl | Unknown KOH |
|---|---|---|
| Initial reading | 9.08 mL | 0.55 mL |
| Final reading | 19.09 mL | 5.56 mL |

32. When calculating the molarity of the KOH, how many significant figures can be reported?

_____

33. A student titrates 60.0 mL of $HNO_3(aq)$ with 0.30 M NaOH(aq). Phenolphthalein is used as an indicator. After adding 42.2 mL of NaOH(aq), a color change remains for 25 seconds, and the student stops the titration.

How many significant figures should be present in the calculated molarity of the $HNO_3(aq)$?

**Base your answer to question 34 on the information provided and the data table below.**

In preparing to titrate an acid with a base, a student puts on goggles and an apron. The students uses burets to dispense and measure the acid and the base in the titration. In each of two trials, a 0.500 M NaOH(aq) solution is added to a flask containing a volume of HCl(aq) solution of unknown concentration. Phenolphthalein is the indicator used in the titration. The calculated volumes used for the two trials are recorded in the table below.

| Volumes of Base and Acid Used in Titration Trials | | | |
|---|---|---|---|
| | | Trial 1 | Trial 2 |
| Solution (aq) | Molarity (M) | Volume Used | Volume Used |
| NaOH | 0.500 | 17.03 | 16.87 |
| HCl | ? | 10.22 | 10.12 |

34. How many significant figures should be shown in the calculated molarity of the HCl(aq) used in trial 2?

# Glossary

**acidity** a measure of the hydrogen (hydronium) ion concentration of a solution

**activated complex** the temporary, intermediate product in a chemical reaction

**activation energy** the amount of energy needed to form an activated complex from reactants

**addition polymerization** joining of monomers of unsaturated compounds

**addition reaction** an organic reaction in which a substance such as hydrogen or a halogen is added to the site of a double or triple bond

**alcohol** an organic compound containing the hydroxyl group ($-OH$) as the functional group

**aldehyde** an organic compound in which the carbonyl group ($-C=O$) is at the end of a carbon chain

**alkali metal** an element of Group 1

**alkaline earth metal** an element of Group 2

**alkalinity** a measure of the hydroxide ion concentration of a solution

**alkane** one of a homologous series of saturated hydrocarbons

**alkene** one of a homologous series of hydrocarbons that contain one double covalent bond

**alkyl group** a group that contains one less hydrogen atom than an alkane with the same number of carbon atoms

**alkyne** one of a homologous series of hydrocarbons that contain one triple covalent bond

**allotrope** one of two or more different forms of an element in the same phase

**alloy** a homogeneous mixture of a metal with another element, usually another metal

**alpha particle** a helium nucleus

**amide** the product obtained from the reaction of an organic acid with an amine

**amine** an ammonia derivative in which one or more of the hydrogen atoms are replaced by an alkyl group

**amino acid** an organic compound containing both the amine group ($-NH_2$) and the carboxylic group ($-COOH$)

**analysis** a chemical reaction in which a compound is broken down (decomposed) into simpler substances

**anode** the site in an electrochemical cell where oxidation occurs

**Arrhenius acid** a substance that produces hydronium ions ($H_3O^+$) as the only positive ions when dissolved in water

**Arrhenius base** a substance that produces hydroxide ions ($OH^-$) as the only negative ions when dissolved in water

**artificial transmutation** a transmutation caused by bombarding a nucleus with a high-energy particle, such as a neutron or an alpha particle

**asymmetrical molecule** a molecule that lacks identical atomic structure on each side of an axis

**atom** the smallest particle of an element that can enter into a chemical reaction

**atomic mass** the average mass of all the isotopes in a sample of an element

**atomic mass unit** one-twelfth the mass of a carbon-12 atom

**atomic number** the number of protons in the nucleus of an atom

**atomic radius** half the distance between two adjacent atoms in a crystal or half the distance between nuclei of identical atoms bonded together

**Avogadro's number** the number of representative particles contained in one mole of a substance; equal to $6.02 \times 10^{23}$ particles

**beta particles** high-energy electrons whose source is an atomic nucleus

**boiling point** the temperature at which the vapor pressure of a liquid is equal to the atmospheric pressure

**catalyst** a substance that alters the speed of a chemical reaction without being permanently changed

**cathode** the site in an electrochemical cell where reduction occurs

**chemical change** a reaction in which the composition of a substance is changed

**chemistry** the study of the composition of matter and changes that occur in it

**coefficient** the number placed before a formula indicating the number of units of that substance

**collision theory** for a chemical reaction to occur, reactant particles must collide

**combustion** an exothermic reaction with oxygen, releasing heat

**compound** a substance composed of two or more elements that are chemically combined in definite proportions by mass

**condensation** an exothermic process in which a vapor or a gas changes into the liquid phase; the potential energy of the substance decreases during this constant temperature process; the reverse of the vaporization process

**condensation polymerization** the bonding of monomers by removing water from hydroxyl groups and joining the monomers by an ether or ester linkage

**conductivity** a measure of the ability of an electric current to flow through a substance

**conjugate acid–base pair** a pair of chemical formulas that differ only by the presence of a hydrogen ion

**covalent bond** a bond formed by the sharing of electrons between two nuclei

**decomposition** a chemical reaction in which a compound is broken down into simpler substances

**deposition** the process in which a gas changes directly into a solid; the reverse of sublimation

**diatomic molecule** a molecule containing two identical atoms

**double covalent bond** the sharing of two pairs of electrons between two nuclei

**double replacement** a chemical reaction in which ions exchange places

**ductility** property of a metal that enables it to be drawn into a wire

**electrochemical cell** a system in which there is an electric current flowing while a chemical reaction occurs

**electrode** the site at which oxidation or reduction occurs; an anode or a cathode

**electrolysis** a process in which an electric current forces a nonspontaneous redox reaction to occur

**electrolyte** a substance whose water solution conducts an electric current

**electrolytic cell** a cell that requires electricity to cause a nonspontaneous chemical reaction to occur

**electron** a fundamental particle of matter having a negative charge

**electron configuration** the distribution of the electrons in an atom

**electronegativity** a measure of the attraction of a nucleus for a bonded electron

**element** substances that cannot be broken down or decomposed into simpler substances by chemical means

**empirical formula** the simplest integer ratio in which atoms combine to form a compound

**endothermic** a chemical reaction that absorbs heat, producing products with more potential energy than the reactants

**entropy** a measure of the disorder or randomness of a system

**equilibrium** a condition in which the rates of opposing reactions are equal

**equilibrium expression** a mathematical expression that shows the relationship of reactants and products of a system at equilibrium

**ester** the organic product of an esterification reaction containing $-COOC-$ as the functional group

**esterification** a chemical reaction between an alcohol and an acid to produce an ester and water

**ether** an organic compound in which oxygen is bonded to two carbon atoms ($R_1-O-R_2$)

**evaporation** the process by which molecules in the liquid phase escape into the gaseous phase

**excited state** the condition that exists when the electrons of an atom occupy higher energy levels while lower energy levels are vacant

**exothermic** a chemical reaction that releases heat, producing products with less potential energy than the reactants

**family** a vertical column on the periodic table

**fermentation** an organic reaction in which ethanol and carbon dioxide are produced from a carbohydrate

**fission** splitting of large nuclei into middle-weight nuclei and neutrons

**formula mass** the sum of the atomic masses of all atoms present

**formula** symbols and subscripts used to represent the composition of a substance

**freezing point** the temperature at which both the solid and liquid phases of a substance exist in equilibrium; the same temperature as the substance's melting point

**freezing** the constant temperature process in which particles in the liquid phase lose energy and change into the solid phase; also known as solidification; the reverse of the melting process

**functional group** the atom or atoms that replace a hydrogen atom in a hydrocarbon and give a class of organic compounds characteristic properties

**fusion** the constant temperature process in which particles in the solid phase gain enough energy to break away into the liquid phase; also known as melting; the reverse of the freezing process; (in nuclear chemistry) the combining of light nuclei into a heavier nucleus

**gamma ray** high-energy ray similar to an X ray

**gaseous phase** a phase of matter without definite shape or volume

**gram formula mass** the formula mass expressed in grams instead of atomic mass units

**ground state** the condition of an atom or ion in which the electrons occupy the lowest available energy levels

**group** a vertical column on the periodic table

**half-life** the length of time for half of a given sample of a radioisotope to decay

**half-reaction** a reaction that shows either the oxidation or reduction portion of a redox reaction

**halide** a salt that includes a halogen

**halogen** an element of Group 17

**heat** energy transferred from one substance to another; measured in units of calories or joules

**heat of fusion** the amount of heat needed to convert a unit mass of a substance from a solid to a liquid at its melting point

**heat of vaporization** the amount of heat needed to convert a unit mass of a substance from a liquid to a vapor at its boiling point

**heterogeneous** a mixture in which the substances are not uniformly mixed

**homogeneous** a substance in which the particles are uniformly mixed

**homologous series** a group of related compounds in which each member differs from the one before it by the same additional unit

**hydrate** the crystalline form of an ionic substance that contains a definite number of water molecules

**hydrocarbon** organic compound containing only hydrogen and carbon atoms

**hydrogen bond** the attraction of a hydrogen atom in one molecule for an oxygen, nitrogen, or fluorine atom in another molecule

**hydrogen ion** a hydrogen atom without its electron (consisting solely of a proton)

**hydronium ion** $H_3O^+$, formed by the combination of water with a hydrogen ion

**hydroxide ion** the polyatomic anion produced by the ionization of a water molecule

**hydroxyl group** the group comprised of an oxygen atom and a hydrogen atom ($-OH$) responsible for the properties of alcohols

**indicator** a substance that undergoes a color change that can be used to determine when a reaction is complete

**inert gas group** former name of the Group 18 noble gases

**insoluble** material with a low solubility

**ionic bond** a bond formed by the transfer of electrons from one atom to another

**ionic radius** the distance from the nucleus to the outer energy level of the ion

**ionization energy** the amount of energy needed to remove the most loosely bound electron from a neutral gaseous atom

**isomers** compounds with the same molecular formula but different structural arrangement

**isotope** atom of an element that has a specific number of protons and neutrons

**ketone** an organic compound in which the carbonyl group ($-C=O$) is joined to two other carbon atoms

**kinetic molecular theory** a theory used to explain the behavior of gases in terms of the motion of their particles

**law of conservation of mass** matter is neither created nor destroyed in chemical reactions

**law of definite proportions** types of atoms in a compound exist in a fixed ratio

**Le Châtelier's principle** a system at equilibrium will react to reduce a stress

**Lewis dot diagram** a diagram that depicts valence electrons as dots around the atomic symbol (representing the nucleus and nonvalence electrons) of the element

**liquid phase** a phase of matter having definite volume but no definite shape (takes the shape of its container)

**malleability** the property of metals that allows them to be hammered into shapes

**mass number** the total number of protons and neutrons in the nucleus of an atom

**matter** anything that has mass and volume

**melting point** the temperature at which both the solid and liquid phases exist in equilibrium; the same temperature as the substance's freezing point

**metal** element whose atoms lose electrons in chemical reactions to become positive ions

**metallic bond** the attraction of valence electrons for the positive kernels of metallic atoms

**metalloid** an element that has both metallic and nonmetallic properties

**molarity** the concentration of a substance in moles per liter of solution

**mole** the number of atoms of carbon present in 12.000 g of carbon-12

**molecular formula** the actual ratio of the atoms in a molecule

**molecule** the smallest unit of a covalently bonded substance that has the properties of that substance

**monomer** each individual unit of a polymer

**multiple covalent bond** a double or triple covalent bond

**neutralization** the reaction between an acid and a base to produce water and a salt

**neutron** the uncharged particle in the nucleus of an atom

**noble gas** a nonreactive element that is in group 18 on the periodic table

**nonmetal** element whose atoms will gain or share electrons in chemical reactions

**nonpolar covalent bond** a bond formed by the equal sharing of a pair of electrons between two nuclei

**nucleus** the dense, positively charged central core of an atom

**octet of electrons** the stable valence electron configuration of eight electrons

**orbital** a region in an atom in which an electron of a particular amount of energy is most likely to be located

**organic acid** an organic compound containing one or more carboxyl groups ($-COOH$)

**organic halide** an organic compound in which one or more hydrogen atoms have been replaced by an atom of a halogen; also known as a halocarbon

**oxidation number (state)** number assigned to keep track of electron gain or loss in redox reactions

**oxidation** the loss of electrons and an increase in oxidation state

**oxidizing agent** the substance reduced in a redox reaction

**parts per million** the ratio between the parts of solute per million parts of solution

**percent by volume** the concentration of a solution expressed as the ratio between the volume of the solute and total volume of the solution, expressed as a percent

**percent mass** the concentration of a solution expressed as the ratio between the mass of the solute and the total mass of the solution, expressed as a percent

**percentage composition** the composition of a compound as a percentage of each element compared with the total mass of the compound

**period** a horizontal row of the periodic table

**periodic law** the properties of elements are periodic functions of their atomic numbers

**pH scale** a logarithmic scale that measures the acidity or alkalinity of a solution on a scale of 1 to 14

**pH** the negative logarithm of a solution's hydrogen ion concentration

**physical change** a change that does not alter the chemical properties of a substance

**polar covalent bond** a bond formed by the unequal sharing of electrons between two nuclei

**polyatomic ion** a covalently bonded group of atoms that have a net electric charge

**polymer** organic compound made up of chains of smaller units bonded together

**polymerization** an organic reaction in which many small units are joined together to form a long chain

**positron** particle identical to an electron except that it has a positive charge

**potential energy diagram** a diagram showing the changes in potential energy as a reaction proceeds

**primary alcohol** an alcohol with a hydroxyl group attached to a carbon atom at the end of a chain

**product** a substance formed in a chemical reaction, shown to the right of the arrow in an equation

**proton** the positively charged particle in the nucleus of an atom

**pure substance** a compound or an element; a material in which the composition is the same throughout

**qualitative** information that cannot be counted or measured

**quantitative** information that can be either counted or measured

**quantum number** one of a set of four numbers that describes a property of an electron in an atom

**quantum theory** a concept that relates the chemical behavior of atoms to energy being transferred in discrete units called quanta

**radioisotope** an unstable nucleus that is radioactive

**reactant** a starting substance in a reaction, shown to the left of the arrow in an equation

**redox** an oxidation-reduction reaction

**reducing agent** the substance oxidized in a redox reaction

**reduction** the gain of electrons and the loss of oxidation number

**salt** the product (other than water) of a neutralization reaction; an ionic substance consisting of a metallic cation and anion other than the hydroxide ion

**salt bridge** a part of a voltaic cell that connects two containers and allows the flow of ions

**saponification** the reaction of an alkali and a fat to produce glycerol and a soap

**saturated** (in regard to a solution) a solution containing the maximum amount of solute that will dissolve at a given temperature; (in regard to organic chemistry) organic compounds containing only single covalent bonds

**secondary alcohol** an alcohol with a hydroxyl group attached to a carbon atom that is attached to two other carbon atoms

**single covalent bond** only one pair of electrons is shared between two atoms

**single replacement** a reaction in which an element replaces a less reactive element in a compound

**solid phase** a phase of matter having a definite shape and volume; particles in this phase have a definite crystalline arrangement

**solubility** a measure of how much solute will dissolve in a certain amount of solvent at a specific temperature

**soluble** material with a high solubility

**solute** the substance being dissolved

**solution** a homogeneous mixture of substances in the same physical state

**solvent** the substance that dissolves the solute

**stress** any change in concentration, pressure, or temperature on an equilibrium system

**sublimation** the process in which a solid changes directly into a gas; the reverse of deposition

**subscript** the number written after a chemical symbol in a formula indicating the number of atoms present

**substitution reaction** one or more hydrogen atoms is removed from a saturated hydrocarbon and replaced by another atom

**supersaturated** a solution that contains more solute than would dissolve in a saturated solution at a given temperature

**symbol** a one-, two- or three-letter designation of an element

**symmetrical molecule** a molecule with identical atomic structure on each side of an axis

**synthesis** a reaction in which two or more substances combine to form one product

**temperature** the measure of the average kinetic energy of a substance's particles

**tertiary alcohol** an alcohol with a hydroxyl group attached to a carbon atom that is attached to three other carbon atoms

**titration** the process of determining the concentration of an unknown solution by a reaction with a solution of known concentration

**tracer** a radioisotope used to track a chemical reaction

**transmutation** the changing of a nucleus of one element into that of a different element

**triple bond** the sharing of three pairs of electrons between two nuclei

**unsaturated** (in regard to a solution) a solution in which more solute can be dissolved at a given temperature; (in regard to organic chemistry) an organic compound containing one or more double or triple covalent bond

**valence electrons** the electrons in the outer energy level of an atom

**vapor** the gaseous state of a substance that is normally a liquid at room temperature

**vapor pressure** the pressure that a vapor exerts

**vaporization** the constant temperature process in which particles in the liquid phase gain enough energy to break away into the gaseous phase; also known as boiling; the reverse of the condensation process

**voltaic cell** an electrochemical cell in which a spontaneous chemical reaction causes a flow of electrons

**wave-mechanical model** the current model of the atom that deals with the wave-particle duality of nature

# Index

as conductors 111
and filtration 71
as solutes or solutions
118–119

**magnesium**
in redox reactions 158
**malleability** 103
**mass**
of atoms 6–8, 46–47
in balancing equations 41, 163,
218
conversion to energy 221–222
**mass defect** 222
**mass number** 6
**matter** 1, 2
as particles and waves 4–5
phases or states of 33, 58
types of 17–19
**melting** 59, 64
bond types and melting
points 111
**Mendeleev, Dmitri** 78
**metallic bonds** 102–103, 110–111
**metalloids** 80–81
**metals** 80–81, A-5
in compounds 31–32
ion formation in 108–109
properties of 81–82
reactions with acids 175,
178–179
in replacement reactions 38
**methyl orange** 186
**miscible liquids** 72
**mixtures** 19
distinguishing from
compounds 16
separating components 71–73
**models**
in science 66, 68
**molarity** 124, A-12
and equilibrium expressions
150
and titration 182–184
**molecular formulas** 28–29, 51
**molecules** 28–29, 106–107
asymmetrical 106
diatomic 27
symmetrical polar 106–107
**moles** 45, 49
molarity 124, A-12
ratios in equations 52–53
**Moseley, Henry** 78
**multiple covalent bonds** 104

**network structures** 195
**neutralization reactions** 174,

179–180, 182–183, 186
**neutrons** 6
and artificial transmutation
220
composed of quarks 6
and fission reactions 222
and isotopes 7
mass of 6
role in nuclear stability 216
**nitrogen** 88
as a diatomic molecule 27
**noble gases** 83, 86, 90, 103
**nonmetals** 81, 82–83
covalent bonds 104
ion formation 109
properties of 82
**nonpolar covalent bonds** 104
**nonpolar molecules** 106–107
in solution formation 119–120
**nuclear chemistry** 215–228
**nuclear equations** 218–219
**nuclear wastes** 228
**nucleus, atomic**
alpha emitters 217
beta emitters 217–218
discovery of 3–4
stability of 216
structure of 6

**octet rule** 103–104
and ion formation 108–109
and oxidation-reduction 158
**orbitals** 5, 8–9
and energy levels 12–14
notation 14–15
**organic acids** 203
**organic chemistry** 193–208
**organic compounds** 194–200
alcohols 201–202
aldehydes 202–203
alkanes 196–197, 199–200
alkenes 196–197
alkynes 197
amides 204
amines 203
amino acids 203
branched 199
esters 203
ethers 203
homologous series 195–197
ketones 203
naming 199–200
organic acids 203
saturated 195
straight-chain 199–200
unsaturated 195
**organic reactions** 206–208

addition 206–207
combustion 206
esterification 207
fermentation 207
polymerization 208
saponification 207
substitution 206
**oxidation** 158
half reactions 163–164
**oxidation numbers** 158–160
and half reactions 163–164
and naming compounds
31–32
and the periodic table 79
**oxidizing agents** 161–162
**oxygen** 83, 88–89
as a diatomic molecule 27
and oxidation numbers 159
and oxidation-reduction 158
**ozone** 83

**particles**
and atomic models 3–5
**peptides** 204
**percentage composition** 47
**percent by mass** 125–126
**percent by volume** 125–126
**periodic law** 78
**periodic table** 77–90, A-9
and electron dot diagrams
99–100
Mendeleev's 78
**periods** 80–81
trends in atomic radii 86
trends in ionization energy 85
**phases of matter** 33, 57–58
and entropy 149
phase changes 59–60, 149
phase equilibrium 142
in replacement reactions 39–40
in writing chemical
equations 36
**phenolphthalein** 186
**phosphate ions** 29
**phosphorus** 83
**pH scale** 186
**physical changes** 33
**plasma** 58
**plating** 167
**polar covalent bonds** 104–105
**polar molecules** 106–107
dipole-dipole forces 112
in solution formation 119–120
**polyatomic ions** 29, 31–32,
109–110
in balancing equations 35–36
**polymerization** 208

# Acknowledgments

**Staff Credits:**

The people who make up the *Chemistry Science Brief Review team*—representing design, editorial, marketing, and production services—are listed below. Bold type denotes the core team members.

Lynn Baldridge, **Jane Breen, Glen Dixon, Becky Napoleon,** Linda Johnson, Rachel Youdelman

**Additional Credits:**

The Quarasan Group, Inc.: Chicago, IL

Lapiz Digital Services: Chennai, India
Lapiz, Inc.: Boston, MA

Independent Reviewer: Alfred E. Snider

**Cover Image:**

Ryan McVay/Photodisc/Getty Images

**Photo Credits:**

**Pages 1, 17, 77, and 145,** Dorling Kindersley; **193,** Education Management Group (EMG); **215,** Dorling Kindersley.

All uncredited photos © 2010 Pearson Education

# New York Regents Examinations

The New York Regents Examinations that follow are provided so that you can practice taking actual Chemistry Regents Examinations. All of the tests included in this book cover the key concepts of the Physical Setting: Chemistry Core Curriculum. You will find that the content of this book provides specifically what you need to review for the Physical Setting: Chemistry Regents Examination.

## Using the Regents Examinations

The best way to use these examinations is to take the entire test after you have reviewed the course content. Use the tests to determine if you have reviewed enough to do well on the Regents Examination and to determine where further review will be most helpful.

Do not look up any information or answers while you take the examinations. Answer each question just as you would during a real test. As you take the examination, use the margin of the paper to note any question where you are just guessing. Leave the more difficult questions for last, but be sure to answer each question. Every point counts so do not skip over a long question that is only worth a point or two. A long question could be easier than it looks and may make the difference between an A or a B or between passing or failing.

When you finish, have your teacher score your Examination and help you determine the areas where you need the most work. Also review the "guesses" you noted in the margin to find out what you need to study to ensure that you will be able to answer similar questions on the next test. Once you have determined your weaknesses, you can focus your review on those topics in this book.

Reviewing the areas where you know the least will give you the best chance of improving your final score. Spending time on areas where you are doing quite well will not produce much improvement in your total score, but it is still important if time permits.

**Answer Key** All answers to these Regents Examinations are included in the Answer Key, which also includes Diagnostic Tests to help you assess what you know before starting to study a topic.

# Part A

## Answer all questions in this part.

*Directions* (1–30): For *each* statement or question, write on the separate answer sheet the *number* of the word or expression that, of those given, best completes the statement or answers the question. Some questions may require the use of the *Reference Tables for Physical Setting/Chemistry*.

1 Which two particles have opposite charges?

(1) an electron and a neutron
(2) an electron and a proton
(3) a proton and a neutron
(4) a proton and a positron

2 Which statement describes how an atom in the ground state becomes excited?

(1) The atom absorbs energy, and one or more electrons move to a higher electron shell.
(2) The atom absorbs energy, and one or more electrons move to a lower electron shell.
(3) The atom releases energy, and one or more electrons move to a higher electron shell.
(4) The atom releases energy, and one or more electrons move to a lower electron shell.

3 An element that has a low first ionization energy and good conductivity of heat and electricity is classified as a

(1) metal           (3) nonmetal
(2) metalloid       (4) noble gas

4 The chemical properties of calcium are most similar to the chemical properties of

(1) Ar      (3) Mg
(2) K       (4) Sc

5 Which element is a liquid at STP?

(1) argon       (3) chlorine
(2) bromine     (4) sulfur

6 Which statement describes a chemical property of aluminum?

(1) Aluminum is malleable.
(2) Aluminum reacts with sulfuric acid.
(3) Aluminum conducts an electric current.
(4) Aluminum has a density of 2.698 $g/cm^3$ at STP.

7 Which element has an atom in the ground state with a total of three valence electrons?

(1) aluminum    (3) phosphorus
(2) lithium     (4) scandium

8 Which substance can be broken down by chemical means?

(1) magnesium   (3) mercury
(2) manganese   (4) methanol

9 The gram-formula mass of $NO_2$ is defined as the mass of

(1) one mole of $NO_2$
(2) one molecule of $NO_2$
(3) two moles of NO
(4) two molecules of NO

10 In which type of reaction do two or more substances combine to produce a single substance?

(1) synthesis
(2) decomposition
(3) single replacement
(4) double replacement

11 Which formula represents a nonpolar molecule?

(1) HCl     (3) $NH_3$
(2) $H_2O$  (4) $CH_4$

12 Which symbol represents an atom in the ground state with the most stable valence electron configuration?

(1) B   (3) Li
(2) O   (4) Ne

13 Which element has an atom with the greatest tendency to attract electrons in a chemical bond?

(1) carbon      (3) silicon
(2) chlorine    (4) sulfur

14 The nitrogen atoms in a molecule of $N_2$ share a total of

(1) one pair of electrons
(2) one pair of protons
(3) three pairs of electrons
(4) three pairs of protons

15 An ionic compound is formed when there is a reaction between the elements

(1) strontium and chlorine
(2) hydrogen and chlorine
(3) nitrogen and oxygen
(4) sulfur and oxygen

16 Which compound has both ionic and covalent bonding?

(1) $CaCO_3$      (3) $CH_3OH$
(2) $CH_2Cl_2$      (4) $C_6H_{12}O_6$

17 The liquids hexane and water are placed in a test tube. The test tube is stoppered, shaken, and placed in a test tube rack. The liquids separate into two distinct layers because hexane and water have different

(1) formula masses
(2) molecular polarities
(3) pH values
(4) specific heats

18 Which statement describes the particles of an ideal gas based on the kinetic molecular theory?

(1) The gas particles are relatively far apart and have negligible volume.
(2) The gas particles are in constant, nonlinear motion.
(3) The gas particles have attractive forces between them.
(4) The gas particles have collisions without transferring energy.

19 Under which conditions of temperature and pressure would a 1-liter sample of a real gas behave most like an ideal gas?

(1) 100 K and 0.1 atm
(2) 100 K and 10 atm
(3) 500 K and 0.1 atm
(4) 500 K and 10 atm

20 Which type of energy is associated with the random motion of the particles in a sample of gas?

(1) chemical energy
(2) electromagnetic energy
(3) nuclear energy
(4) thermal energy

21 The particles in which sample of LiCl(s) have the same average kinetic energy as the particles in a 2.0-mole sample of $H_2O(\ell)$ at 25°C?

(1) 1.0 mol at 75°C
(2) 2.0 mol at 50.°C
(3) 3.0 mol at 25°C
(4) 4.0 mol at 0°C

22 Which rigid cylinder contains the same number of gas molecules at STP as a 2.0-liter rigid cylinder containing $H_2(g)$ at STP?

(1) 1.0-L cylinder of $O_2(g)$
(2) 2.0-L cylinder of $CH_4(g)$
(3) 1.5-L cylinder of $NH_3(g)$
(4) 4.0-L cylinder of He(g)

23 Hydrogen bonding is a type of

(1) strong covalent bond
(2) weak ionic bond
(3) strong intermolecular force
(4) weak intermolecular force

24 The data collected from a laboratory titration are used to calculate the

(1) rate of a chemical reaction
(2) heat of a chemical reaction
(3) concentration of a solution
(4) boiling point of a solution

25 When one compound dissolves in water, the only positive ion produced in the solution is $H_3O^+(aq)$. This compound is classified as

(1) a salt
(2) a hydrocarbon
(3) an Arrhenius acid
(4) an Arrhenius base

26 Which nuclear emission has the greatest mass and the *least* penetrating power?

(1) an alpha particle    (3) a neutron
(2) a beta particle      (4) a positron

27 Which radioisotope has an atom that emits a particle with a mass number of 0 and a charge of +1?

(1) $^3H$    (3) $^{19}Ne$
(2) $^{16}N$    (4) $^{239}Pu$

28 In which type of reaction do two lighter nuclei combine to form one heavier nucleus?

(1) combustion    (3) nuclear fission
(2) reduction      (4) nuclear fusion

29 For which compound is the process of dissolving in water exothermic?

(1) NaCl    (3) $NH_4Cl$
(2) NaOH    (4) $NH_4NO_3$

30 Which quantities must be equal for a chemical reaction at equilibrium?

(1) the activation energies of the forward and reverse reactions
(2) the rates of the forward and reverse reactions
(3) the concentrations of the reactants and products
(4) the potential energies of the reactants and products

**January '10   Regents Examination**

# Part B–1

## Answer all questions in this part.

*Directions* (31–50): For *each* statement or question, write on the separate answer sheet the *number* of the word or expression that, of those given, best completes the statement or answers the question. Some questions may require the use of the *Reference Tables for Physical Setting/Chemistry*.

31 Which formula represents copper(I) oxide?

(1) CuO      (3) $Cu_2O$
(2) $CuO_2$      (4) $Cu_2O_2$

32 At STP, a 7.49-gram sample of an element has a volume of 1.65 cubic centimeters. The sample is most likely

(1) Ta      (3) Te
(2) Tc      (4) Ti

33 Which element, represented by *X*, reacts with fluorine to produce the compound $XF_2$?

(1) aluminum      (3) magnesium
(2) argon      (4) sodium

34 Each diagram below represents the nucleus of a different atom.

D      E      Q      R

Which diagrams represent nuclei of the same element?

(1) *D* and *E*, only      (3) *Q* and *R*, only
(2) *D*, *E*, and *Q*      (4) *Q*, *R*, and *E*

35 As atomic number increases within Group 15 on the Periodic Table, atomic radius

(1) decreases, only
(2) increases, only
(3) decreases, then increases
(4) increases, then decreases

36 Given the balanced equation representing a reaction:

$$CaO(s) + CO_2(g) \rightarrow CaCO_3(s) + heat$$

What is the total mass of CaO(s) that reacts completely with 88 grams of $CO_2(g)$ to produce 200. grams of $CaCO_3(s)$?

(1) 56 g      (3) 112 g
(2) 88 g      (4) 288 g

37 What is the empirical formula of a compound that has a carbon-to-hydrogen ratio of 2 to 6?

(1) $CH_3$      (3) $C_3H$
(2) $C_2H_6$      (4) $C_6H_2$

38 Given the balanced equation representing a reaction:

$$H_2(g) + Cl_2(g) \rightarrow 2HCl(g) + energy$$

Which statement describes the energy changes in this reaction?

(1) Energy is absorbed as bonds are formed, only.
(2) Energy is released as bonds are broken, only.
(3) Energy is absorbed as bonds are broken, and energy is released as bonds are formed.
(4) Energy is absorbed as bonds are formed, and energy is released as bonds are broken.

39 Which solution has the highest boiling point at standard pressure?

(1) 0.10 M KCl(aq)
(2) 0.10 M $K_2SO_4$(aq)
(3) 0.10 M $K_3PO_4$(aq)
(4) 0.10 M $KNO_3$(aq)

40 What is the molarity of 1.5 liters of an aqueous solution that contains 52 grams of lithium fluoride, LiF, (gram-formula mass = 26 grams/mole)?

(1) 1.3 M        (3) 3.0 M
(2) 2.0 M        (4) 0.75 M

41 What occurs when a 35-gram aluminum cube at 100.°C is placed in 90. grams of water at 25°C in an insulated cup?

(1) Heat is transferred from the aluminum to the water, and the temperature of the water decreases.
(2) Heat is transferred from the aluminum to the water, and the temperature of the water increases.
(3) Heat is transferred from the water to the aluminum, and the temperature of the water decreases.
(4) Heat is transferred from the water to the aluminum, and the temperature of the water increases.

42 Which temperature is equal to 120. K?

(1) −153°C        (3) +293°C
(2) −120.°C       (4) +393°C

43 A rigid cylinder contains a sample of gas at STP. What is the pressure of this gas after the sample is heated to 410 K?

(1) 1.0 atm       (3) 0.67 atm
(2) 0.50 atm      (4) 1.5 atm

44 Given the balanced equation representing a phase change:

$$C_6H_4Cl_2(s) + energy \rightarrow C_6H_4Cl_2(g)$$

Which statement describes this change?

(1) It is endothermic, and entropy decreases.
(2) It is endothermic, and entropy increases.
(3) It is exothermic, and entropy decreases.
(4) It is exothermic, and entropy increases.

45 In a biochemical reaction, an enzyme acts as a catalyst, causing the

(1) activation energy of the reaction to decrease
(2) potential energy of the reactants to decrease
(3) kinetic energy of the reactants to increase
(4) heat of reaction to increase

46 Given the formula for an organic compound:

This compound is classified as an

(1) aldehyde       (3) ester
(2) amine         (4) organic acid

47 Butanal and butanone have different chemical and physical properties primarily because of differences in their

(1) functional groups
(2) molecular masses
(3) molecular formulas
(4) number of carbon atoms per molecule

48 Which salt is produced when sulfuric acid and calcium hydroxide react completely?

(1) $CaH_2$        (3) CaS
(2) CaO         (4) $CaSO_4$

49 Which radioisotope is used to treat thyroid disorders?

(1) Co-60        (3) C-14
(2) I-131         (4) U-238

50 The diagram below represents an operating electrochemical cell and the balanced ionic equation for the reaction occurring in the cell.

$$Zn(s) + Ni^{2+}(aq) \longrightarrow Zn^{2+}(aq) + Ni(s)$$

Which statement identifies the part of the cell that conducts electrons and describes the direction of electron flow as the cell operates?

(1) Electrons flow through the salt bridge from the Ni(s) to the Zn(s).
(2) Electrons flow through the salt bridge from the Zn(s) to the Ni(s).
(3) Electrons flow through the wire from the Ni(s) to the Zn(s).
(4) Electrons flow through the wire from the Zn(s) to the Ni(s).

## Part B–2

### Answer all questions in this part.

*Directions* (51–65): Record your answers in the spaces provided in your answer booklet. Some questions may require the use of the *Reference Tables for Physical Setting/Chemistry*.

51 Based on Table *G*, determine the total mass of $NH_3$ that must be dissolved in 200. grams of water to produce a saturated solution at 20.°C. [1]

52 Determine the total time that must elapse until only ¼ of an original sample of the radioisotope Rn-222 remains unchanged. [1]

Base your answers to questions 53 through 55 on the information below.

A phase change for carbon dioxide that occurs spontaneously at 20.°C and 1.0 atmosphere is represented by the balanced equation below.

$$CO_2(s) + energy \rightarrow CO_2(g)$$

53 Write the name of this phase change. [1]

54 Describe what happens to the potential energy of the $CO_2$ molecules as this phase change occurs. [1]

55 *In your answer booklet,* use the key to draw *at least five* molecules in the box to represent $CO_2$ after this phase change is completed. [1]

Base your answers to questions 56 and 57 on the information below.

The dissolving of solid lithium bromide in water is represented by the balanced equation below.

$$LiBr(s) \xrightarrow{H_2O} Li^+(aq) + Br^-(aq)$$

56 Calculate the total mass of LiBr(s) required to make 500.0 grams of an aqueous solution of LiBr that has a concentration of 388 parts per million. Your response must include *both* a correct numerical setup and the calculated result. [2]

57 Based on Table *F*, identify *one* ion that reacts with $Br^-$ ions in an aqueous solution to form an insoluble compound. [1]

Base your answers to questions 58 through 60 on the information below.

The formula below represents a hydrocarbon.

58 Identify the homologous series to which this hydrocarbon belongs.  [1]

59 Explain, in terms of carbon-carbon bonds, why this hydrocarbon is saturated.  [1]

60 In the space *in your answer booklet,* draw a structural formula for *one* isomer of this hydrocarbon.  [1]

_____

Base your answers to questions 61 through 63 on the information below.

The atomic and ionic radii for sodium and chlorine are shown in the table below.

**Atomic and Ionic Radii**

| Particle | Radius (pm) |
| --- | --- |
| Na atom | 190. |
| Na$^+$ ion | 102 |
| Cl atom | 97 |
| Cl$^-$ ion | 181 |

61 Write the ground state electron configuration for the ion that has a radius of 181 picometers.  [1]

62 Convert the radius of an Na$^+$ ion to meters.  [1]

63 Explain, in terms of atomic structure, why the radius of an Na atom is larger than the radius of an Na$^+$ ion.  [1]

_____

Base your answers to questions 64 and 65 on the information below.

The nucleus of one boron atom has five protons and four neutrons.

64 Determine the total number of electrons in the boron atom.   [1]

65 Determine the total charge of the boron nucleus.   [1]

_____

# Part C

## Answer all questions in this part.

*Directions* (66–84): Record your answers in the spaces provided in your answer booklet. Some questions may require the use of the *Reference Tables for Physical Setting/Chemistry*.

Base your answers to questions 66 through 68 on the information below.

> At STP, iodine, $I_2$, is a crystal, and fluorine, $F_2$, is a gas. Iodine is soluble in ethanol, forming a tincture of iodine. A typical tincture of iodine is 2% iodine by mass.

66 Compare the strength of the intermolecular forces in a sample of $I_2$ at STP to the strength of the intermolecular forces in a sample of $F_2$ at STP. [1]

67 In the space *in your answer booklet,* draw a Lewis electron-dot diagram for a molecule of $I_2$. [1]

68 Determine the total mass of $I_2$ in 25 grams of this typical tincture of iodine. [1]

Base your answers to questions 69 through 71 on the information below.

> In a laboratory investigation, magnesium reacts with hydrochloric acid to produce hydrogen gas and magnesium chloride. This reaction is represented by the unbalanced equation below.

$$Mg(s) + HCl(aq) \rightarrow H_2(g) + MgCl_2(aq)$$

69 State, in terms of the relative activity of elements, why this reaction is spontaneous. [1]

70 Balance the equation *in your answer booklet,* using the smallest whole-number coefficients. [1]

71 Write a balanced half-reaction equation for the oxidation that occurs. [1]

Base your answers to questions 72 through 75 on the information below.

An experiment is performed to determine how concentration affects the rate of reaction. In each of four trials, equal volumes of solution A and solution B are mixed while temperature and pressure are held constant. The concentration of solution B is held constant, but the concentration of solution A is varied. The concentration of solution A and the time for the reaction to go to completion for each trial are recorded in the data table below.

**Data Table**

| Trial | Concentration of Solution A (M) | Reaction Time (s) |
|-------|---------------------------------|-------------------|
| 1 | 0.0200 | 4.5 |
| 2 | 0.0150 | 7.0 |
| 3 | 0.0100 | 12.0 |
| 4 | 0.0050 | 20.0 |

72 Describe the relationship between the concentration of solution A and the time for the reaction to go to completion.   [1]

73 On the grid *in your answer booklet,* mark an appropriate scale on the axis labeled "Reaction Time (s)."   [1]

74 On the same grid, plot the data from the data table. Circle and connect the points.   [1]

75 Identify *one* factor, other than the concentration of the solutions, that can affect the rate of this reaction.   [1]

Base your answers to questions 76 through 78 on the information below.

Carbon has three naturally occurring isotopes, C-12, C-13, and C-14. Diamond and graphite are familiar forms of solid carbon. Diamond is one of the hardest substances known, while graphite is a very soft substance. Diamond has a rigid network of bonded atoms. Graphite has atoms bonded in thin layers that are held together by weak forces.

Recent experiments have produced new forms of solid carbon called fullerenes. One fullerene, $C_{60}$, is a spherical, cagelike molecule of carbon.

76 Determine *both* the total number of protons and the total number of neutrons in an atom of the naturally occurring carbon isotope with the largest mass number. [1]

77 Identify the type of bonding in a fullerene molecule. [1]

78 State, in terms of the arrangement of atoms, the difference in hardness between diamond and graphite. [1]

---

Base your answers to questions 79 through 81 on the information below.

Hydrocarbons and fissionable nuclei are among the sources used for the production of energy in the United States. A chemical reaction produces much less energy than a nuclear reaction per mole of reactant.

The balanced chemical equation below represents the reaction of one molecule of a hydrocarbon with two molecules of oxygen.

Chemical equation: $CH_4 + 2O_2 \rightarrow CO_2 + 2H_2O + 1.48 \times 10^{-18}$ J

The nuclear equation below represents one of the many possible reactions for one fissionable nucleus. In this equation, $X$ represents a missing product.

Nuclear equation: $^{1}_{0}n + ^{235}_{92}U \rightarrow ^{89}_{36}Kr + X + 3^{1}_{0}n + 3.36 \times 10^{-11}$ J

79 Identify the type of organic reaction represented by the chemical equation. [1]

80 On the labeled axes *in your answer booklet,* draw a potential energy diagram for the reaction of the hydrocarbon with oxygen. [1]

81 Write an isotopic notation for the missing product represented by $X$ in the nuclear equation. [1]

---

Base your answers to questions 82 through 84 on the information below.

The diagram below shows a system in which water is being decomposed into oxygen gas and hydrogen gas. Litmus is used as an indicator in the water. The litmus turns red in test tube 1 and blue in test tube 2.

The oxidation and reduction occurring in the test tubes are represented by the balanced equations below.

Test tube 1: $2H_2O(\ell) \rightarrow O_2(g) + 4H^+(aq) + 4e^-$

Test tube 2: $4H_2O(\ell) + 4e^- \rightarrow 2H_2(g) + 4OH^-(aq)$

82 Identify the information in the diagram that indicates this system is an electrolytic cell. [1]

83 Determine the change in oxidation number of oxygen during the reaction in test tube 1. [1]

84 Explain, in terms of the products formed in test tube 2, why litmus turns blue in test tube 2. [1]

# PHYSICAL SETTING
# CHEMISTRY

**Thursday,** January 28, 2010 — 1:15 to 4:15 p.m., only

---

## ANSWER SHEET

Student ................................................ Sex: ☐ Male ☐ Female  Grade ............

Teacher ................................................  School ..................................

**Record your answers to Part A and Part B–1 on this answer sheet.**

| Part A | | | Part B–1 | |
|---|---|---|---|---|
| 1 ............. | 11 ............. | 21 ............. | 31 ............. | 41 ............. |
| 2 ............. | 12 ............. | 22 ............. | 32 ............. | 42 ............. |
| 3 ............. | 13 ............. | 23 ............. | 33 ............. | 43 ............. |
| 4 ............. | 14 ............. | 24 ............. | 34 ............. | 44 ............. |
| 5 ............. | 15 ............. | 25 ............. | 35 ............. | 45 ............. |
| 6 ............. | 16 ............. | 26 ............. | 36 ............. | 46 ............. |
| 7 ............. | 17 ............. | 27 ............. | 37 ............. | 47 ............. |
| 8 ............. | 18 ............. | 28 ............. | 38 ............. | 48 ............. |
| 9 ............. | 19 ............. | 29 ............. | 39 ............. | 49 ............. |
| 10 ............. | 20 ............. | 30 ............. | 40 ............. | 50 ............. |

Part A Score

Part B–1 Score

**Write your answers to Part B–2 and Part C in your answer booklet.**

**The declaration below must be signed when you have completed the examination.**

I do hereby affirm, at the close of this examination, that I had no unlawful knowledge of the questions or answers prior to the examination and that I have neither given nor received assistance in answering any of the questions during the examination.

_____
Signature

Tear Here

# PHYSICAL SETTING
# CHEMISTRY

**Thursday,** January 28, 2010 — 1:15 to 4:15 p.m., only

### ANSWER BOOKLET

Student...................................... Sex: ☐ Male
☐ Female

Teacher.................................................

School...................................... Grade .........

**Answer all questions in Part B–2 and Part C. Record your answers in this booklet.**

| Part | Maximum Score | Student's Score |
|------|---------------|-----------------|
| A | 30 | |
| B–1 | 20 | |
| B–2 | 16 | |
| C | 19 | |

Total Written Test Score
(Maximum Raw Score: 85)

Final Score
(from conversion chart)

Raters' Initials:

Rater 1 ......... Rater 2 .........

**Part B–2**

51 _____ g

52 _____ d

53 _____

54 _____

55

| Key |
|-----|
| ◯ = $CO_2$ molecule |

**For Raters Only**

51 ☐

52 ☐

53 ☐

54 ☐

55 ☐

56

_____ g

57 _____

58 _____

59 _____

_____

_____

60

61 _____     61 [ ]

62 _____ m     62 [ ]

63 _____

_____     63 [ ]

_____

64 _____     64 [ ]

65 _____     65 [ ]

[ ]

Total Score
for Part B–2

66 _____

_____

66 ☐

67

67 ☐

68 _____ g

68 ☐

69 _____

_____

69 ☐

70 _____ Mg(s) + _____ HCl(aq) → _____ H$_2$(g) + _____ MgCl$_2$(aq)

70 ☐

71 _____

71 ☐

72 _____

72 [ ]

**73 and 74**

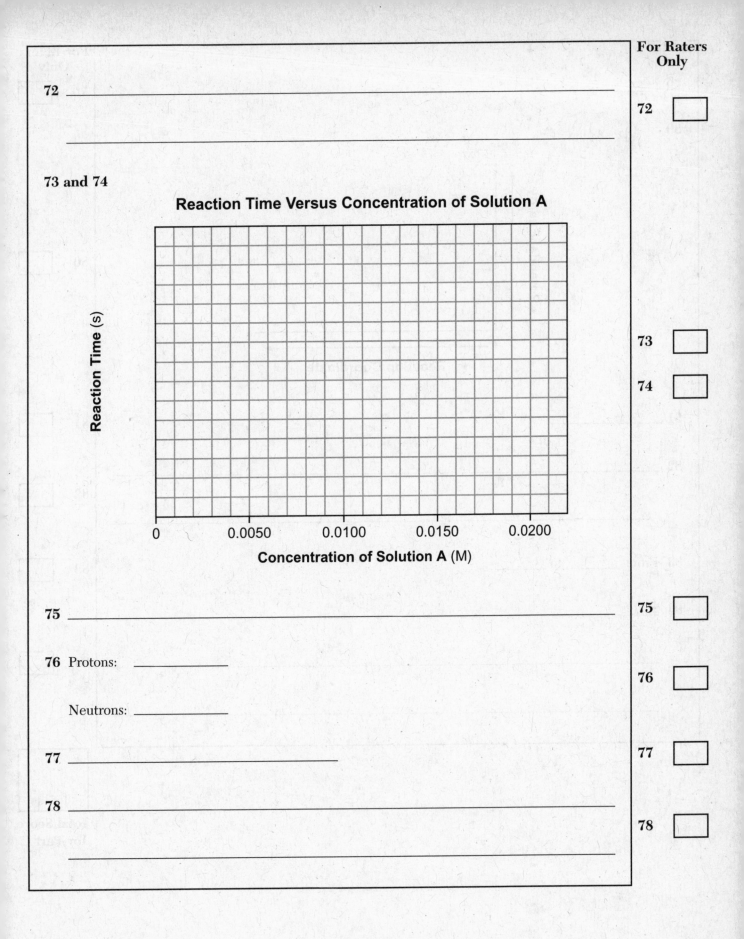

**Reaction Time Versus Concentration of Solution A**

Reaction Time (s)

0          0.0050          0.0100          0.0150          0.0200

**Concentration of Solution A** (M)

73 [ ]

74 [ ]

75 _____

75 [ ]

76 Protons: _____

Neutrons: _____

76 [ ]

77 _____

77 [ ]

78 _____

_____

78 [ ]

79 _____    79 [ ]

80                                                80 [ ]

**Potential Energy**

**Reaction Coordinate**

81 _____                              81 [ ]

82 _____   82 [ ]

_____

83 From _____ to _____                    83 [ ]

84 _____   84 [ ]

_____     84 [ ]

_____

**Total Score
for Part C** [ ]

## Part A

### Answer all questions in this part.

*Directions* (1–30): For *each* statement or question, write on the separate answer sheet the *number* of the word or expression that, of those given, best completes the statement or answers the question. Some questions may require the use of the *Reference Tables for Physical Setting/Chemistry*.

1 Which particle has the *least* mass?

(1) $^4_2He$
(2) $^1_1H$
(3) $^1_0n$
(4) $^0_{-1}e$

2 What information is necessary to determine the atomic mass of the element chlorine?

(1) the atomic mass of each artificially produced isotope of chlorine, only
(2) the relative abundance of each naturally occurring isotope of chlorine, only
(3) the atomic mass and the relative abundance of each naturally occurring isotope of chlorine
(4) the atomic mass and the relative abundance of each naturally occurring and artificially produced isotope of chlorine

3 In an atom of argon-40, the number of protons

(1) equals the number of electrons
(2) equals the number of neutrons
(3) is less than the number of electrons
(4) is greater than the number of electrons

4 An electron in a sodium atom moves from the third shell to the fourth shell. This change is a result of the atom

(1) absorbing energy
(2) releasing energy
(3) gaining an electron
(4) losing an electron

5 Which statement describes oxygen gas, $O_2(g)$, and ozone gas, $O_3(g)$?

(1) They have different molecular structures, only.
(2) They have different properties, only.
(3) They have different molecular structures and different properties.
(4) They have the same molecular structure and the same properties.

6 Which statement describes a chemical property of bromine?

(1) Bromine is soluble in water.
(2) Bromine has a reddish-brown color.
(3) Bromine combines with aluminum to produce $AlBr_3$.
(4) Bromine changes from a liquid to a gas at 332 K and 1 atm.

7 An atom of aluminum in the ground state and an atom of gallium in the ground state have the same

(1) mass
(2) electronegativity
(3) total number of protons
(4) total number of valence electrons

8 Which type of matter is composed of two or more elements that are chemically combined in a fixed proportion?

(1) solution
(2) compound
(3) homogeneous mixture
(4) heterogeneous mixture

9 Which type of substance can conduct electricity in the liquid phase but *not* in the solid phase?

(1) ionic compound
(2) molecular compound
(3) metallic element
(4) nonmetallic element

10 Why is a molecule of $CO_2$ nonpolar even though the bonds between the carbon atom and the oxygen atoms are polar?

(1) The shape of the $CO_2$ molecule is symmetrical.
(2) The shape of the $CO_2$ molecule is asymmetrical.
(3) The $CO_2$ molecule has a deficiency of electrons.
(4) The $CO_2$ molecule has an excess of electrons.

11 Which formula represents a molecular compound?

(1) HI         (3) KCl
(2) KI         (4) LiCl

12 Which element has the greatest density at STP?

(1) scandium         (3) silicon
(2) selenium         (4) sodium

13 Particles are arranged in a crystal structure in a sample of

(1) $H_2(g)$         (3) $Ar(g)$
(2) $Br_2(\ell)$         (4) $Ag(s)$

14 The relatively high boiling point of water is due to water having

(1) hydrogen bonding
(2) metallic bonding
(3) nonpolar covalent bonding
(4) strong ionic bonding

15 Matter is classified as a

(1) substance, only
(2) substance or as a mixture of substances
(3) homogenous mixture, only
(4) homogenous mixture or as a heterogeneous mixture

16 Which substance can *not* be decomposed by a chemical change?

(1) ammonia         (3) propanol
(2) copper         (4) water

17 A beaker contains both alcohol and water. These liquids can be separated by distillation because the liquids have different

(1) boiling points         (3) particle sizes
(2) densities         (4) solubilities

18 Which term is defined as a measure of the average kinetic energy of the particles in a sample of matter?

(1) activation energy         (3) temperature
(2) potential energy         (4) entropy

19 How do the boiling point and freezing point of a solution of water and calcium chloride at standard pressure compare to the boiling point and freezing point of water at standard pressure?

(1) Both the freezing point and boiling point of the solution are higher.
(2) Both the freezing point and boiling point of the solution are lower.
(3) The freezing point of the solution is higher and the boiling point of the solution is lower.
(4) The freezing point of the solution is lower and the boiling point of the solution is higher.

20 Under which conditions of temperature and pressure does a sample of neon behave most like an ideal gas?

(1) 100 K and 0.25 atm
(2) 100 K and 25 atm
(3) 400 K and 0.25 atm
(4) 400 K and 25 atm

21 According to the kinetic molecular theory, which statement describes the particles in a sample of an ideal gas?

(1) The force of attraction between the gas particles is strong.
(2) The motion of the gas particles is random and straight-line.
(3) The collisions between the gas particles cannot result in a transfer of energy between the particles.
(4) The separation between the gas particles is smaller than the size of the gas particles themselves.

22 The activation energy of a chemical reaction can be *decreased* by the addition of

(1) a catalyst         (3) electrical energy
(2) an indicator         (4) thermal energy

23 A straight-chain hydrocarbon that has only one double bond in each molecule has the general formula

(1) $C_nH_{2n-6}$         (3) $C_nH_{2n}$
(2) $C_nH_{2n-2}$         (4) $C_nH_{2n+2}$

24 Why can an increase in temperature lead to more effective collisions between reactant particles and an increase in the rate of a chemical reaction?

(1) The activation energy of the reaction increases.

(2) The activation energy of the reaction decreases.

(3) The number of molecules with sufficient energy to react increases.

(4) The number of molecules with sufficient energy to react decreases.

25 Which reaction results in the production of soap?

(1) esterification
(2) fermentation
(3) polymerization
(4) saponification

26 Which substance is always a product when an Arrhenius acid in an aqueous solution reacts with an Arrhenius base in an aqueous solution?

(1) HBr
(2) $H_2O$
(3) KBr
(4) KOH

27 Which substance is an electrolyte?

(1) $CCl_4$
(2) $C_2H_6$
(3) HCl
(4) $H_2O$

28 One acid-base theory defines a base as an

(1) $H^+$ donor
(2) $H^+$ acceptor
(3) H donor
(4) H acceptor

29 A change in the nucleus of an atom that converts the atom from one element to another element is called

(1) combustion
(2) neutralization
(3) polymerization
(4) transmutation

30 Which particle is emitted from a hydrogen-3 nucleus when it undergoes radioactive decay?

(1) $\alpha$
(2) $\beta^-$
(3) $\beta^+$
(4) $\gamma$

# Part B–1

## Answer all questions in this part.

*Directions* (31–50): For *each* statement or question, write on the separate answer sheet the *number* of the word or expression that, of those given, best completes the statement or answers the question. Some questions may require the use of the *Reference Tables for Physical Setting/Chemistry*.

31 Which electron configuration represents an excited state for a potassium atom?

(1) 2-8-7-1      (3) 2-8-8-1
(2) 2-8-7-2      (4) 2-8-8-2

32 A sample of an element is malleable and can conduct electricity. This element could be

(1) H      (3) S
(2) He      (4) Sn

33 Which general trend is demonstrated by the Group 17 elements as they are considered in order from top to bottom on the Periodic Table?

(1) a decrease in atomic radius
(2) a decrease in electronegativity
(3) an increase in first ionization energy
(4) an increase in nonmetallic behavior

34 Which element is a liquid at 758 K and standard pressure?

(1) gold      (3) platinum
(2) silver      (4) thallium

35 Which equation represents a decomposition reaction?

(1) $CaCO_3(s) \rightarrow CaO(s) + CO_2(g)$
(2) $Cu(s) + 2AgNO_3(aq) \rightarrow 2Ag(s) + Cu(NO_3)_2(aq)$
(3) $2H_2(g) + O_2(g) \rightarrow 2H_2O(\ell)$
(4) $KOH(aq) + HCl(aq) \rightarrow KCl(aq) + H_2O(\ell)$

36 A compound has the empirical formula $CH_2O$ and a gram-formula mass of 60. grams per mole. What is the molecular formula of this compound?

(1) $CH_2O$      (3) $C_3H_8O$
(2) $C_2H_4O_2$      (4) $C_4H_8O_4$

37 Which formula represents strontium phosphate?

(1) $SrPO_4$      (3) $Sr_2(PO_4)_3$
(2) $Sr_3PO_8$      (4) $Sr_3(PO_4)_2$

38 Which Lewis electron-dot diagram represents calcium oxide?

39 Which statement describes the transfer of heat energy that occurs when an ice cube is added to an insulated container with 100 milliliters of water at 25°C?

(1) Both the ice cube and the water lose heat energy.
(2) Both the ice cube and the water gain heat energy.
(3) The ice cube gains heat energy and the water loses heat energy.
(4) The ice cube loses heat energy and the water gains heat energy.

40 What is the mass of $NH_4Cl$ that must dissolve in 200. grams of water at 50.°C to make a saturated solution?

(1) 26 g      (3) 84 g
(2) 42 g      (4) 104 g

41 Given the bright-line spectra of three elements and the spectrum of a mixture formed from at least two of these elements:

**Bright-Line Spectra**

Element D

Element E

Element G

Mixture

750 nm                                                    360 nm

Which elements are present in this mixture?

(1) *E* and *D*, only
(2) *E* and *G*, only
(3) *D* and *G*, only
(4) *D*, *E*, and *G*

42 Given the balanced particle-diagram equation:

| Key |
| --- |
| ◯ = an atom of an element |
| ● = an atom of a different element |

Which statement describes the type of change and the chemical properties of the product and reactants?

(1) The equation represents a physical change, with the product and reactants having different chemical properties.
(2) The equation represents a physical change, with the product and reactants having identical chemical properties.
(3) The equation represents a chemical change, with the product and reactants having different chemical properties.
(4) The equation represents a chemical change, with the product and reactants having identical chemical properties.

43 Which quantity of heat is equal to 200. joules?

(1) 20.0 kJ      (3) 0.200 kJ

(2) 2.00 kJ      (4) 0.0200 kJ

44 Which graph represents the relationship between pressure and volume for a sample of an ideal gas at constant temperature?

45 The entropy of a sample of $H_2O$ increases as the sample changes from a

(1) gas to a liquid      (3) liquid to a gas

(2) gas to a solid      (4) liquid to a solid

46 Ethanol and dimethyl ether have different chemical and physical properties because they have different

(1) functional groups
(2) molecular masses
(3) numbers of covalent bonds
(4) percent compositions by mass

47 Which formula represents an unsaturated hydrocarbon?

48 What is the oxidation state of nitrogen in the compound $NH_4Br$?

(1) –1      (3) –3

(2) +2      (4) +4

49 A student completes a titration by adding 12.0 milliliters of NaOH(aq) of unknown concentration to 16.0 milliliters of 0.15 M HCl(aq). What is the molar concentration of the NaOH(aq)?

(1) 0.11 M      (3) 1.1 M

(2) 0.20 M      (4) 5.0 M

50 What is the half-life of a radioisotope if 25.0 grams of an original 200.-gram sample of the isotope remains unchanged after 11.46 days?

(1) 2.87 d      (3) 11.46 d

(2) 3.82 d      (4) 34.38 d

# Part B–2

## Answer all questions in this part.

*Directions* (51–63): Record your answers in the spaces provided in your answer booklet. Some questions may require the use of the *Reference Tables for Physical Setting/Chemistry.*

51 Identify the element in Period 3 of the Periodic Table that reacts with oxygen to form an ionic compound represented by the formula $X_2O$. [1]

52 Given the balanced equation representing a reaction:

$$2C_2H_6 + 7O_2 \rightarrow 4CO_2 + 6H_2O$$

Determine the total number of moles of oxygen that react completely with 8.0 moles of $C_2H_6$. [1]

53 On the potential energy diagram *in your answer booklet*, draw an arrow to represent the activation energy of the forward reaction. [1]

54 Describe the electrons in an atom of carbon in the ground state. Your response must include:

- the charge of an electron [1]
- the location of electrons based on the wave-mechanical model [1]
- the total number of electrons in a carbon atom [1]

55 Determine the mass of 5.20 moles of $C_6H_{12}$ (gram-formula mass = 84.2 grams/mole). [1]

---

Base your answers to questions 56 through 58 on the information below.

A 1.0-gram strip of zinc is reacted with hydrochloric acid in a test tube. The unbalanced equation below represents the reaction.

$$Zn(s) + HCl(aq) \rightarrow H_2(g) + ZnCl_2(aq)$$

56 Balance the equation *in your answer booklet* for the reaction of zinc and hydrochloric acid, using the smallest whole-number coefficients. [1]

57 Explain, using information from Reference Table *F*, why the symbol (aq) is used to describe the product $ZnCl_2$. [1]

58 Explain, in terms of collision theory, why using 1.0 gram of powdered zinc, instead of the 1.0-gram strip of zinc, would have increased the rate of the reaction. [1]

---

[8]

**August '09  Regents Examination**

Base your answers to questions 59 through 63 on the information below.

Bond energy is the amount of energy required to break a chemical bond. The table below gives a formula and the carbon-nitrogen bond energy for selected nitrogen compounds.

### Selected Nitrogen Compounds

| Compound | Formula | Carbon-Nitrogen Bond Energy (kJ/mol) |
|---|---|---|
| hydrogen cyanide | H—C≡N | 890. |
| isocyanic acid | H—N=C=O | 615 |
| methanamine | H<br>\|<br>H—C—N—H<br>\|  \|<br>H  H | 293 |

59 Describe, in terms of electrons, the type of bonding between the carbon atom and the nitrogen atom in a molecule of methanamine. [1]

60 Identify the noble gas that has atoms in the ground state with the same electron configuration as the nitrogen in a molecule of isocyanic acid. [1]

61 State the relationship between the number of electrons in a carbon-nitrogen bond and carbon-nitrogen bond energy. [1]

62 Explain, in terms of charge distribution, why a molecule of hydrogen cyanide is polar. [1]

63 A 3.2-gram sample of air contains 0.000 74 gram of hydrogen cyanide. Determine the concentration, in parts per million, of the hydrogen cyanide in this sample. [1]

# Part C

## Answer all questions in this part.

*Directions* (64–81): Record your answers in the spaces provided in your answer booklet. Some questions may require the use of the *Reference Tables for Physical Setting/Chemistry*.

64 Based on data collected during a laboratory investigation, a student determined an experimental value of 322 joules per gram for the heat of fusion of $H_2O$. Calculate the student's percent error. Your response must include a correct numerical setup and the calculated result. [2]

Base your answers to questions 65 through 67 on the information below.

A student used blue litmus paper and phenolphthalein paper as indicators to test the pH of distilled water and five aqueous household solutions. Then the student used a pH meter to measure the pH of the distilled water and each solution. The results of the student's work are recorded in the table below.

### Testing Results

| Liquid Tested | Color of Blue Litmus Paper | Color of Phenolphthalein Paper | Measured pH Value Using a pH Meter |
|---|---|---|---|
| 2% milk | blue | colorless | 6.4 |
| distilled water | blue | colorless | 7.0 |
| household ammonia | blue | pink | 11.5 |
| lemon juice | red | colorless | 2.3 |
| tomato juice | red | colorless | 4.3 |
| vinegar | red | colorless | 3.3 |

65 Identify the liquid tested that has the *lowest* hydronium ion concentration. [1]

66 Explain, in terms of the pH range for color change on Reference Table *M*, why litmus is *not* appropriate to differentiate the acidity levels of tomato juice and vinegar. [1]

67 Based on the measured pH values, identify the liquid tested that is 10 times more acidic than vinegar. [1]

Base your answers to questions 68 through 72 on the information below.

Biodiesel is an alternative fuel for vehicles that use petroleum diesel. Biodiesel is produced by reacting vegetable oil with $CH_3OH$. Methyl palmitate, $C_{15}H_{31}COOCH_3$, a compound found in biodiesel, is made from soybean oil. One reaction of methyl palmitate with oxygen is represented by the balanced equation below.

$$2C_{15}H_{31}COOCH_3 + 49O_2 \rightarrow 34CO_2 + 34H_2O + energy$$

68 Write an IUPAC name for the compound that reacts with vegetable oil to produce biodiesel. [1]

69 Explain, in terms of *both* atoms and molecular structure, why there is no isomer of $CH_3OH$. [1]

70 Identify the class of organic compounds to which methyl palmitate belongs. [1]

71 Identify the type of organic reaction represented by the balanced equation. [1]

72 State evidence from the balanced equation that indicates the reaction is exothermic. [1]

_____

Base your answers to questions 73 through 76 on the information below.

In a laboratory investigation, a student constructs a voltaic cell with iron and copper electrodes. Another student constructs a voltaic cell with zinc and iron electrodes. Testing the cells during operation enables the students to write the balanced ionic equations below.

Cell with iron and copper electrodes: $Cu^{2+}(aq) + Fe(s) \rightarrow Cu(s) + Fe^{2+}(aq)$

Cell with zinc and iron electrodes: $Fe^{2+}(aq) + Zn(s) \rightarrow Fe(s) + Zn^{2+}(aq)$

73 State evidence from the balanced equation for the cell with iron and copper electrodes that indicates the reaction in the cell is an oxidation-reduction reaction. [1]

74 Identify the particles transferred between $Fe^{2+}$ and $Zn$ during the reaction in the cell with zinc and iron electrodes. [1]

75 Write a balanced half-reaction equation for the reduction that takes place in the cell with zinc and iron electrodes. [1]

76 State the relative activity of the three metals used in these two voltaic cells. [1]

_____

**August '09   Regents Examination**

Base your answers to questions 77 through 79 on the information below.

A method used by ancient Egyptians to obtain copper metal from copper(I) sulfide ore was heating the ore in the presence of air. Later, copper was mixed with tin to produce a useful alloy called bronze.

77 Calculate the density of a 129.5-gram sample of bronze that has a volume of 14.8 cubic centimeters. Your response must include a correct numerical setup and the calculated result. [2]

78 Convert the melting point of the metal obtained from copper(I) sulfide ore to degrees Celsius. [1]

79 A 133.8-gram sample of bronze was 10.3% tin by mass. Determine the total mass of tin in the sample. [1]

_____

Base your answers to questions 80 and 81 on the information below.

Scientists are investigating the production of energy using hydrogen-2 nuclei (deuterons) and hydrogen-3 nuclei (tritons). The balanced equation below represents one nuclear reaction between two deuterons.

$$_1^2\text{H} + _1^2\text{H} \rightarrow _2^3\text{He} + _0^1\text{n} + 5.23 \times 10^{-13} \text{ J}$$

80 State, in terms of subatomic particles, how a deuteron differs from a triton. [1]

81 Identify the type of nuclear reaction represented by the equation. [1]

_____

# PHYSICAL SETTING
# CHEMISTRY

**Thursday,** August 13, 2009 — 12:30 to 3:30 p.m., only

## ANSWER SHEET

Student ................................................... Sex: ☐ Male ☐ Female Grade ...........

Teacher ................................................ School ...............................

**Record your answers to Part A and Part B–1 on this answer sheet.**

| Part A | | | Part B–1 | |
|---|---|---|---|---|
| 1 ............ | 11 ............ | 21 ............ | 31 ............ | 41 ............ |
| 2 ............ | 12 ............ | 22 ............ | 32 ............ | 42 ............ |
| 3 ............ | 13 ............ | 23 ............ | 33 ............ | 43 ............ |
| 4 ............ | 14 ............ | 24 ............ | 34 ............ | 44 ............ |
| 5 ............ | 15 ............ | 25 ............ | 35 ............ | 45 ............ |
| 6 ............ | 16 ............ | 26 ............ | 36 ............ | 46 ............ |
| 7 ............ | 17 ............ | 27 ............ | 37 ............ | 47 ............ |
| 8 ............ | 18 ............ | 28 ............ | 38 ............ | 48 ............ |
| 9 ............ | 19 ............ | 29 ............ | 39 ............ | 49 ............ |
| 10 ............ | 20 ............ | 30 ............ | 40 ............ | 50 ............ |

Part A Score

Part B–1 Score

**Write your answers to Part B–2 and Part C in your answer booklet.**

**The declaration below should be signed when you have completed the examination.**

I do hereby affirm, at the close of this examination, that I had no unlawful knowledge of the questions or answers prior to the examination and that I have neither given nor received assistance in answering any of the questions during the examination.

_____

Signature

Tear Here

# PHYSICAL SETTING
# CHEMISTRY

**Thursday,** August 13, 2009 — 12:30 to 3:30 p.m., only

## ANSWER BOOKLET

Student . . . . . . . . . . . . . . . . . . . . . . . . . . . . . . . . . . . .  Sex:  ☐ Male
☐ Female

Teacher . . . . . . . . . . . . . . . . . . . . . . . . . . . . . . . . . . . . . . . . . . . . . . . . . . .

School . . . . . . . . . . . . . . . . . . . . . . . . . . . . . . . .  Grade . . . . . . . . .

Answer all questions in Part B–2 and Part C. Record your answers in this booklet.

| Part | Maximum Score | Student's Score |
|------|---------------|-----------------|
| A | 30 | |
| B–1 | 20 | |
| B–2 | 15 | |
| C | 20 | |

**Total Written Test Score** (Maximum Raw Score: 85) ☐

**Final Score** (from conversion chart) ☐

Raters' Initials:

Rater 1 . . . . . . . . . .  Rater 2 . . . . . . . . . .

---

**Part B–2**

**For Raters Only**

51 _____

51 ☐

52 _____ mol

52 ☐

53

**Reaction Coordinate** (x-axis label), **Potential Energy** (y-axis label)

53 ☐

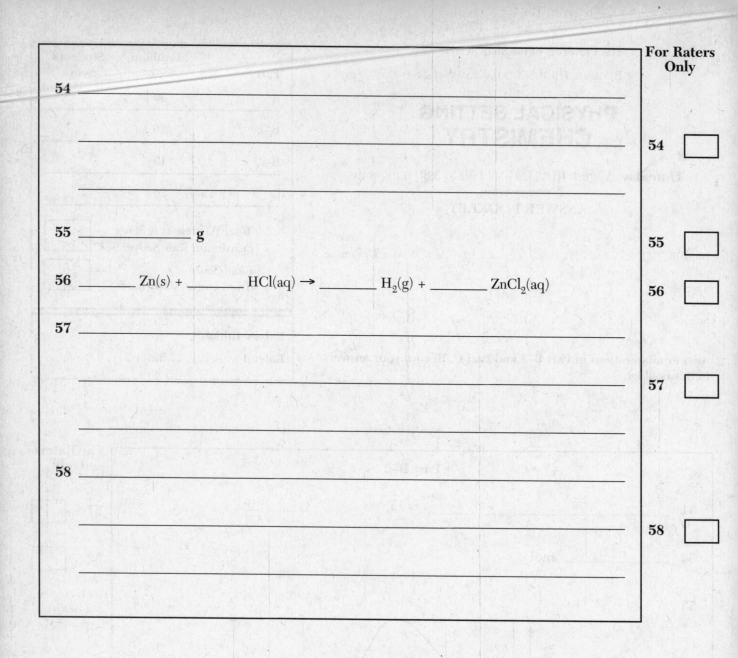

54 _____

_____

_____

54 ☐

55 _____ g

55 ☐

56 _____ Zn(s) + _____ HCl(aq) → _____ $H_2$(g) + _____ $ZnCl_2$(aq)

56 ☐

57 _____

_____

_____

57 ☐

58 _____

_____

_____

58 ☐

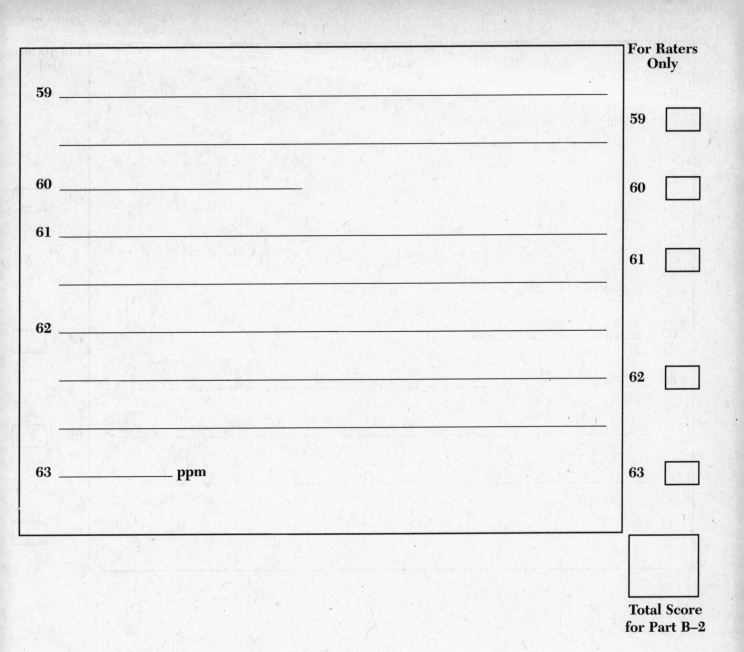

**For Raters Only**

59 ☐

60 ☐

61 ☐

62 ☐

63 ☐

☐

**Total Score for Part B–2**

59 _____

_____

60 _____

61 _____

_____

62 _____

_____

63 _____ ppm

[3]

[OVER]

**August '09   Regents Examination**

**64**

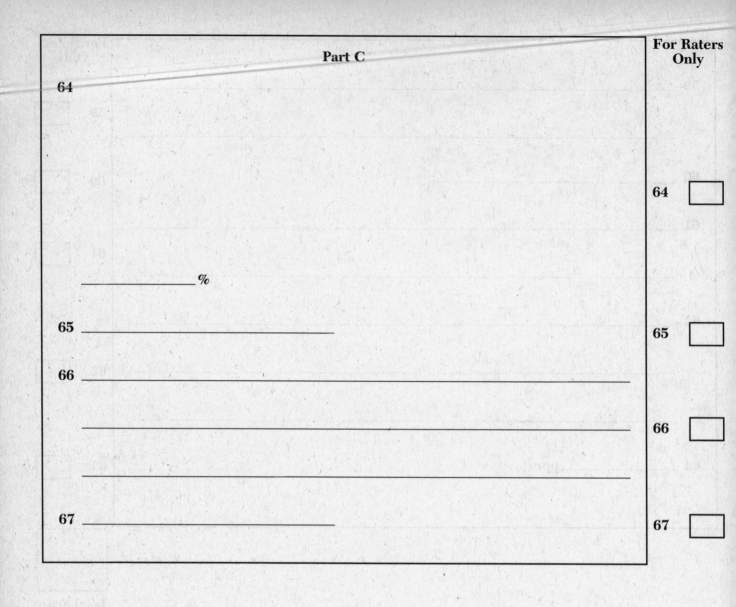

_____%

**64** ☐

**65** _____

**65** ☐

**66** _____

_____

_____

**66** ☐

**67** _____

**67** ☐

[4]

68 _____

68 [ ]

69 _____

_____

69 [ ]

_____

70 _____

70 [ ]

71 _____

71 [ ]

72 _____

72 [ ]

_____

73 _____

73 [ ]

_____

74 _____

74 [ ]

75 _____

75 [ ]

76 _____

76 [ ]

_____

77

77 ☐

_____ g/cm³

78 _____ °C

78 ☐

79 _____ g

79 ☐

80 _____

_____

80 ☐

81 _____

81 ☐

☐

[6]

## Part A

### Answer all questions in this part.

*Directions* (1–30): For *each* statement or question, write on the separate answer sheet the *number* of the word or expression that, of those given, best completes the statement or answers the question. Some questions may require the use of the *Reference Tables for Physical Setting/Chemistry*.

1 Which subatomic particle is negatively charged?

(1) electron     (3) positron
(2) neutron     (4) proton

2 Which element has the greatest density at STP?

(1) barium     (3) magnesium
(2) beryllium     (4) radium

3 What is the mass number of a carbon atom that contains six protons, eight neutrons, and six electrons?

(1) 6     (3) 14
(2) 8     (4) 20

4 Which element is a metalloid?

(1) Al     (3) As
(2) Ar     (4) Au

5 Which substance can be decomposed by chemical means?

(1) aluminum     (3) silicon
(2) octane     (4) xenon

6 An element that is malleable and a good conductor of heat and electricity could have an atomic number of

(1) 16     (3) 29
(2) 18     (4) 35

7 A 1.0-mole sample of krypton gas has a mass of

(1) 19 g     (3) 39 g
(2) 36 g     (4) 84 g

8 An atom in the ground state has a stable valence electron configuration. This atom could be an atom of

(1) Al     (3) Na
(2) Cl     (4) Ne

9 An atom of an element has a total of 12 electrons. An ion of the same element has a total of 10 electrons. Which statement describes the charge and radius of the ion?

(1) The ion is positively charged and its radius is smaller than the radius of the atom.
(2) The ion is positively charged and its radius is larger than the radius of the atom.
(3) The ion is negatively charged and its radius is smaller than the radius of the atom.
(4) The ion is negatively charged and its radius is larger than the radius of the atom.

10 Which formula represents a nonpolar molecule?

(1) $CH_4$     (3) $H_2O$
(2) HCl     (4) $NH_3$

11 The compound $XCl$ is classified as ionic if $X$ represents the element

(1) H     (3) Rb
(2) I     (4) Br

12 The chemical bonding in sodium phosphate, $Na_3PO_4$, is classified as

(1) ionic, only
(2) metallic, only
(3) both covalent and ionic
(4) both covalent and metallic

13 Which element is composed of molecules that each contain a multiple covalent bond?

(1) chlorine      (3) hydrogen
(2) fluorine      (4) nitrogen

14 Which equation represents an exothermic reaction at 298 K?

(1) $N_2(g) + O_2(g) \rightarrow 2NO(g)$

(2) $C(s) + O_2(g) \rightarrow CO_2(g)$

(3) $KNO_3(s) \xrightarrow{H_2O} K^+(aq) + NO_3^-(aq)$

(4) $NH_4Cl(s) \xrightarrow{H_2O} NH_4^+(aq) + Cl^-(aq)$

15 Standard pressure is equal to

(1) 1 atm      (3) 273 atm
(2) 1 kPa      (4) 273 kPa

16 A large sample of solid calcium sulfate is crushed into smaller pieces for testing. Which two physical properties are the same for both the large sample and one of the smaller pieces?

(1) mass and density
(2) mass and volume
(3) solubility and density
(4) solubility and volume

17 According to the kinetic molecular theory, the molecules of an ideal gas

(1) have a strong attraction for each other
(2) have significant volume
(3) move in random, constant, straight-line motion
(4) are closely packed in a regular repeating pattern

18 At 65°C, which compound has a vapor pressure of 58 kilopascals?

(1) ethanoic acid      (3) propanone
(2) ethanol      (4) water

19 At STP, which 2.0-gram sample of matter uniformly fills a 340-milliliter closed container?

(1) $Br_2(\ell)$      (3) KCl(aq)
(2) $Fe(NO_3)_2(s)$      (4) Xe(g)

20 Compared to the freezing point and boiling point of water at 1 atmosphere, a solution of a salt and water at 1 atmosphere has a

(1) lower freezing point and a lower boiling point
(2) lower freezing point and a higher boiling point
(3) higher freezing point and a lower boiling point
(4) higher freezing point and a higher boiling point

21 Changes in activation energy during a chemical reaction are represented by a

(1) cooling curve
(2) heating curve
(3) ionization energy diagram
(4) potential energy diagram

22 Under which conditions of temperature and pressure would a real gas behave most like an ideal gas?

(1) 200. K and 50.0 kPa
(2) 200. K and 200.0 kPa
(3) 600. K and 50.0 kPa
(4) 600. K and 200.0 kPa

23 Given the equation representing a reaction:

$$N_2O_4(g) \rightleftharpoons 2NO_2(g)$$

Which statement describes this reaction at equilibrium?

(1) The concentration of $N_2O_4(g)$ must equal the concentration of $NO_2(g)$.
(2) The concentration of $N_2O_4(g)$ and the concentration of $NO_2(g)$ must be constant.
(3) The rate of the forward reaction is greater than the rate of the reverse reaction.
(4) The rate of the reverse reaction is greater than the rate of the forward reaction.

24 Which compound is a saturated hydrocarbon?

(1) propanal      (3) propene
(2) propane      (4) propyne

25 The isomers butane and methylpropane differ in their

(1) molecular formulas
(2) structural formulas
(3) total number of atoms per molecule
(4) total number of bonds per molecule

26 Which word equation represents a neutralization reaction?

(1) base + acid → salt + water
(2) base + salt → water + acid
(3) salt + acid → base + water
(4) salt + water → acid + base

27 An aqueous solution of lithium hydroxide contains hydroxide ions as the only negative ion in the solution. Lithium hydroxide is classified as an

(1) aldehyde          (3) Arrhenius acid
(2) alcohol           (4) Arrhenius base

28 One alternate acid-base theory states that an acid is an

(1) $H^+$ donor        (3) $OH^-$ donor
(2) $H^+$ acceptor     (4) $OH^-$ acceptor

29 Which particle has the greatest mass?

(1) an alpha particle   (3) a neutron
(2) a beta particle     (4) a positron

30 A beta particle may be spontaneously emitted from

(1) a ground-state electron
(2) a stable nucleus
(3) an excited electron
(4) an unstable nucleus

**Answer all questions in this part.**

*Directions* (31–50): For *each* statement or question, write on the separate answer sheet the *number* of the word or expression that, of those given, best completes the statement or answers the question. Some questions may require the use of the *Reference Tables for Physical Setting/Chemistry*.

31 Which electron configuration represents an atom in an excited state?

(1) 2–7      (3) 2–8–1
(2) 2–6–2      (4) 2–8–8–2

32 Magnesium and calcium have similar chemical properties because a magnesium atom and a calcium atom have the same

(1) atomic number
(2) mass number
(3) total number of electron shells
(4) total number of valence electrons

33 What is the empirical formula for a compound with the molecular formula $C_6H_{12}Cl_2O_2$?

(1) $CHClO$      (3) $C_3H_6ClO$
(2) $CH_2ClO$      (4) $C_6H_{12}Cl_2O_2$

34 Given the balanced equation representing a reaction:

$$4Al(s) + 3O_2(g) \rightarrow 2Al_2O_3(s)$$

Which type of chemical reaction is represented by this equation?

(1) double replacement
(2) single replacement
(3) substitution
(4) synthesis

35 A person with a body temperature of 37°C holds an ice cube with a temperature of 0°C in a room where the air temperature is 20.°C. The direction of heat flow is

(1) from the person to the ice, only
(2) from the person to the ice and air, and from the air to the ice
(3) from the ice to the person, only
(4) from the ice to the person and air, and from the air to the person

36 What is the total mass of solute in 1000. grams of a solution having a concentration of 5 parts per million?

(1) 0.005 g      (3) 0.5 g
(2) 0.05 g      (4) 5 g

37 Which compound is *least* soluble in water at 60.°C?

(1) $KClO_3$      (3) $NaCl$
(2) $KNO_3$      (4) $NH_4Cl$

38 At standard pressure, which element has a freezing point *below* standard temperature?

(1) In      (3) Hf
(2) Ir      (4) Hg

39 Which two particle diagrams represent mixtures of diatomic elements?

(1) A and B

(2) A and C

(3) B and C

(4) B and D

40 The graph below represents the relationship between temperature and time as heat is added to a sample of $H_2O$.

Which statement correctly describes the energy of the particles of the sample during interval BC?

(1) Potential energy decreases and average kinetic energy increases.

(2) Potential energy increases and average kinetic energy increases.

(3) Potential energy increases and average kinetic energy remains the same.

(4) Potential energy remains the same and average kinetic energy increases.

41 Given the balanced equation representing a reaction:

$$2HCl(aq) + Na_2S_2O_3(aq) \rightarrow S(s) + H_2SO_3(aq) + 2NaCl(aq)$$

Decreasing the concentration of $Na_2S_2O_3(aq)$ *decreases* the rate of reaction because the

(1) activation energy decreases

(2) activation energy increases

(3) frequency of effective collisions decreases

(4) frequency of effective collisions increases

42 Given the equation representing a reaction at equilibrium:

$$H_2(g) + I_2(g) + heat \rightleftharpoons 2HI(g)$$

Which change favors the reverse reaction?

(1) decreasing the concentration of HI(g)
(2) decreasing the temperature
(3) increasing the concentration of $I_2(g)$
(4) increasing the pressure

43 Which formula represents 2-butene?

(1)                        (3)

(2)                        (4)

44 Given the balanced equation representing a reaction:

$$Fe_2O_3 + 2Al \rightarrow Al_2O_3 + 2Fe$$

During this reaction, the oxidation number of Fe changes from

(1) +2 to 0 as electrons are transferred
(2) +2 to 0 as protons are transferred
(3) +3 to 0 as electrons are transferred
(4) +3 to 0 as protons are transferred

45 Which reaction occurs spontaneously?

(1) $Cl_2(g) + 2NaBr(aq) \rightarrow Br_2(\ell) + 2NaCl(aq)$
(2) $Cl_2(g) + 2NaF(aq) \rightarrow F_2(g) + 2NaCl(aq)$
(3) $I_2(s) + 2NaBr(aq) \rightarrow Br_2(\ell) + 2NaI(aq)$
(4) $I_2(s) + 2NaF(aq) \rightarrow F_2(g) + 2NaI(aq)$

46 Which sample of HCl(aq) contains the greatest number of moles of solute particles?

(1) 1.0 L of 2.0 M HCl(aq)
(2) 2.0 L of 2.0 M HCl(aq)
(3) 3.0 L of 0.50 M HCl(aq)
(4) 4.0 L of 0.50 M HCl(aq)

47 Which change in pH represents a hundredfold increase in the concentration of hydronium ions in a solution?

(1) pH 1 to pH 2        (3) pH 2 to pH 1
(2) pH 1 to pH 3        (4) pH 3 to pH 1

48 Which indicator would best distinguish between a solution with a pH of 3.5 and a solution with a pH of 5.5?

(1) bromthymol blue      (3) litmus
(2) bromcresol green     (4) thymol blue

49 Given the equation:

$$HCl(g) + H_2O(\ell) \rightarrow X(aq) + Cl^-(aq)$$

Which ion is represented by $X$?

(1) hydroxide          (3) hypochlorite
(2) hydronium          (4) perchlorate

50 Which nuclide is used to investigate human thyroid gland disorders?

(1) carbon-14          (3) cobalt-60
(2) potassium-37       (4) iodine-131

## Answer all questions in this part.

*Directions* (51–65): Record your answers in the spaces provided in your answer booklet. Some questions may require the use of the *Reference Tables for Physical Setting/Chemistry*.

Base your answers to questions 51 through 53 on the information below.

A sample of helium gas is in a closed system with a movable piston. The volume of the gas sample is changed when both the temperature and the pressure of the sample are increased. The table below shows the initial temperature, pressure, and volume of the gas sample, as well as the final temperature and pressure of the sample.

**Helium Gas in a Closed System**

| Condition | Temperature (K) | Pressure (atm) | Volume (mL) |
|-----------|-----------------|----------------|-------------|
| initial   | 200.            | 2.0            | 500.        |
| final     | 300.            | 7.0            | ?           |

51 In the space *in your answer booklet*, show a correct numerical setup for calculating the final volume of the helium gas sample. [1]

52 Convert the final temperature of the helium gas sample to degrees Celsius. [1]

53 Compare the total number of gas particles in the sample under the initial conditions to the total number of gas particles in the sample under the final conditions. [1]

Base your answers to questions 54 through 57 on the information below.

**Molar Mass and Boiling Point of Four Substances**

| Substance | Molar Mass (g/mol) | Boiling Point at 1 atm (K) |
|-----------|--------------------|----------------------------|
| methane | 16 | 112 |
| ethane | 30. | 185 |
| propane | 44 | 231 |
| butane | 58 | 273 |

54 On the grid *in your answer booklet*, mark an appropriate scale on the axis labeled "Boiling Point (K)."  [1]

55 On the same grid, plot the data from the data table. Circle and connect the points.  [1]

56 Based on the data in the table, state the relationship between the boiling point at 1 atmosphere and molar mass for these four substances.  [1]

57 State, in terms of intermolecular forces, why the boiling point of propane at 1 atmosphere is *lower* than the boiling point of butane at 1 atmosphere.  [1]

Base your answers to questions 58 and 59 on the information below.

At a pressure of 101.3 kilopascals and a temperature of 373 K, heat is removed from a sample of water vapor, causing the sample to change from the gaseous phase to the liquid phase. This phase change is represented by the equation below.

$$H_2O(g) \rightarrow H_2O(\ell) + heat$$

58 Explain, in terms of particle arrangement, why entropy *decreases* during this phase change.  [1]

59 Determine the total amount of heat released by 5.00 grams of water vapor during this phase change.  [1]

Base your answers to questions 60 through 62 on the information below.

A voltaic cell with magnesium and copper electrodes is shown in the diagram below. The copper electrode has a mass of 15.0 grams.

**Voltaic Cell**

$$Mg(s) + Cu^{2+}(aq) \longrightarrow Mg^{2+}(aq) + Cu(s)$$

When the switch is closed, the reaction in the cell begins. The balanced ionic equation for the reaction in the cell is shown below the cell diagram. After several hours, the copper electrode is removed, rinsed with water, and dried. At this time, the mass of the copper electrode is greater than 15.0 grams.

60 State the direction of electron flow through the wire between the electrodes when the switch is closed. [1]

61 State the purpose of the salt bridge in this cell. [1]

62 Explain, in terms of copper ions and copper atoms, why the mass of the copper electrode increases as the cell operates. Your response must include information about *both* copper ions and copper atoms. [1]

Base your answers to questions 63 through 65 on the information below.

**Naturally Occurring Isotopes of Sulfur**

| Isotope | Atomic Mass (atomic mass units, u) | Natural Abundance (%) |
|---------|-----------------------------------|----------------------|
| $^{32}$S | 31.97 | 94.93 |
| $^{33}$S | 32.97 | 0.76 |
| $^{34}$S | 33.97 | 4.29 |
| $^{36}$S | 35.97 | 0.02 |

63  State, in terms of the number of subatomic particles, *one* similarity and *one* difference between the atoms of these isotopes of sulfur.  [1]

64  In the space *in your answer booklet*, draw a Lewis electron-dot diagram for an atom of sulfur-33.  [1]

65  In the space *in your answer booklet*, show a correct numerical setup for calculating the atomic mass of sulfur.  [1]

## Part C

### Answer all questions in this part.

*Directions* (66–83): Record your answers in the spaces provided in your answer booklet. Some questions may require the use of the *Reference Tables for Physical Setting/Chemistry*.

Base your answers to questions 66 and 67 on the information below.

In 1897, J. J. Thomson demonstrated in an experiment that cathode rays were deflected by an electric field. This suggested that cathode rays were composed of negatively charged particles found in all atoms. Thomson concluded that the atom was a positively charged sphere of almost uniform density in which negatively charged particles were embedded. The total negative charge in the atom was balanced by the positive charge, making the atom electrically neutral.

In the early 1900s, Ernest Rutherford bombarded a very thin sheet of gold foil with alpha particles. After interpreting the results of the gold foil experiment, Rutherford proposed a more sophisticated model of the atom.

66 State *one* conclusion from Rutherford's experiment that contradicts one conclusion made by Thomson. [1]

67 State *one* aspect of the modern model of the atom that agrees with a conclusion made by Thomson. [1]

Base your answers to questions 68 through 70 on the information below.

Cobalt-60 is commonly used as a source of radiation for the prevention of food spoilage. Bombarding cobalt-59 nuclei with neutrons produces the nuclide cobalt-60. A food irradiation facility replaces the cobalt-60, a source of gamma rays, when the radioactivity level falls to $\frac{1}{8}$ of its initial level. The nuclide cesium-137 is also a source of radiation for the prevention of food spoilage.

68 Identify *one* emission spontaneously released by a cobalt-60 nucleus. [1]

69 Determine the total number of years that elapse before an original cobalt-60 source in an irradiation facility must be replaced. [1]

70 Complete the nuclear equation *in your answer booklet* for the decay of cesium-137. Your response must include the symbol, atomic number, and mass number of the missing particle. [1]

Base your answers to questions 71 through 73 on the information below.

A soft-drink bottling plant makes a colorless, slightly acidic carbonated beverage called soda water. During production of the beverage, $CO_2(g)$ is dissolved in water at a pressure greater than 1 atmosphere. The bottle containing the solution is capped to maintain that pressure above the solution. As soon as the bottle is opened, fizzing occurs due to $CO_2(g)$ being released from the solution.

71 Explain why $CO_2(g)$ is released when a bottle of soda water is opened. [1]

72 Write the chemical name of the acid in soda water. [1]

73 State the relationship between the solubility of $CO_2(g)$ in water and the temperature of the aqueous solution. [1]

_____

Base your answers to questions 74 through 76 on the information below.

During a bread-making process, glucose is converted to ethanol and carbon dioxide, causing the bread dough to rise. Zymase, an enzyme produced by yeast, is a catalyst needed for this reaction.

74 Balance the equation *in your answer booklet* for the reaction that causes bread dough to rise, using the smallest whole-number coefficients. [1]

75 In the space *in your answer booklet*, draw a structural formula for the alcohol formed in this reaction. [1]

76 State the effect of zymase on the activation energy for this reaction. [1]

_____

Base your answers to questions 77 and 78 on the information below.

In performing a titration, a student adds three drops of phenolphthalein to a flask containing 25.00 milliliters of HCl(aq). Using a buret, the student slowly adds 0.150 M NaOH(aq) to the flask until one drop causes the indicator to turn light pink. The student determines that a total volume of 20.20 milliliters of NaOH(aq) was used in this titration.

77 The concentration of the NaOH(aq) used in the titration is expressed to what number of significant figures? [1]

78 Calculate the molarity of the HCl(aq) used in this titration. Your response must include *both* a correct numerical setup and the calculated result. [2]

Base your answers to questions 79 through 83 on the information below.

Arsenic is often obtained by heating the ore arsenopyrite, FeAsS. The decomposition of FeAsS is represented by the balanced equation below.

$$FeAsS(s) \xrightarrow{\text{heat}} FeS(s) + As(g)$$

In the solid phase, arsenic occurs in two forms. One form, yellow arsenic, has a density of 1.97 $g/cm^3$ at STP. The other form, gray arsenic, has a density of 5.78 $g/cm^3$ at STP. When arsenic is heated rapidly in air, arsenic(III) oxide is formed.

Although arsenic is toxic, it is needed by the human body in very small amounts. The body of a healthy human adult contains approximately 5 milligrams of arsenic.

79 Convert the mass of arsenic found in the body of a healthy human adult to grams. [1]

80 When heated, a 125.0-kilogram sample of arsenopyrite yields 67.5 kilograms of FeS. Determine the total mass of arsenic produced in this reaction. [1]

81 Write the formula for the compound produced when arsenic is heated rapidly in air. [1]

82 Explain, in terms of the arrangement of atoms, why the two forms of arsenic have different densities at STP. [1]

83 Calculate the percent composition by mass of arsenic in arsenopyrite. Your response must include *both* a correct numerical setup and the calculated result. [2]

The University of the State of New York

REGENTS HIGH SCHOOL EXAMINATION

# PHYSICAL SETTING
# CHEMISTRY

**Wednesday,** June 17, 2009 — 1:15 to 4:15 p.m., only

## ANSWER SHEET

Student .......................................................... Sex: ☐ Male ☐ Female  Grade ...........

Teacher ...................................................... School ....................................

**Record your answers to Part A and Part B–1 on this answer sheet.**

| Part A | | | Part B–1 | |
|---|---|---|---|---|
| 1 .......... | 11 .......... | 21 .......... | 31 .......... | 41 .......... |
| 2 .......... | 12 .......... | 22 .......... | 32 .......... | 42 .......... |
| 3 .......... | 13 .......... | 23 .......... | 33 .......... | 43 .......... |
| 4 .......... | 14 .......... | 24 .......... | 34 .......... | 44 .......... |
| 5 .......... | 15 .......... | 25 .......... | 35 .......... | 45 .......... |
| 6 .......... | 16 .......... | 26 .......... | 36 .......... | 46 .......... |
| 7 .......... | 17 .......... | 27 .......... | 37 .......... | 47 .......... |
| 8 .......... | 18 .......... | 28 .......... | 38 .......... | 48 .......... |
| 9 .......... | 19 .......... | 29 .......... | 39 .......... | 49 .......... |
| 10 .......... | 20 .......... | 30 .......... | 40 .......... | 50 .......... |

Part A Score

Part B–1 Score

**Write your answers to Part B–2 and Part C in your answer booklet.**

**The declaration below should be signed when you have completed the examination.**

I do hereby affirm, at the close of this examination, that I had no unlawful knowledge of the questions or answers prior the examination and that I have neither given nor received assistance in answering any of the questions during the examination

Signature

# PHYSICAL SETTING CHEMISTRY

**Wednesday,** June 17, 2009 — 1:15 to 4:15 p.m., only

## ANSWER BOOKLET

Student.....................................  Sex: ☐ Male  ☐ Female

Teacher.............................................................

School.....................................  Grade .........

Answer all questions in Part B–2 and Part C. Record your answers in this booklet.

| Part | Maximum Score | Student's Score |
|------|---------------|-----------------|
| A | 30 | |
| B–1 | 20 | |
| B–2 | 15 | |
| C | 20 | |

**Total Written Test Score** (Maximum Raw Score: 85) ☐

**Final Score** (from conversion chart) ☐

**Raters' Initials:**

Rater 1 ......... Rater 2 .........

---

## Part B–2

| | For Raters Only |
|---|---|
| **51** | |
| | 51 ☐ |
| **52** _____ °C | 52 ☐ |
| **53** _____ | 53 ☐ |

**54** and **55**

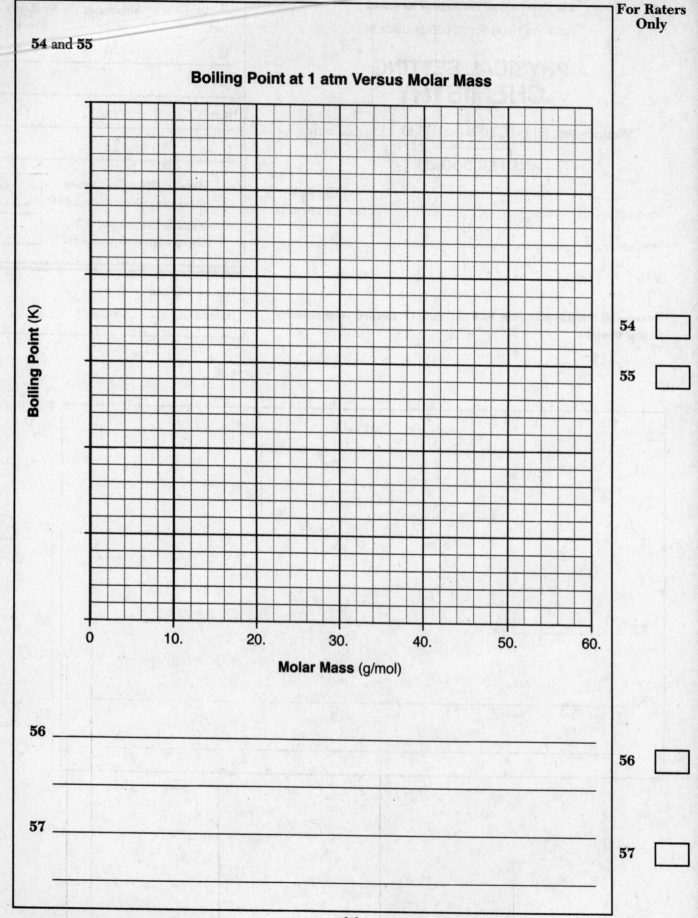

**Boiling Point at 1 atm Versus Molar Mass**

Boiling Point (K)

Molar Mass (g/mol)

0   10.   20.   30.   40.   50.   60.

56 _____

_____

57 _____

_____

**58** _____

_____

_____

58 ☐

**59** _____ J

59 ☐

**60** _____

60 ☐

_____

**61** _____

61 ☐

_____

**62** _____

62 ☐

_____

_____

For Rater
Only

63 Similarity: _____

_____

63 ☐

Difference: _____

_____

64

64 ☐

65

65 ☐

Total Score
for Part B–2

[4]

June '09   Regents Examination

66 _____

66 ☐

_____

67 _____

67 ☐

_____

68 _____

68 ☐

69 _____ y

69 ☐

70 $^{137}_{55}Cs \rightarrow {}^{0}_{-1}e + $ _____

70 ☐

71 _____

_____

71 ☐

_____

72 _____

72 ☐

73 _____

73 ☐

_____

74 _____ $C_6H_{12}O_6$ $\xrightarrow{\text{zymase}}$ _____ $C_2H_5OH$ + _____ $CO_2$ + energy

74 ☐

75

75 ☐

76 _____

_____

76 ☐

77 _____

77 ☐

78

78 ☐

_____ **M**

79 _____ g

80 _____ kg

81 _____

82 _____

_____

_____

83

_____ %

*Directions* (1–30): For *each* statement or question, write on the separate answer sheet the *number* of the word or expression that, of those given, best completes the statement or answers the question. Some questions may require the use of the *Reference Tables for Physical Setting/Chemistry*.

1 On the modern Periodic Table, the elements are arranged in order of increasing

(1) atomic mass  (3) mass number
(2) atomic number  (4) oxidation number

2 Which particle has a mass that is approximately the same as the mass of a proton?

(1) an alpha particle  (3) a neutron
(2) a beta particle  (4) a positron

3 An atom of an element forms a $2^+$ ion. In which group on the Periodic Table could this element be located?

(1) 1  (3) 13
(2) 2  (4) 17

4 Which statement describes the relative energy of the electrons in the shells of a calcium atom?

(1) An electron in the first shell has more energy than an electron in the second shell.
(2) An electron in the first shell has the same amount of energy as an electron in the second shell.
(3) An electron in the third shell has more energy than an electron in the second shell.
(4) An electron in the third shell has less energy than an electron in the second shell.

5 According to the electron-cloud model of the atom, an orbital is a

(1) circular path traveled by an electron around the nucleus
(2) spiral path traveled by an electron toward the nucleus
(3) region of the most probable proton location
(4) region of the most probable electron location

6 What can be determined if only the atomic number of an atom is known?

(1) the total number of neutrons in the atom, only
(2) the total number of protons in the atom, only
(3) the total number of protons and the total number of neutrons in the atom
(4) the total number of protons and the total number of electrons in the atom

7 The most common isotope of chromium has a mass number of 52. Which notation represents a different isotope of chromium?

(1) $^{52}_{24}Cr$  (3) $^{24}_{52}Cr$
(2) $^{54}_{24}Cr$  (4) $^{24}_{54}Cr$

8 Which Group 14 element is a metalloid?

(1) tin  (3) lead
(2) silicon  (4) carbon

9 Samples of four Group 15 elements, antimony, arsenic, bismuth, and phosphorus, are in the gaseous phase. An atom in the ground state of which element requires the *least* amount of energy to remove its most loosely held electron?

(1) As  (3) P
(2) Bi  (4) Sb

10 Which substance can be broken down by chemical means?

(1) CO  (3) Ca
(2) Ce  (4) Cu

11 During all chemical reactions, mass, energy, and charge are

(1) absorbed  (3) formed
(2) conserved  (4) released

12 Which formula represents a molecular compound?

(1) Kr        (3) $N_2O_4$

(2) LiOH      (4) NaI

13 The bonds in BaO are best described as

(1) covalent, because valence electrons are shared
(2) covalent, because valence electrons are transferred
(3) ionic, because valence electrons are shared
(4) ionic, because valence electrons are transferred

14 In which sample of water do the molecules have the highest average kinetic energy?

(1) 20. mL at 100.°C     (3) 60. mL at 60.°C
(2) 40. mL at 80.°C      (4) 80. mL at 40.°C

15 Which compound is insoluble in water?

(1) calcium bromide     (3) silver bromide
(2) potassium bromide   (4) sodium bromide

16 Which element is a brittle solid with low conductivity at STP?

(1) sulfur         (3) argon
(2) sodium       (4) aluminum

17 Which two samples of gas at STP contain the same total number of molecules?

(1) 1 L of CO(g) and 0.5 L of $N_2$(g)
(2) 2 L of CO(g) and 0.5 L of $NH_3$(g)
(3) 1 L of $H_2$(g) and 2 L of $Cl_2$(g)
(4) 2 L of $H_2$(g) and 2 L of $Cl_2$(g)

18 A reaction is most likely to occur when reactant particles collide with

(1) proper energy, only
(2) proper orientation, only
(3) both proper energy and proper orientation
(4) neither proper energy nor proper orientation

19 The net energy released or absorbed during a reversible chemical reaction is equal to

(1) the activation energy of the endothermic reaction
(2) the activation energy of the exothermic reaction
(3) the difference between the potential energy of the products and the potential energy of the reactants
(4) the sum of the potential energy of the products and the potential energy of the reactants

20 A catalyst lowers the activation energy of a reaction by

(1) providing an alternate reaction pathway
(2) decreasing the heat of reaction
(3) increasing the mass of the reactants
(4) changing the mole ratio of the reactants

21 Which element is present in every organic compound?

(1) carbon       (3) nitrogen
(2) fluorine      (4) oxygen

22 Given the balanced equation representing a reaction:

$$2Fe + 3Cu^{2+} \rightarrow 2Fe^{3+} + 3Cu$$

When the iron atoms lose six moles of electrons, how many moles of electrons are gained by the copper ions?

(1) 12 moles     (3) 3 moles
(2) 2 moles      (4) 6 moles

23 Which statement describes electrolysis?

(1) Chemical energy is used to produce an electrical change.
(2) Chemical energy is used to produce a thermal change.
(3) Electrical energy is used to produce a chemical change.
(4) Thermal energy is used to produce a chemical change.

24 During which process does an atom gain one or more electrons?

(1) transmutation     (3) oxidation
(2) reduction        (4) neutralization

25 Which substance is an Arrhenius base?

(1) $CH_3OH$      (3) LiOH
(2) $CH_3Cl$       (4) LiCl

26 Which statement describes an alternate theory of acids and bases?

(1) Acids and bases are both $H^+$ acceptors.
(2) Acids and bases are both $H^+$ donors.
(3) Acids are $H^+$ acceptors, and bases are $H^+$ donors.
(4) Acids are $H^+$ donors, and bases are $H^+$ acceptors.

27 Which two compounds are electrolytes?

(1) $C_6H_{12}O_6$ and $CH_3CH_2OH$
(2) $C_6H_{12}O_6$ and HCl
(3) NaOH and HCl
(4) NaOH and $CH_3CH_2OH$

28 The only positive ion found in $H_2SO_4$(aq) is the

(1) ammonium ion     (3) hydroxide ion
(2) hydronium ion     (4) sulfate ion

29 Which risk is associated with using nuclear fission to produce energy in a power plant?

(1) depletion of hydrocarbons
(2) depletion of atmospheric oxygen
(3) exposure of workers to radiation
(4) exposure of workers to sulfur dioxide

30 An unstable nucleus loses the most mass if the nucleus emits

(1) an alpha particle     (3) a positron
(2) a beta particle      (4) a gamma ray

## Part B–1

### Answer all questions in this part.

*Directions* (31–50): For *each* statement or question, write on the separate answer sheet the *number* of the word or expression that, of those given, best completes the statement or answers the question. Some questions may require the use of the *Reference Tables for Physical Setting/Chemistry*.

31 The diagram below represents the bright-line spectra of four elements and a bright-line spectrum produced by a mixture of two of these elements.

**Bright-Line Spectra**

Which two elements are in this mixture?

(1) barium and hydrogen        (3) helium and hydrogen
(2) barium and lithium          (4) helium and lithium

---

32 The table below gives information about the nucleus of each of four atoms.

**Nuclei of Four Atoms**

| Atom | Number of Protons | Number of Neutrons |
|------|------|------|
| A | 6 | 6 |
| D | 6 | 7 |
| E | 7 | 7 |
| G | 7 | 8 |

How many different elements are represented by the nuclei in the table?

(1) 1          (3) 3
(2) 2          (4) 4

33 What is the total number of valence electrons in an atom of germanium in the ground state?

(1) 8          (3) 14
(2) 2          (4) 4

34 In the formula $X_2O_5$, the symbol $X$ could represent an element in Group

(1) 1          (3) 15
(2) 2          (4) 18

35 A 50.0-gram block of copper at 10.0°C is carefully lowered into 100.0 grams of water at 90.0°C in an insulated container. Which statement describes the transfer of heat in this system?

(1) The water loses heat to the block until both are at 10.0°C.
(2) The block gains heat from the water until both are at 90.0°C.
(3) The water loses heat and the block gains heat until both are at the same temperature that is between 10.0°C and 90.0°C.
(4) The water gains heat and the block loses heat until both are at the same temperature that is between 10.0°C and 90.0°C.

36 The compounds $C_2H_4$ and $C_4H_8$ have the same

(1) freezing point at standard pressure
(2) boiling point at standard pressure
(3) molecular formula
(4) empirical formula

37 The chemical bond between which two atoms is most polar?

(1) C–N        (3) S–Cl
(2) H–H        (4) Si–O

38 What is the total amount of heat absorbed by 100.0 grams of water when the temperature of the water is increased from 30.0°C to 45.0°C?

(1) 418 J       (3) 12 500 J
(2) 6270 J      (4) 18 800 J

39 Which process is exothermic?

(1) boiling of water
(2) melting of copper
(3) condensation of ethanol vapor
(4) sublimation of iodine

40 Which sample, when dissolved in 1.0 liter of water, produces a solution with the *lowest* freezing point?

(1) 0.1 mol of $C_2H_5OH$
(2) 0.1 mol of LiBr
(3) 0.2 mol of $C_6H_{12}O_6$
(4) 0.2 mol of $CaCl_2$

41 Which particle diagram represents a mixture of an element and a compound?

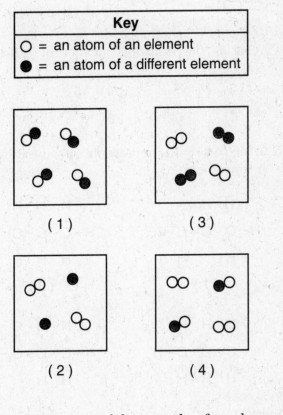

(1)        (3)

(2)        (4)

42 Starting as a solid, a sample of a substance is heated at a constant rate. The graph below shows the changes in temperature of this sample.

**Temperature Versus Time for a Sample**

What is the melting point of the sample and the total time required to completely melt the sample after it has reached its melting point?

(1) 50°C and 3 min       (3) 110°C and 4 min
(2) 50°C and 5 min       (4) 110°C and 14 min

43 Which compound is an alkyne?

(1) $C_2H_2$  (3) $C_4H_8$
(2) $C_2H_4$  (4) $C_4H_{10}$

44 What is the oxidation number of sulfur in $Na_2S_2O_3$?

(1) –1  (3) +6
(2) +2  (4) +4

45 Which formula represents an unsaturated hydrocarbon?

(1)

(3)

(2)

(4)

46 Which balanced equation represents a redox reaction?

(1) $PCl_5 \rightarrow PCl_3 + Cl_2$
(2) $KOH + HCl \rightarrow KCl + H_2O$
(3) $LiBr \rightarrow Li^+ + Br^-$
(4) $Ca^{2+} + SO_4{}^{2-} \rightarrow CaSO_4$

47 A 25.0-milliliter sample of $HNO_3(aq)$ is neutralized by 32.1 milliliters of 0.150 M KOH(aq). What is the molarity of the $HNO_3(aq)$?

(1) 0.117 M  (3) 0.193 M
(2) 0.150 M  (4) 0.300 M

48 Which nuclide has a half-life that is *less* than one minute?

(1) cesium-137  (3) phosphorus-32
(2) francium-220  (4) strontium-90

49 The table below indicates the stability of six nuclides.

**Stability of Six Nuclides**

| Nuclide | Stability |
|---------|-----------|
| C-12 | stable |
| C-14 | unstable |
| N-14 | stable |
| N-16 | unstable |
| O-16 | stable |
| O-19 | unstable |

All atoms of the unstable nuclides listed in this table have

(1) an odd number of neutrons
(2) an odd number of protons
(3) more neutrons than protons
(4) more protons than neutrons

50 Cobalt-60 and iodine-131 are radioactive isotopes that are used in

(1) dating geologic formations
(2) industrial measurements
(3) medical procedures
(4) nuclear power

## Part B–2

## Answer all questions in this part.

*Directions* (51–66): Record your answers in the spaces provided in your answer booklet. Some questions may require the use of the *Reference Tables for Physical Setting/Chemistry.*

51 In the box *in your answer booklet*, draw a Lewis electron-dot diagram for an atom of boron. [1]

52 Explain, in terms of atomic structure, why the noble gas neon is an unreactive element. [1]

53 Given the equation representing a reaction at equilibrium:

$$N_2(g) + 3H_2(g) \rightleftharpoons 2NH_3(g)$$

Explain, in terms of collision theory, why the rate of the forward reaction *decreases* when the concentration of $N_2(g)$ is decreased. [1]

Base your answers to questions 54 and 55 on the information below.

A 4.86-gram sample of calcium reacted completely with oxygen to form 6.80 grams of calcium oxide. This reaction is represented by the balanced equation below.

$$2Ca(s) + O_2(g) \rightarrow 2CaO(s)$$

54 Determine the total mass of oxygen that reacted. [1]

55 Explain, in terms of electrons, why the radius of a calcium ion is smaller than the radius of a calcium atom. [1]

Base your answers to questions 56 through 58 on the information below.

The compounds $NH_4Br(s)$ and $NH_3(g)$ are soluble in water. Solubility data for $NH_4Br(s)$ in water are listed in the table below.

**Solubility of $NH_4Br$ in $H_2O$**

| Temperature (°C) | Mass of $NH_4Br$ per 100. g of $H_2O$ (g) |
|---|---|
| 0 | 60. |
| 20. | 75 |
| 40. | 90. |
| 60. | 105 |
| 80. | 120. |
| 100. | 135 |

56 On the grid *in your answer booklet*, plot the data from the data table. Circle and connect the points. [1]

57 Determine the total mass of $NH_4Br(s)$ that must be dissolved in 200. grams of $H_2O$ at 60.°C to produce a saturated solution. [1]

58 Compare the solubilities of $NH_4Br(s)$ and $NH_3(g)$, each in 100. grams of $H_2O$, as temperature increases at standard pressure. Your response must include *both* $NH_4Br(s)$ and $NH_3(g)$. [1]

_____

Base your answers to questions 59 through 61 on the information below.

Carbon forms molecular compounds with some elements from Group 16. Two of these compounds are carbon dioxide, $CO_2$, and carbon disulfide, $CS_2$.
Carbon dioxide is a colorless, odorless gas at room temperature. At standard temperature and pressure, $CO_2(s)$ changes directly to $CO_2(g)$.
Carbon disulfide is formed by a direct reaction of carbon and sulfur. At room temperature, $CS_2$ is a colorless liquid with an offensive odor. Carbon disulfide vapors are flammable.

59 Identify *one* physical property and *one* chemical property of $CS_2$. [1]

60 State what happens to the potential energy of $CO_2$ molecules during this phase change of $CO_2$. [1]

61 Compare the intermolecular forces in $CO_2$ and $CS_2$ at room temperature. [1]

_____

**January '09   Regents Examination**

Base your answers to questions 62 through 64 on the data table below.

**Formulas and Boiling Points
of Selected Alkanes**

| Name | Formula | Boiling Point at 1 Atm (°C) |
|---|---|---|
| methane | $CH_4$ | −162 |
| ethane | $C_2H_6$ | −89 |
| propane | $C_3H_8$ | −42 |
| butane | $C_4H_{10}$ | −0.5 |
| pentane | $C_5H_{12}$ | 36 |

62 In the space *in your answer booklet*, draw a structural formula for butane. [1]

63 At standard pressure and 298 K, which alkane is a liquid? [1]

64 What is the boiling point of propane at 1 atmosphere, in kelvins? [1]

---

Base your answers to questions 65 and 66 on the information below.

The balanced equation below represents the reaction between magnesium metal and hydrochloric acid to produce aqueous magnesium chloride and hydrogen gas.

$$Mg(s) + 2HCl(aq) \rightarrow MgCl_2(aq) + H_2(g)$$

A piece of Mg(s) has a volume of 0.0640 cubic centimeters. This piece of Mg(s) reacts completely with HCl(aq) to produce $H_2(g)$. The $H_2(g)$ produced has a volume of 112 milliliters and a pressure of 1.00 atmosphere at 298 K.

65 The volume of the piece of Mg(s) is expressed to what number of significant figures? [1]

66 In the space *in your answer booklet*, show a correct numerical setup for calculating the volume of the $H_2(g)$ produced if the conditions are changed to STP. [1]

---

## Part C

### Answer all questions in this part.

*Directions* (67–81): Record your answers in the spaces provided in your answer booklet. Some questions may require the use of the *Reference Tables for Physical Setting/Chemistry*.

Base your answers to questions 67 and 68 on the information below.

Underground iron pipes in contact with moist soil are likely to corrode. This corrosion can be prevented by applying the principles of electrochemistry. Connecting an iron pipe to a magnesium block with a wire creates an electrochemical cell. The magnesium block acts as the anode and the iron pipe acts as the cathode. A diagram of this system is shown below.

**Cross-Sectional View of**
**Underground Pipe Protection System**

67 State the direction of the flow of electrons between the electrodes in this cell. [1]

68 Explain, in terms of reactivity, why magnesium is preferred over zinc to protect underground iron pipes. Your response must include *both* magnesium and zinc. [1]

Base your answers to questions 69 through 71 on the information below.

In a laboratory, 0.100 mole of colorless hydrogen iodide gas at room temperature is placed in a 1.00-liter flask. The flask is sealed and warmed, causing the HI(g) to start decomposing to $H_2(g)$ and $I_2(g)$. Then the temperature of the contents of the flask is kept constant.

During this reaction, the contents of the flask change to a pale purple-colored mixture of HI(g), $H_2(g)$, and $I_2(g)$. When the color of the mixture in the flask stops changing, the concentration of $I_2(g)$ is determined to be 0.013 mole per liter. The relationship between concentration and time for the reactant and products is shown in the graph below.

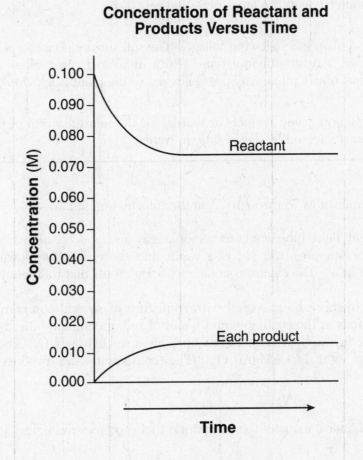

**Concentration of Reactant and Products Versus Time**

69 Write a balanced equation to represent the decomposition reaction occurring in the flask. [1]

70 State, in terms of concentration, evidence that indicates the system in the flask has reached equilibrium. [1]

71 Calculate the mass of $I_2(g)$ in the flask at equilibrium. Your response must include *both* a correct numerical setup and the calculated result. [2]

Base your answers to questions 72 through 74 on the information below.

Soil pH can affect the development of plants. For example, a hydrangea plant produces blue flowers when grown in acidic soil but pink flowers when grown in basic soil. Evergreen plants can show a yellowing of foliage, called chlorosis, when grown in soil that is too basic.

Acidic soil can be neutralized by treating it with calcium hydroxide, $Ca(OH)_2$, commonly called slaked lime. Slaked lime is slightly soluble in water.

72 Compare the hydrogen ion concentration to the hydroxide ion concentration in soil when a hydrangea plant produces pink flowers. [1]

73 An evergreen plant has yellowing foliage. The soil surrounding the plant is tested with methyl orange and bromthymol blue. Both indicators turn yellow in the soil tests. State, in terms of pH value, why the yellowing of the plant is *not* due to chlorosis. [1]

74 Write an equation, using symbols *or* words, for the neutralization of the ions in acidic soil by the ions released by slaked lime in water. [1]

_____

Base your answers to questions 75 through 77 on the information below.

A fluorescent light tube contains a noble gas and a drop of mercury. When the fluorescent light operates, the Hg is a vapor and there are free-flowing Hg ions and electrons in the tube. The electrons collide with Hg atoms that then emit ultraviolet (UV) radiation.

The inside of the tube is coated with a mixture of several compounds that absorbs UV radiation. Ions in the coating emit a blend of red, green, and blue light that together appears as white light. The compound that produces red light is $Y_2O_3$. The compound that produces green light is $CeMgAl_{11}O_{19}$. The compound that produces blue light is $BaMgAl_{10}O_{17}$.

75 Write the chemical name of the compound that produces red light. [1]

76 Calculate the percent composition by mass of aluminum in the compound that produces green light. Your response must include *both* a correct numerical setup and the calculated result. [2]

77 Explain, in terms of *both* electrons and energy, how ions in the coating emit light. [1]

_____

Base your answers to questions 78 and 79 on the information below.

A substance known as heavy water can be obtained from ordinary water and could be a significant source of energy in the future. Heavy water contains deuterium, H-2. Instead of the two hydrogen atoms in a typical water molecule, a heavy water molecule has two deuterium atoms. In 3.78 kilograms of ordinary water, the percent composition by mass of heavy water is approximately 0.0156%.

Deuterium atoms completely ionize at approximately $10^8$ K. The result is an ionized gas consisting of electrons and deuterons (the nuclei of deuterium). A triton is the nucleus of a tritium atom, H-3. These particles react according to the equations below. In the second equation, $X$ represents an unidentified product.

$$^2_1H + {}^2_1H \rightarrow {}^3_1H + {}^1_1H + \text{energy}$$

$$^2_1H + {}^3_1H \rightarrow {}^4_2He + X + \text{energy}$$

78 Calculate the mass of heavy water in a 3.78-kilogram sample of ordinary water. Your response must include *both* a correct numerical setup and the calculated result. [2]

79 Identify particle $X$ in the second nuclear equation. Your response must include the symbol, atomic number, and mass number of the particle. [1]

_____

Base your answers to questions 80 and 81 on the information below.

Ethyl butanoate is an organic compound that contributes to the odor of pineapple. Ethyl butanoate is one of the products formed by the reaction of butanoic acid with ethanol.

80 Identify *two* differences in the structures between a molecule of butanoic acid and a molecule of ethanol. *Each* of your responses must include *both* compounds. [2]

81 Identify the type of organic reaction that produces the compound that contributes to the odor of pineapple. [1]

_____

The University of the State of New York

REGENTS HIGH SCHOOL EXAMINATION

# PHYSICAL SETTING
# CHEMISTRY

**Thursday,** January 29, 2009 — 1:15 to 4:15 p.m., only

## ANSWER SHEET

Student .......................................... Sex: ☐ Male ☐ Female  Grade ...........

Teacher ............................................ School ...............................

**Record your answers to Part A and Part B–1 on this answer sheet.**

| Part A | | | | Part B–1 | |
|---|---|---|---|---|---|
| 1 ............ | 11 ............ | 21 ............ | | 31 ............ | 41 ............ |
| 2 ............ | 12 ............ | 22 ............ | | 32 ............ | 42 ............ |
| 3 ............ | 13 ............ | 23 ............ | | 33 ............ | 43 ............ |
| 4 ............ | 14 ............ | 24 ............ | | 34 ............ | 44 ............ |
| 5 ............ | 15 ............ | 25 ............ | | 35 ............ | 45 ............ |
| 6 ............ | 16 ............ | 26 ............ | | 36 ............ | 46 ............ |
| 7 ............ | 17 ............ | 27 ............ | | 37 ............ | 47 ............ |
| 8 ............ | 18 ............ | 28 ............ | | 38 ............ | 48 ............ |
| 9 ............ | 19 ............ | 29 ............ | | 39 ............ | 49 ............ |
| 10 ............ | 20 ............ | 30 ............ | | 40 ............ | 50 ............ |

Part A Score ☐

Part B–1 Score ☐

**Write your answers to Part B–2 and Part C in your answer booklet.**

**The declaration below should be signed when you have completed the examination.**

I do hereby affirm, at the close of this examination, that I had no unlawful knowledge of the questions or answers prior to the examination and that I have neither given nor received assistance in answering any of the questions during the examination.

_____
Signature

**January '09   Regents Examination**

# PHYSICAL SETTING
# CHEMISTRY

**Thursday,** January 29, 2009 — 1:15 to 4:15 p.m., only

## ANSWER BOOKLET

Student ........................................  Sex: ☐ Male  ☐ Female

Teacher ..................................................

School ...................................... Grade .........

Answer all questions in Part B–2 and Part C. Record your answers in this booklet.

| Part | Maximum Score | Student's Score |
|------|---------------|-----------------|
| A | 30 | |
| B–1 | 20 | |
| B–2 | 16 | |
| C | 19 | |

Total Written Test Score
(Maximum Raw Score: 85)

Final Score
(from conversion chart)

Raters' Initials:

Rater 1 ......... Rater 2 ..........

**For Raters Only**

## Part B–2

**51**

**51** ☐

**52** _____

_____

_____

**52** ☐

**53** _____

_____

_____

**53** ☐

54 _____ g                54 ☐

55 _____

_____        55 ☐

56                                    56 ☐

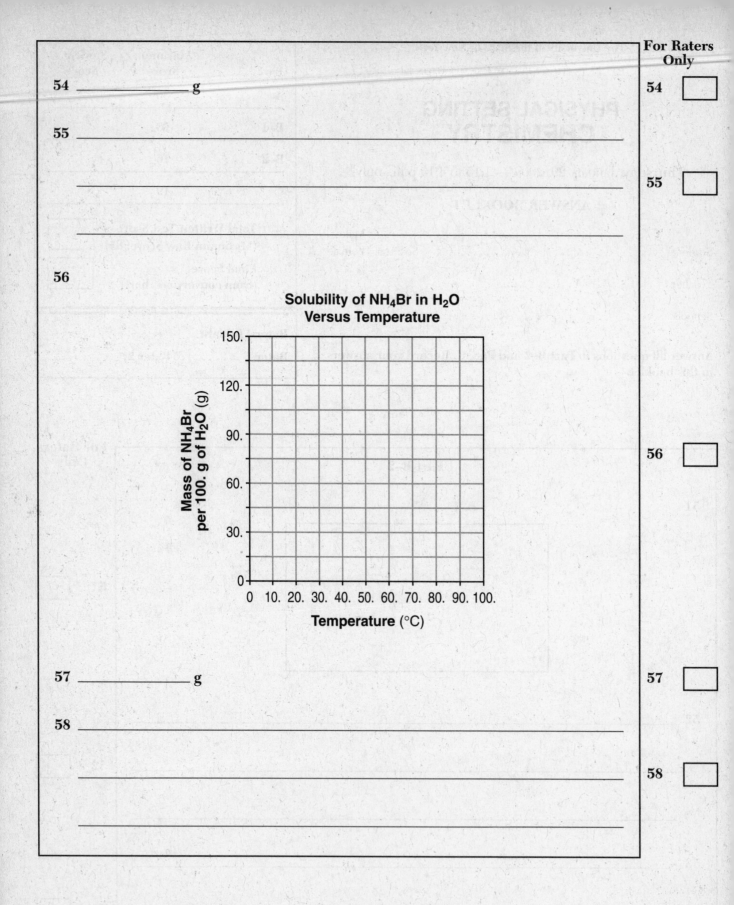

**Solubility of NH₄Br in H₂O
Versus Temperature**

57 _____ g                57 ☐

58 _____

_____        58 ☐

_____

[2]

**59** Physical property: _____

   Chemical property: _____

**60** _____

   _____

**61** _____

   _____

   _____

**62**

**63** _____

**64** _____ **K**

**65** _____

**66**

67 _____

67 ☐

68 _____

68 ☐

69 _____

69 ☐

70 _____

70 ☐

71

71 ☐

_____ g

[4]

72 _____

_____

_____

72 ☐

73 _____

_____

73 ☐

74 _____

74 ☐

75 _____

75 ☐

76

76 ☐

_____ %

77 _____

_____

77 ☐

_____

[OVER]

**January '09   Regents Examination**

**78**

78 ☐

_____ kg

**79** _____

79 ☐

**80** Difference 1: _____

_____

_____

Difference 2: _____

80 ☐

_____

_____

**81** _____

81 ☐

☐

**Total Score
for Part C**

## Part A

### Answer all questions in this part.

*Directions* (1–30): For *each* statement or question, write on the separate answer sheet the *number* of the word or expression that, of those given, best completes the statement or answers the question. Some questions may require the use of the *Reference Tables for Physical Setting/Chemistry*.

1 In the wave-mechanical model of the atom, orbitals are regions of the most probable locations of

(1) protons
(2) positrons
(3) neutrons
(4) electrons

2 Which phrase describes an atom?

(1) a positively charged electron cloud surrounding a positively charged nucleus
(2) a positively charged electron cloud surrounding a negatively charged nucleus
(3) a negatively charged electron cloud surrounding a positively charged nucleus
(4) a negatively charged electron cloud surrounding a negatively charged nucleus

3 Which total mass is the *smallest*?

(1) the mass of 2 electrons
(2) the mass of 2 neutrons
(3) the mass of 1 electron plus the mass of 1 proton
(4) the mass of 1 neutron plus the mass of 1 electron

4 Elements on the modern Periodic Table are arranged in order of increasing

(1) atomic mass
(2) atomic number
(3) number of neutrons
(4) number of valence electrons

5 As the elements of Group 17 are considered in order of increasing atomic number, there is an increase in

(1) atomic radius
(2) electronegativity
(3) first ionization energy
(4) number of electrons in the first shell

6 Chlorine-37 can be represented as

(1) $_{35}^{17}\text{Cl}$
(2) $_{37}^{20}\text{Cl}$
(3) $_{20}^{35}\text{Cl}$
(4) $_{17}^{37}\text{Cl}$

7 Which element is a metal that is in the liquid phase at STP?

(1) bromine
(2) cobalt
(3) hydrogen
(4) mercury

8 Which list of formulas represents compounds, only?

(1) $CO_2$, $H_2O$, $NH_3$
(2) $H_2$, $N_2$, $O_2$
(3) $H_2$, Ne, NaCl
(4) MgO, NaCl, $O_2$

9 What is the chemical formula for iron(III) oxide?

(1) FeO
(2) $Fe_2O_3$
(3) $Fe_3O$
(4) $Fe_3O_2$

10 An atom of which element has the greatest attraction for the electrons in a bond with a hydrogen atom?

(1) chlorine
(2) phosphorus
(3) silicon
(4) sulfur

11 Which property could be used to identify a compound in the laboratory?

(1) mass
(2) melting point
(3) temperature
(4) volume

12 Which statement describes what occurs as two atoms of bromine combine to become a molecule of bromine?

(1) Energy is absorbed as a bond is formed.
(2) Energy is absorbed as a bond is broken.
(3) Energy is released as a bond is formed.
(4) Energy is released as a bond is broken.

13 Given a formula for oxygen:

$$:O=O:$$

What is the total number of electrons shared between the atoms represented in this formula?

(1) 1                    (3) 8
(2) 2                    (4) 4

14 Solid $ZnCl_2$ and liquid $ZnCl_2$ have different

(1) empirical formulas     (3) ion ratios
(2) formula masses         (4) physical properties

15 Which phrase describes the molarity of a solution?

(1) liters of solute per mole of solution
(2) liters of solution per mole of solution
(3) moles of solute per liter of solution
(4) moles of solution per liter of solution

16 Which substance can *not* be decomposed by a chemical change?

(1) $AlCl_3$              (3) HI
(2) $H_2O$               (4) Cu

17 Tetrachloromethane, $CCl_4$, is classified as a

(1) compound because the atoms of the elements are combined in a fixed proportion
(2) compound because the atoms of the elements are combined in a proportion that varies
(3) mixture because the atoms of the elements are combined in a fixed proportion
(4) mixture because the atoms of the elements are combined in a proportion that varies

18 Which formulas represent two polar molecules?

(1) $CO_2$ and HCl       (3) $H_2O$ and HCl
(2) $CO_2$ and $CH_4$    (4) $H_2O$ and $CH_4$

19 Hydrocarbons are compounds that contain

(1) carbon, only
(2) carbon and hydrogen, only
(3) carbon, hydrogen, and oxygen, only
(4) carbon, hydrogen, oxygen, and nitrogen, only

20 The reaction that joins thousands of small, identical molecules to form one very long molecule is called

(1) esterification       (3) polymerization
(2) fermentation         (4) substitution

21 What is the IUPAC name of the organic compound that has the formula shown below?

(1) 1,1-dimethylbutane   (3) hexane
(2) 2-methylpentane      (4) 4-methylpentane

22 A voltaic cell spontaneously converts chemical energy to

(1) electrical energy    (3) mechanical energy
(2) geothermal energy    (4) nuclear energy

23 Given the balanced equation representing a reaction:

$$Mg(s) + Ni^{2+}(aq) \rightarrow Mg^{2+}(aq) + Ni(s)$$

What is the total number of moles of electrons lost by Mg(s) when 2.0 moles of electrons are gained by $Ni^{2+}(aq)$?

(1) 1.0 mol              (3) 3.0 mol
(2) 2.0 mol              (4) 4.0 mol

**August '08   Regents Examination**

24 Which half-reaction correctly represents reduction?

(1) $Mn^{4+} \rightarrow Mn^{3+} + e^-$
(2) $Mn^{4+} \rightarrow Mn^{7+} + 3e^-$
(3) $Mn^{4+} + e^- \rightarrow Mn^{3+}$
(4) $Mn^{4+} + 3e^- \rightarrow Mn^{7+}$

25 Which indicator is blue in a solution that has a pH of 5.6?

(1) bromcresol green    (3) methyl orange
(2) bromthymol blue    (4) thymol blue

26 The Arrhenius theory explains the behavior of

(1) acids and bases
(2) alcohols and amines
(3) isomers and isotopes
(4) metals and nonmetals

27 In which laboratory process could a student use 0.10 M NaOH(aq) to determine the concentration of an aqueous solution of HBr?

(1) chromatography
(2) decomposition of the solute
(3) evaporation of the solvent
(4) titration

28 A nuclear reaction in which two light nuclei combine to form a more massive nucleus is called

(1) addition    (3) fusion
(2) fission    (4) substitution

29 The nucleus of a radium-226 atom is unstable, which causes the nucleus to spontaneously

(1) absorb electrons    (3) decay
(2) absorb protons    (4) oxidize

30 A serious risk factor associated with the operation of a nuclear power plant is the production of

(1) acid rain
(2) helium gas
(3) greenhouse gases, such as $CO_2$
(4) radioisotopes with long half-lives

**August '08   Regents Examination**

### Answer all questions in this part.

* *Directions* (31–50): For *each* statement or question, write on the separate answer sheet the *number* of the word or expression that, of those given, best completes the statement or answers the question. Some questions may require the use of the *Reference Tables for Physical Setting/Chemistry*.

31 What is the total number of protons in an atom with the electron configuration 2-8-18-32-18-1?

(1) 69      (3) 118
(2) 79      (4) 197

32 Which two elements have the most similar chemical properties?

(1) Be and Mg      (3) Cl and Ar
(2) Ca and Br      (4) Na and P

33 In the ground state, each atom of an element has two valence electrons. This element has a lower first ionization energy than calcium. Where is this element located on the Periodic Table?

(1) Group 1, Period 4      (3) Group 2, Period 3
(2) Group 2, Period 5      (4) Group 3, Period 4

34 Which equation shows conservation of mass and charge?

(1) $NH_4Br \rightarrow NH_3 + Br_2$
(2) $2Mg + Fe^{3+} \rightarrow Mg^{2+} + 3Fe$
(3) $H_2SO_4 + LiOH \rightarrow Li_2SO_4 + H_2O$
(4) $Cu + 2Ag^+ \rightarrow Cu^{2+} + 2Ag$

35 What is the percent composition by mass of hydrogen in $NH_4HCO_3$ (gram-formula mass = 79 grams/mole)?

(1) 5.1%      (3) 10.%
(2) 6.3%      (4) 50.%

36 What is the total number of valence electrons in a sulfide ion in the ground state?

(1) 8      (3) 16
(2) 2      (4) 18

37 A temperature of 37°C is equivalent to a temperature of

(1) 98.6 K      (3) 310. K
(2) 236 K      (4) 371 K

38 Which balanced equation represents a chemical change?

(1) $H_2O(\ell) + energy \rightarrow H_2O(g)$
(2) $2H_2O(\ell) + energy \rightarrow 2H_2(g) + O_2(g)$
(3) $H_2O(\ell) \rightarrow H_2O(s) + energy$
(4) $H_2O(g) \rightarrow H_2O(\ell) + energy$

39 When 5 grams of KCl are dissolved in 50. grams of water at 25°C, the resulting mixture can be described as

(1) heterogeneous and unsaturated
(2) heterogeneous and supersaturated
(3) homogeneous and unsaturated
(4) homogeneous and supersaturated

40 Which aqueous solution of KI freezes at the *lowest* temperature?

(1) 1 mol of KI in 500. g of water
(2) 2 mol of KI in 500. g of water
(3) 1 mol of KI in 1000. g of water
(4) 2 mol of KI in 1000. g of water

41 Which compound is a member of the same homologous series as $C_3H_8$?

(1) $CH_4$      (3) $C_5H_8$
(2) $C_4H_8$      (4) $C_5H_{10}$

42 Which equation represents an oxidation-reduction reaction?

(1) $CH_4 + 2O_2 \rightarrow CO_2 + 2H_2O$
(2) $H_2SO_4 + Ca(OH)_2 \rightarrow CaSO_4 + 2H_2O$
(3) $MgCrO_4 + BaCl_2 \rightarrow MgCl_2 + BaCrO_4$
(4) $Zn(NO_3)_2 + Na_2CO_3 \rightarrow 2NaNO_3 + ZnCO_3$

43 Given the balanced equation representing a reaction:

$$2KClO_3(s) \rightarrow 2KCl(s) + 3O_2(g)$$

The oxidation state of chlorine in this reaction changes from

(1) –1 to +1        (3) +1 to –1
(2) –1 to +5        (4) +5 to –1

44 The potential energy diagram for a chemical reaction is shown below.

**Reaction Coordinate**

Each interval on the axis labeled "Potential Energy (kJ)" represents 40 kilojoules. What is the heat of reaction?

(1) –120 kJ        (3) +40 kJ
(2) –40 kJ         (4) +160 kJ

45 Given the balanced equation representing a reaction occurring in an electrolytic cell:

$$2NaCl(\ell) \rightarrow 2Na(\ell) + Cl_2(g)$$

Where is $Na(\ell)$ produced in the cell?

(1) at the anode, where oxidation occurs
(2) at the anode, where reduction occurs
(3) at the cathode, where oxidation occurs
(4) at the cathode, where reduction occurs

46 Given the balanced equation representing a reaction:

$$NH_3(g) + H_2O(\ell) \rightarrow NH_4^+(aq) + OH^-(aq)$$

According to one acid-base theory, the $NH_3(g)$ molecules act as

(1) an acid because they accept $H^+$ ions
(2) an acid because they donate $H^+$ ions
(3) a base because they accept $H^+$ ions
(4) a base because they donate $H^+$ ions

47 What volume of 0.120 M $HNO_3(aq)$ is needed to completely neutralize 150.0 milliliters of 0.100 M $NaOH(aq)$?

(1) 62.5 mL        (3) 180. mL
(2) 125 mL         (4) 360. mL

48 Given the balanced equation representing a nuclear reaction:

$$^{235}_{92}U + ^1_0n \rightarrow ^{142}_{56}Ba + ^{91}_{36}Kr + 3X + energy$$

Which particle is represented by $X$?

(1) $^0_{-1}e$        (3) $^4_2He$
(2) $^1_1H$          (4) $^1_0n$

49 An original sample of the radioisotope fluorine-21 had a mass of 80.0 milligrams. Only 20.0 milligrams of this original sample remain unchanged after 8.32 seconds. What is the half-life of fluorine-21?

(1) 1.04 s         (3) 4.16 s
(2) 2.08 s         (4) 8.32 s

50 Which nuclide is paired with a specific use of that nuclide?

(1) carbon-14, treatment of cancer
(2) cobalt-60, dating of rock formations
(3) iodine-131, treatment of thyroid disorders
(4) uranium-238, dating of once-living organisms

## Part B–2

### Answer all questions in this part.

*Directions* (51–65): Record your answers in the spaces provided in your answer booklet. Some questions may require the use of the *Reference Tables for Physical Setting/Chemistry.*

51 Identify *one* ion from Table *F* that can combine with $Pb^{2+}$(aq) to produce an insoluble compound. [1]

52 Describe *one* appropriate laboratory test that can be used to determine the malleability of a solid sample of an element at room temperature. [1]

53 State *two* methods to increase the rate of a chemical reaction and explain, in terms of particle behavior, how *each* method increases the reaction rate. [2]

Base your answers to questions 54 through 57 on the information below.

**Naturally Occurring Isotopes of Copper**

| Isotope Notation | Percent Natural Abundance (%) | Atomic Mass (atomic mass units, u) |
|---|---|---|
| Cu-63 | 69.17 | 62.930 |
| Cu-65 | 30.83 | 64.928 |

54 State, in terms of subatomic particles, how an atom of Cu-63 differs from an atom of Cu-65. [1]

55 What is the total number of electrons in an atom of Cu-65? [1]

56 The atomic mass of Cu-63 is expressed to what number of significant figures? [1]

57 In the space *in your answer booklet*, show a correct numerical setup for calculating the atomic mass of copper. [1]

Base your answers to questions 58 and 59 on the information below.

The boiling point of a liquid is the temperature at which the vapor pressure of the liquid is equal to the pressure on the surface of the liquid. The heat of vaporization of ethanol is 838 joules per gram. A sample of ethanol has a mass of 65.0 grams and is boiling at 1.00 atmosphere.

58 Based on Table $H$, what is the temperature of this sample of ethanol? [1]

59 Calculate the minimum amount of heat required to completely vaporize this sample of ethanol. Your response must include *both* a correct numerical setup and the calculated result. [2]

---

Base your answers to questions 60 through 62 on the information below.

The equation below represents the reaction between butanoic acid and an unidentified reactant, $X$.

60 Identify the type of organic reaction represented by the equation. [1]

61 Write the molecular formula of the organic product in the equation. [1]

62 In the space *in your answer booklet*, draw a structural formula for the unidentified reactant, $X$, in the equation. [1]

---

Base your answers to questions 63 through 65 on the information below.

A piece of magnesium ribbon is reacted with excess hydrochloric acid to produce aqueous magnesium chloride and hydrogen gas. The volume of the dry hydrogen gas produced is 45.6 milliliters. The temperature of the gas is 293 K, and the pressure is 99.5 kilopascals.

63 Balance the equation *in your answer booklet*, using the smallest whole-number coefficients. [1]

64 Identify the type of bond between the atoms in a molecule of the gas produced in this laboratory investigation. [1]

65 Calculate the volume this dry hydrogen gas would occupy at STP. Your response must include *both* a correct numerical setup and the calculated result. [2]

# Part C

## Answer all questions in this part.

*Directions* (66–80): Record your answers in the spaces provided in your answer booklet. Some questions may require the use of the *Reference Tables for Physical Setting/Chemistry*.

Base your answers to questions 66 through 69 on the information below.

In a laboratory, a glass tube is filled with hydrogen gas at a very low pressure. When a scientist applies a high voltage between metal electrodes in the tube, light is emitted. The scientist analyzes the light with a spectroscope and observes four distinct spectral lines. The table below gives the color, frequency, and energy for each of the four spectral lines. The unit for frequency is hertz, Hz.

### Visible Spectrum of Hydrogen

| Color | Frequency ($\times 10^{14}$ Hz) | Energy ($\times 10^{-19}$ J) |
|-------|---------|--------|
| red | 4.6 | 3.0 |
| blue green | 6.2 | 4.1 |
| blue | 6.9 | 4.6 |
| violet | 7.3 | 4.8 |

66 On the grid *in your answer booklet*, plot the data from the data table for frequency and energy. Circle and connect the points, including the point (0,0) that has already been plotted and circled for you. [1]

67 A spectral line in the infrared region of the spectrum of hydrogen has a frequency of $2.3 \times 10^{14}$ hertz. Using your graph, estimate the energy associated with this spectral line. [1]

68 Explain, in terms of subatomic particles and energy states, why light is emitted by the hydrogen gas. [1]

69 Identify *one* condition *not* mentioned in the passage, under which hydrogen gas behaves most like an ideal gas. [1]

Base your answers to questions 70 through 72 on the information below.

Carbon and oxygen are examples of elements that exist in more than one form in the same phase.

Graphite and diamond are two crystalline arrangements for carbon. The crystal structure of graphite is organized in layers. The bonds between carbon atoms within each layer of graphite are strong. The bonds between carbon atoms that connect different layers of graphite are weak because the shared electrons in these bonds are loosely held by the carbon atoms. The crystal structure of diamond is a strong network of atoms in which all the shared electrons are strongly held by the carbon atoms. Graphite is an electrical conductor, but diamond is not. At 25°C, graphite has a density of 2.2 $g/cm^3$ and diamond has a density of 3.51 $g/cm^3$.

The element oxygen can exist as diatomic molecules, $O_2$, and as ozone, $O_3$. At standard pressure the boiling point of ozone is 161 K.

70 Explain, in terms of electrons, why graphite is an electrical conductor and diamond is *not*. Your response must include information about *both* graphite and diamond.   [1]

71 Calculate the volume, in $cm^3$, of a diamond at 25°C that has a mass of 0.200 gram. Your response must include *both* a correct numerical setup and the calculated result.   [2]

72 Explain, in terms of intermolecular forces, the difference in the boiling points of $O_2$ and $O_3$ at standard pressure. Your response must include information about *both* $O_2$ and $O_3$.   [1]

Base your answers to questions 73 through 76 on the information below.

A portable propane-fueled lantern contains a mesh silk bag coated with metal hydroxides. The primary metal hydroxide is yttrium hydroxide. When the silk bag is installed, it is ignited and burned away, leaving the metal hydroxide coating. The coating forms metal oxides that glow brightly when heated to a high temperature.

During a test, a propane lantern is operated for three hours and consumes 5.0 moles of propane from the lantern's tank. The balanced equation below represents the combustion of propane.

$$C_3H_8 + 5O_2 \rightarrow 3CO_2 + 4H_2O + energy$$

73 At standard pressure, the boiling point of propane is 231 K. In the box *in your answer booklet*, draw a particle diagram to represent the phase of the propane as it leaves the tank at 294 K. Your response must include *at least six* molecules. [1]

74 Calculate the total mass of propane consumed during the lantern test. Your response must include *both* a correct numerical setup and the calculated result. [2]

75 Determine the total number of moles of $CO_2$ produced during the lantern test. [1]

76 Write the formula for the primary metal hydroxide used in the lantern. [1]

Base your answers to questions 77 through 80 on the information below.

When a person perspires (sweats), the body loses many sodium ions and potassium ions. The evaporation of sweat cools the skin.

After a strenuous workout, people often quench their thirst with sports drinks that contain NaCl and KCl. A single 250.-gram serving of one sports drink contains 0.055 gram of sodium ions.

77 In the space *in your answer booklet*, show a correct numerical setup for calculating the concentration of sodium ions in this sports drink, expressed as percent by mass. [1]

78 Describe the transfer of energy between the skin and the surroundings as a person perspires and the sweat evaporates. [1]

79 State why the salts in sports drinks are classified as electrolytes. [1]

80 In the space *in your answer booklet*, draw a Lewis electron-dot diagram for *one* of the positive ions lost by the body as a person perspires. [1]

# PHYSICAL SETTING
# CHEMISTRY

**Wednesday,** August 13, 2008 — 12:30 to 3:30 p.m., only

---

## ANSWER SHEET

Student .......................................................... Sex: ☐ Male ☐ Female  Grade ...........

Teacher ................................................. School ...........................................

### Record your answers to Part A and Part B–1 on this answer sheet.

| Part A | | | Part B–1 | |
|---|---|---|---|---|
| 1 .......... | 11 .......... | 21 .......... | 31 .......... | 41 .......... |
| 2 .......... | 12 .......... | 22 .......... | 32 .......... | 42 .......... |
| 3 .......... | 13 .......... | 23 .......... | 33 .......... | 43 .......... |
| 4 .......... | 14 .......... | 24 .......... | 34 .......... | 44 .......... |
| 5 .......... | 15 .......... | 25 .......... | 35 .......... | 45 .......... |
| 6 .......... | 16 .......... | 26 .......... | 36 .......... | 46 .......... |
| 7 .......... | 17 .......... | 27 .......... | 37 .......... | 47 .......... |
| 8 .......... | 18 .......... | 28 .......... | 38 .......... | 48 .......... |
| 9 .......... | 19 .......... | 29 .......... | 39 .......... | 49 .......... |
| 10 .......... | 20 .......... | 30 .......... | 40 .......... | 50 .......... |

Part A Score

Part B–1 Score

### Write your answers to Part B–2 and Part C in your answer booklet.

### The declaration below should be signed when you have completed the examination.

I do hereby affirm, at the close of this examination, that I had no unlawful knowledge of the questions or answers prior to the examination and that I have neither given nor received assistance in answering any of the questions during the examination.

_____
Signature

Tear Here

# PHYSICAL SETTING
# CHEMISTRY

**Wednesday,** August 13, 2008 — 12:30 to 3:30 p.m., only

## ANSWER BOOKLET

Student.....................................  Sex: ☐ Male  ☐ Female

Teacher.............................................................

School.......................................  Grade .........

**Answer all questions in Part B–2 and Part C. Record your answers in this booklet.**

| Part | Maximum Score | Student's Score |
|------|---------------|-----------------|
| A | 30 | |
| B–1 | 20 | |
| B–2 | 18 | |
| C | 17 | |

**Total Written Test Score**
**(Maximum Raw Score: 85)**

**Final Score**
**(from conversion chart)**

**Raters' Initials:**

Rater 1 .......... Rater 2 ..........

---

## Part B–2

For Raters Only

51 _____

52 _____

_____

53 Method and explanation 1: _____

_____

_____

Method and explanation 2: _____

_____

_____

51 ☐

52 ☐

53 ☐

**54** _____

_____

54 ☐

**55** _____

55 ☐

**56** _____

56 ☐

**57**

57 ☐

**58** _____ °C

58 ☐

**59**

59 ☐

_____ **J**

60 _____

61 _____

62

63 _____ Mg(s) + _____ HCl(aq) → _____ MgCl$_2$(aq) + _____ H$_2$(g)

64 _____

65

_____ mL

**66**

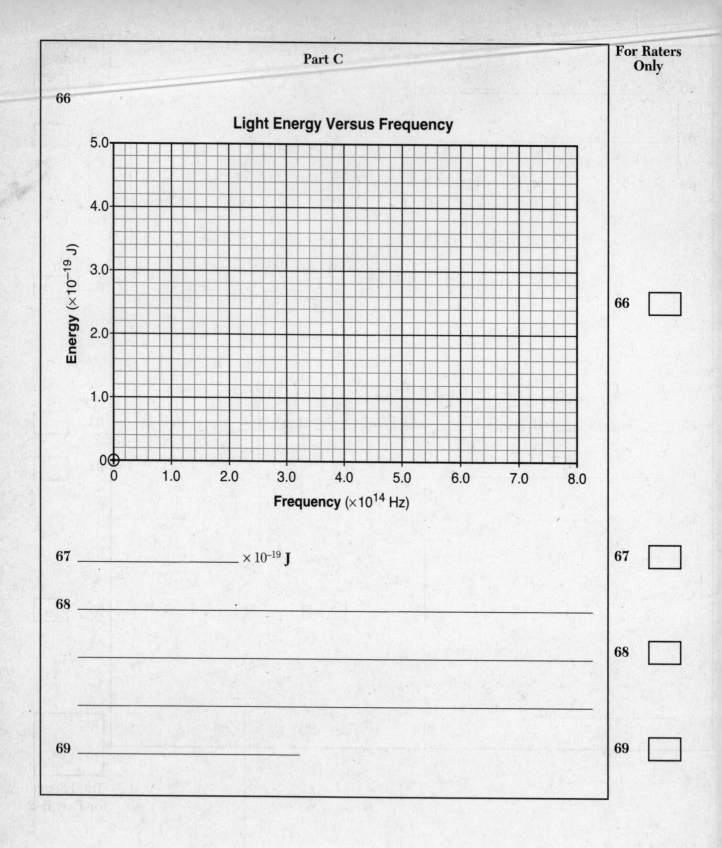

**66** ☐

**67** _____ $\times 10^{-19}$ **J**          **67** ☐

**68** _____

_____

**68** ☐

_____

**69** _____          **69** ☐

[4]

70 _____

70 ☐

_____

_____

_____

71

71 ☐

_____ cm³

72 _____

_____

72 ☐

_____

_____

[OVER]

**August '08   Regents Examination**

73

**Key**

◯ = propane
molecule

74

_____ g

75 _____ mol

76 _____

**August '08   Regents Examination**

77

77 ☐

78 _____

_____

78 ☐

_____

79 _____

_____

79 ☐

_____

80

80 ☐

☐

August '08   Regents Examination